£2.0

PHYSICAL GEOGRAPHY
AND CLIMATOLOGY

The Aletsch Glacier, Switzerland, with the Jungfrau, Mönch and Trugberg in the
background and the Märjelensee in the foreground

Physical Geography and Climatology

N. K. HORROCKS, B.Sc., F.R.Met.S.
Formerly Senior Geography Master, Central High School, Manchester

With a Foreword by
The late **PROFESSOR S. W. WOOLDRIDGE**, C.B.E., D.Sc.,
F.R.S.

LONGMAN

LONGMAN GROUP LIMITED
London

Associated companies, branches and representatives throughout the world

First published 1953
Second edition 1964
Eighth impression with revisions 1973
New impression 1976

ISBN 0 582 31027 X

Printed in Hong Kong by
The Continental Printing Co Ltd

To B. B. in friendship

914 02
912

Cover: Death Valley, California
Reproduced by kind permission of Aerofilms Limited

Foreword

by Professor S. W. Wooldridge, C.B.E., D.Sc.

I am glad to write an introduction to Mr. Horrocks's book because I hope that it will play its part in a revival of the teaching of Physical Geography in schools. Such a revival is now overdue. For many years we have followed a principle established by the pioneers of geographical teaching in Britain that Physical Geography should be subordinate to Regional Geography. Many like myself, proud to number themselves as among the students of James Fairgrieve, will remember his insistence that the 'capes and bays geography' of old unhappy times bade fair at one stage to give place to a rather cold and abstract regimen of 'scientific capes and bays', isotherms, isobars, *et hoc genus omnes*. He and his associates were quite right in their emphasis, but we who learned from them have tended to take a good principle and carry it to extremes. It is one thing, and often a good thing, to teach Physical Geography incidentally, as it were, to Regional Geography; it is quite another to ignore it altogether. Those of us who teach geography in the Universities and are concerned for the good name and future progress of our subject have all too often been confronted with classes essentially ignorant of the build of their planet, the significance of its landscapes, and the mechanism of its climates. These have been ignored as topics too abstract, difficult, or even irrelevant to find place in an admittedly crowded course and University Departments have necessarily had to teach their Physical Geography from the beginning.

I am far from suggesting that the sole purpose of school geography is to provide entrants for the Honours Schools of the Universities. The case for Physical Geography rests on much better and wider grounds than this. It is of high cultural value and upon it rest most of the practical applications of geography of which the modern world finds itself in need. We may perhaps recall G. K. Chesterton's mildly ironical characterization of the geography he knew:

> "Our principal imports come far as Cape Horn,
> For necessities cocoa, for luxuries corn.
> Thus Brahmins are born for the ricefield and thus
> The Gods made the Greeks to grow currants for us."

Even in these wider fields we shall find that as geographers we can have little very significant to say about Brahmins, Greeks, or currants without the underlying discipline and control of Physical Geography.

Mr. Horrocks's book is systematic and detailed. He presents his matter in the light of his experience as a teacher of many years' standing. It is natural and even proper that his friends and colleagues will not always agree with the matter or treatment which commends itself to him. None the less I find myself in substantial agreement with the method and manner he has used and, what is far more important, I am assured that no intelligent boy or girl at the VIth Form stage could read this book without a growing realization that our earth is something more than the sum of its parts, and that geography offers a field of study very attractive and amply repaying to the intelligent and enquiring mind.

I hope this book will be widely used, for I know that if it is, the objectives of geographical education will be soundly advanced.

Preface to the First Edition

The purpose of this book is to provide an account of the several aspects of physical geography which shall be as comprehensive as possible. It is intended primarily for pupils in secondary grammar schools who are preparing for an examination in geography at an advanced level. Nevertheless, it is hoped that some parts of the text may be of value to those pupils who will reach scholarship standard.

In order to give breadth to the discussion of most of the topics it has been necessary to make some selection of material. Thus no systematic account is given of mathematical geography (it is assumed that the reader is in possession of the elementary facts) so that where necessary, as in Chapter X, only the essential facts are stated, quite briefly, in the text. Also it has not been easy, in Chapter 1, to limit the discussion of the basic facts of geology, but the choice which has been made should be sufficient for reading the following chapters in Parts I and II of the book. Rather more detailed treatment has been given to several matters of basic importance which experience has shown can present difficulties to most senior pupils. Throughout the writing of this book every endeavour has been made to present the material in such a manner as to make it possible for the reader who is not studying science at an advanced level to gain an adequate knowledge of physical geography. Every care has been taken to establish a logical sequence. However, the accounts of both vegetation and soils in Part IV are incomplete without reference to related sections in Part V. Furthermore, in order to avoid an unduly large number of cross-references in the text, a limited amount of repetition has been made. It has been decided to omit world distribution maps of temperature, pressure, etc., as these are available in advanced atlases.

The author is indebted to many friends, colleagues, and others for their invaluable assistance in one way or another. The list of these would, indeed, be long if given in full, but a particular debt of gratitude is owing to the following: Professor E. Ashby (who gave much advice for Chapter 15); and to Messrs. E. P. Boon, L. Hadlow, G. C. Rosser, W. Shercliff, M. L. T. Sinclair, A. W. Smith, H. Smith, and R. P. Trueblood. Thanks must also be accorded to Professor Wooldridge for his guidance and his interest in this work of one of his past students; to Professor A. A. Miller, for permission to draw freely on his *Climatology* for statistics and other material; and to Professor S. H. Beaver. Needless to say, the author is responsible for the form in which the material is presented.

The diagrams and pictures have been chosen so as to give as fresh an aspect as possible to the book. However, in several instances it has been considered wise to make use of existing illustrations from other books. Recognition of these and of the sources of photographs is made where necessary and the author thanks all concerned. In some cases sources cannot be traced and it is regretted that acknow-ledgment is therefore not possible.

N. K. HORROCKS

Sale, Cheshire.
May 1st. 1953.

Revised Preface to the Second Edition

With the publication of the seventh impression of this second edition it is desirable to replace the earlier preface of 1964. It was possible with the preparation of the second edition to modify and amplify the contents of this book. Thus, more modern views of some meteorological matters were introduced in Part III and more adequate discussions of soils and vegetation were provided.

In this seventh impression the author has revised completely the opening section of Part VI in the light of modern knowledge of the physical features of the ocean basins. Further, the final part of Part I has been replaced with a discussion of orogenesis in relation to the concept of plate tectonics. Thus, cross references have been necessary between the last part of Chapter 4 and the beginning of Chapter 21. In addition, the Great Barrier Reefs are discussed at greater length in p. 155. These revisions are accompanied by new diagrams.

During the preparation of this second edition, I have been helped by the generous co-operation of many friends. In particular, I am indebted to Professor P. R. Crowe and also, to Dr. R. H. Johnson of the Department of Geography and Dr. F. M. Broadhurst of the Department of Geology, in the University of Manchester.

The Foreword remains, not only as a personal memory of the late Professor S. W. Wooldridge and his wisdom, but also because of my belief that in it there is a valid argument in support of the study of physical geography which is still as true as when it was written in 1953.

I would like to express my gratitude to the publishers and their staff for the great care and attention that they have given to the illustrations, and in providing the book with such an attractive cover.

Marple, Cheshire.   N. K. HORROCKS
May 1973

CONVERSION INFORMATION AND FACTORS

Feet to Metres (1 ft = 0·304 8 m)

ft	0	1	2	3	4	5	6	7	8	9
	m	m	m	m	m	m	m	m	m	m
0	0·00	0·30	0·61	0·91	1·22	1·52	1·83	2·13	2·44	2·74
10	3·05	3·35	3·66	3·96	4·27	4·57	4·88	5·18	5·49	5·79
20	6·10	6·40	6·71	7·01	7·32	7·62	7·92	8·23	8·53	8·84
30	9·14	9·45	7·75	10·06	10·36	10·67	10·97	11·28	11·58	11·89
40	12·19	12·50	12·80	13·11	13·41	13·72	14·02	14·33	14·63	14·94
50	15·24	15·54	15·85	16·15	16·46	16·76	17·07	17·37	17·68	17·98
60	18·29	18·59	18·90	19·20	19·51	19·81	20·12	20·42	20·73	21·03
70	21·34	21·64	21·95	22·25	22·56	22·86	23·16	23·47	23·77	24·08
80	24·38	24·69	24·99	25·30	25·60	25·91	26·21	26·52	26·82	27·13
90	27·43	27·74	28·04	28·35	28·65	28·96	29·26	29·57	29·87	30·18

Miles to Kilometres (1 ml = 1·609 344 km)

mi	0	1	2	3	4	5	6	7	8	9
	km	km	km	km	km	km	km	km	km	km
0	0·0	1·6	3·2	4·8	6·4	8·0	9·7	11·3	12·9	14·5
10	16·1	17·7	19·3	20·9	22·5	24·1	25·7	27·4	29·0	30·6
20	32·2	33·8	35·4	37·0	38·6	40·2	41·8	43·5	45·1	46·7
30	48·3	49·9	51·5	53·1	54·7	56·3	57·9	59·5	61·2	62·8
40	64·4	66·0	67·6	69·2	70·8	72·4	74·0	75·6	77·2	78·9
50	80·5	82·1	83·7	85·3	86·9	88·5	90·1	91·7	93·3	95·0
60	96·6	98·2	99·8	101·4	103·0	104·6	106·2	107·8	109·4	111·0
70	112·7	114·3	115·9	117·5	119·1	120·7	122·3	123·9	125·5	127·1
80	128·7	130·4	132·0	133·6	135·2	136·8	138·4	140·0	141·6	143·2
90	144·8	146·5	148·1	149·7	151·3	152·9	154·5	156·1	157·7	159·3

Contents

Part I   *Structure of the Earth's Surface*

CONTENTS

Part II   Earth Sculpture

Part III   Meteorology

Part IV   Plants and Soils

Part V   Climatology

Part VI   Oceanography

CHAPTER 1

Introduction – Weathering Processes and Rocks

Introduction

In approaching the study of physical geography, it is desirable to make a brief reference to some of the theories and speculations concerning the origin of the earth and kindred topics. These problems rightly belong to the studies of astronomy and cosmogony, and cannot justifiably be discussed at length in this book. It is generally accepted that the earth was originally formed from a hot, gaseous mass which condensed to a liquid state, by cooling, in a relatively short time as measured on the time scales of astronomy and geology (whose units are millions of years rather than centuries). Later, a solid crust was formed on which an atmosphere with water vapour collected, thus providing surface water by condensation.

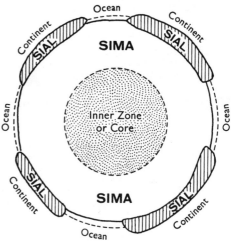

FIG. 1.1.—The Zones of the Earth (not to scale)

Our knowledge of the interior of the earth is limited. The products of volcanic eruptions help us to gain some idea of the probable chemical and physical conditions below the surface whilst seismology (the study of earthquakes) has led to the belief that the interior of the earth has concentric layers of material whose density increases with depth. Observations by geologists suggest that there is a surface layer, represented by the continental masses, which is distinct from the layer immediately below; the upper surface of the second layer forms the floors of the oceans (Fig. 1.1). The continental material is

1

often called sial and that of the ocean floor is known as sima. It seems probable that small areas of the floors of some oceans are formed of sial. These two terms are derived from the names of the elements which are most common in each (viz. *si*licon and *al*uminium, and *si*licon and *mag*nesium respectively) as determined by the chemical analysis of the rock material.

By estimation of the areas of land and ocean, within certain ranges of height and depth respectively, it is possible to plot a hypsographic curve (Fig. 1.2) which gives a generalized cross-section of the continents and the ocean basins. It will be observed that there are

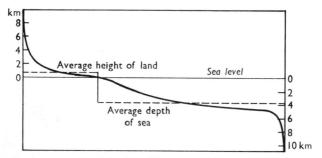

FIG. 1.2.—The Hypsographic Curve

The diagram shows the average level of the land surface at about 840 metres above sea-level and the average level of the ocean floor at about 3,800 metres below sea-level. The continents represent about 30 per cent of the global surface—the remaining 70 per cent is ocean.

two quite definite levels coinciding with the continental surfaces and the ocean floors which gives support to the suggestion of the two superior layers of the earth. Very high land features and very deep oceanic features are minor characteristics of this curve.

Most of the theories which attempt to explain the arrangement of the continents and oceans are based on some aspect of the cooling and contraction of the earth in the past. In the development of these theories, estimations of the rate of cooling of the earth were made, but early estimates have been upset in more recent times by the new knowledge of a source of heat within the earth which was previously unsuspected. It is now known that scattered amongst the materials of the various layers of the earth are radioactive elements, which are, and have been, liberating heat spontaneously as a result of atomic disintegration. The most effective elements in this respect are uranium and thorium. But potassium, although less effective, is far more widespread in the rocks than either of the others, and therefore probably makes a considerable contribution to this heat. This spontaneous disintegration is a constant process, and forms a time measure for the geologist, who has now extended the age of the oldest rocks to some three thousand million years.

The discovery of this internal supply of heat has modified our views of the nature of the material in the deeper zones of the earth. This material must remain at very high temperatures, since there is this supply of radioactive heat to make good heat lost by conduction to the surface. The materials below the upper layers must be so hot that they are capable of flow under great pressure, although it must be appreciated that at these pressures the melting-points of these materials will be raised, and so higher temperatures will be required than those which would produce melting at the surface of the earth. The materials are not liquid as commonly understood, but are capable of movement under great stresses. This conception of the plasticity of the sima in contrast to the rigidity of the sial may help to explain the separation of the earth's surface into continental masses and ocean basins. A glance at Fig. 1.1 will show that the sial is light and that it rests on the sima, which is more dense. We may regard the masses of sial as rafts 'floating' in the sima, which, by virtue of its inherent radioactive heat, can become at times almost 'liquid'.

FIG. 1.3.—A Coarse-grained Igneous Rock as shown by a Microscope Slide

The possibility of lateral movement of a sial raft in the sima sub-stratum has been postulated by Wegener in his theory of continental drift. Wegener found it necessary to envisage a dispersal of the continents, as we see them today on a world map, from a single great land mass of the past in order to explain various apparent discrepancies arising from his study of fossil plants. The mechanism by which this movement of the continents has been effected is not known, but many suggestions, apart from those of Wegener, have been put forward.

Minerals in Rocks

The sial may be regarded mainly as a mass of coarse-grained igneous rock, formed by the cooling of molten material. Examination of such rocks shows that they are made up of various minerals in the form of crystals, which differ in size and chemical composition. Some are large, whilst others are relatively small; some are dark in colour, whilst others are light (Fig. 1.3). In specimens of what, for the moment, may be called sialic rock, light-coloured minerals are generally predominant. Of these, two are very common: (*a*) quartz, which is largely silica, or the oxide of the element silicon, and (*b*) felspar, which contains alumino-silicates, or compounds of silicon with aluminium and oxygen, in association with calcium, potassium, and sodium in varying proportions. Thus there may be several types of felspar in any one specimen of rock. The dark colours are indicative of minerals, such as mica, which are also rich in silicon and aluminium, but dark by virtue of iron oxides and other compounds. A common rock of this type is granite, which has approximately equal proportions of quartz and felspar (the latter is slightly more predominant), which represent about 80 per cent of the various minerals present, the remainder being mainly dark in colour.

Weathering and Erosion ✓

It is of the utmost importance at this stage to distinguish between *weathering* and *erosion*. First, by various means, the sialic rocks are weathered or disintegrated into small fragments by mechanical processes as well as through decomposition by chemical changes. In turn, these fragments are moved by water, wind and ice so that they may rub against other rock surfaces and thus wear them away. This latter process is known as erosion (or the gnawing away of the surface). Whilst weathering of rocks involves no significant movement, erosion depends upon the transport of rock fragments. Denudation (the laying bare of the surface) is sometimes used as a comprehensive term to cover the weathering, transport and erosion of rocks. One mode of transport which is often overlooked is the down-slope movement of material under the action of gravity. These various processes are discussed fully in the next three sections of this chapter.

Mechanical Weathering ✓

The all-important influence of weathering may be due to purely mechanical processes such as:

1. The disintegration of the surface of rocks caused by their exposure to the intense heating by the sun. The minerals in rocks expand by varying amounts so that great forces are created, and some of the particles are ejected from the rock surface. Although this process is universal, it is most common in the hot deserts of the world, where sometimes the rock peels off in layers. This peeling effect is known as exfoliation.

2. At night the opposite effect is frequently produced as a result of intense chilling, and then mineral particles are loosened by the forces developed by excessive contraction.

3. Frequently this last process is assisted by frost action. In surface

crevices water collects and with nocturnal chilling, if this is sufficiently great, a wedge of ice is formed. Since the water expands on freezing, very considerable forces are brought to bear on the mineral particles on the sides of this wedge of ice, and it is usual for these forces to loosen some of the particles, although they are not free to be moved until the ice melts with a rise of temperature. Large-scale frost action is widespread on high mountains, and can result in the formation of extensive layers of shattered rock fragments known as screes (Figs. 1.10 and 7.10), found at the base of a steep slope, having fallen under the action of gravity. Small-scale frost weathering is almost world-wide, and in temperate and cold lands it may be of vital assistance to the farmer in breaking up the soil. It is possible that exfoliation is partly produced by frost action, even in hot deserts where freezing of dew at night can produce frost heaving (see p. 291).

Chemical Weathering ✓

The chemical nature of the various minerals in a rock determines the extent to which weathering may be produced by the action of rain-water. Rain is not merely water, but must be regarded as a mildly acid solution. The following chemical changes may occur:

1. Some mineral particles are removed in solution from the rock.

2. Other minerals absorb water, and new compounds are formed by the process of hydration. Many of these freshly formed substances are soluble in rain-water, whereas before hydration the minerals from which they were formed were insoluble. After hydration some minerals show a great increase in bulk, and are more readily attacked by the agents of mechanical weathering.

3. Since rain-water contains oxygen, there is a considerable oxidation of some minerals and many oxides are produced, particularly those of iron, which are red, yellow, and brown in colour.

4. Carbon-dioxide is another gas which is dissolved in rain-water. The weak acid solution, which is thus formed, produces carbonation, and amongst other compounds, carbonates and bicarbonates are developed. Most of these products are then easily dissolved in the rain-water. Carbonation is of major importance in the weathering of limestone rock (see p. 125).

The result of mechanical and chemical weathering is to reduce the original rock to particles of various compounds—this is known as comminution of the rock. The rock waste of various minerals[1] may be produced directly by either mechanical or chemical weathering but very often both types of weathering are operating together. In some instances, chemical changes in the minerals make it easier for mechanical weathering to proceed. As will be seen later the end-

[1] Mainly compounds of silicon, aluminium, calcium, iron and oxygen.

5

products may be regarded as particles of clay,[1] sand,[2] and carbonates. Common rocks, such as sandstone and grit, are developed from sand fragments; shale from clay fragments; and Chalk and limestone from the carbonates.

Some Forms of Erosion

It is necessary to pause for a moment and consider other mechanical processes which assist in the complete denudation of a rock surface. Without the preliminary comminution of rock particles that has been described, these latter processes could hardly proceed.

Wind is an agent of erosion, because when small hard fragments of rock waste are blown against other rock surfaces there is abrasion which will reduce the less-resistant particles in that rock. Where soft sandstone and brickwork are employed for the facings of buildings, the scouring effect of wind-driven particles may be very apparent. Wind plays its part in some localities on a grand scale, as in deserts and in some coastal districts (see pp. 115 and 140).

FIG. 1.4.—Formation of Earth Pillars

Raindrops, when driven by the wind, behave in very much the same fashion, and drops falling with very heavy rainfall may produce a form of erosion which is quite local, giving rise to the spectacular earth pillars (Fig. 1.4). Such pillars are found in the Italian Alps near Bolzano. Small ones are known in the Findhorn valley of Scotland and near Fochabers in the Lower Spey valley.

Rock waste is eventually transported to a stream by rain-wash and by gravity either as insoluble solid fragments in suspension or as dissolved fragments in solution. The fragments in the water are of various sizes; some are so massive that they move only when the river flows fast, and even then their movement is more akin to rolling and sliding along the river-bed. This movement of solid fragments is important, in that it leads to further wearing down as the fragments are projected on to rock surfaces in the river course. This is sometimes referred to as corrasion.

The work of a river is of such importance that a detailed study is made of it in a later chapter, but for the moment we must follow the suspended fragments as the river makes its way to the sea. In general,

[1] Hydrated aluminium silicate.
[2] Silica with oxides of iron.

6

as a river approaches the sea it can only carry quite small fragments in suspension and, of course, those solids which are in solution. On entering the sea, the flow of the river is almost completely halted. The coarser fragments in suspension are jettisoned as sand, and the very finest move out into the sea for considerable distances before sinking to the sea floor to form muds and clays.

Ice is capable of transporting rock fragments and even large rock masses. By gripping and enclosing fragments of all sizes within its mass, a sheet of ice can erode extensively any rock surface over which it moves. The scope of such ice erosion is limited by temperature and ceases with the melting of the ice. Today the areas of the world which are so affected are restricted to high latitudes or high altitudes.

Finally, mention must be made of the action of the sea along the shores of the land masses. Whilst this form of erosion is relatively restricted in area it calls for special consideration in Chapter 9.

Sedimentary Rocks

It is on the sea floor that new rock formations are produced from the assorted particles derived from the land. In addition, the dissolved solids which have been carried from the land into the sea may be extracted from solution by sea organisms in order that they may build their shells and other body structures of calcium carbonate or silica. When these organisms die, their shells and hard structures sink to the sea floor, thus forming layers of carbonates, although some portions of these layers are formed by the physical condition whereby dissolved carbonates are deposited directly from sea water with an increase of temperature.[1] Some solids remain in solution, thus increasing the salinity of the ocean waters.

Thus are formed new rocks of the type known as sedimentary. Grains of sand which are so accumulated become sandstone and grit by a process of cementation effected largely by iron oxides. Muds become clays and shales as a result of compression of one layer upon another. Carbonates produce limestone and Chalk rock.

Marine Transgressions

At this point it may be asked how such rocks are found today on the land surfaces. The continents may suffer a relative uplift, due to forces which have their application in or below the sialic rafts. Such an uplift of an original continent would expose inshore deposits that had already accumulated as waste from the land in the marginal seas. On the other hand, a depression of a sial block would permit its marginal areas to be flooded by the sea. Such flooding is known as a marine transgression, and in these marginal seas would be laid fresh

[1] It is probable that the presence of ammonia assists this deposition.

deposits from the land. Renewed uplift would expose land areas with a cover of newer surface rocks (Fig. 1.5). Such a sequence of events must have occurred on many occasions in the past. The process of marine transgression is dealt with more fully on p. 20.

Thus the continents have acquired, by a series of such transgressions, a great number of layers of sedimentary rock. These in their turn have undergone denudation, thus providing material for still younger layers of rock to be formed in the course of ages.

FIG. 1.5.—Marine Transgression of Continent (above)
Retreat of Sea after Transgression (below)

Not all sedimentary rocks are laid in marginal seas; some have been formed entirely on the land surfaces, such as certain sandstones which reflect past desert climates. Others indicate that they have been formed from the coarse material laid down by a previous river in its delta. An example of the former is provided by the New Red Sandstones of Permian and Triassic age found extensively in the Midlands of England whilst the Millstone Grit of the Pennine Uplands is largely of deltaic origin.

Rock Structures

It is evident that sedimentary rocks are laid more or less horizontally in the sea, forming layers or strata which are separated by bedding planes. Thus, these rocks show a stratification. However, on land, strata frequently show an inclination to the horizontal, possessing, in geological parlance, a dip (Fig. 1.6). The dip is expressed in degrees by the magnitude of the angle between the hori-

zontal surface and the strata. In some rock exposures it is possible
to note that the dip changes its direction (Fig. 1.7) and, in very
favourable sections, one may note that the strata may exhibit the
appearance shown in Fig. 1.8. The latter example shows folding of

FIG. 1.6.—Stratified Rocks showing Dip, Strike, and Outcrops

FIG. 1.7.—Change of Dip

FIG. 1.8—Folded Strata

FIG. 1.9.—Faulted Strata

the rocks, and this is produced by compressional forces which must
act, presumably, parallel to the surface of the earth.

In other exposures it is possible to see that the strata in two
adjacent sections of rock are displaced in relation to one another
(Fig. 1.9). This is an example of faulting and is the result of either
tensional or compressional forces acting in one or another direction.
In some cases, these forces act in a vertical plane, in other cases
they are horizontal, whilst in many cases they are oblique to these
directions. The cracks or faults which are thus developed may

penetrate deep into the sial. Joints may also occur. In sedimentary rocks these are cracks which intersect strata between the bedding planes. Joints may result from tensional forces or by the shrinkage of sedimentary rocks as they dry out. Some igneous rocks are well jointed as a result of contraction during their solidification from molten material (Fig. 1.10). Joints in rocks are of assistance in giving access to the agents of weathering and erosion.

Erosion of rocks having a dip exposes the eroded edges or out-crops of the strata (Fig. 1.6). These will vary in width and a slight dip will give wide outcrops, whereas if the same strata were dip-

Aerofilms Ltd.

FIG. 1.10.—Cliffs on the Antrim Coast, east of the Giant's Causeway.

The cliffs, some 250 feet high, are formed of a series of lava flows. Note the columnar jointing of the lava and screes at the base of the cliffs.

ping at a high angle, the outcrops would be relatively narrow. The surface trend of an outcrop is known as the strike. Rarely do extensive outcrops show a constant width as in Fig. 1.6. However, the geological map of England shows that in the east and south the out-crops of Jurassic and Cretaceous rocks have a fairly high degree of parallelism.

Igneous Rocks

Faulting which has penetrated the sial blocks may give rise to two other features deserving of comment. These cracks give access to the surface of molten material from the hot inner layers of the earth.

Thus, in certain localities, outpourings of lava (Fig. 1.10) or the building of volcanoes may occur. The molten material is sometimes sidetracked on its way to the surface and seeps in between two strata (Fig. 2.1), producing a sill of rock. The material which rises up a fault may solidify without giving a lava flow on the surface. It then produces a narrow wedge or dyke, which when exposed cuts the surface as a thin outcrop. In either case, whether the surface is reached or not, the molten material cools and solidifies to form a rock which, like granite, is crystalline. To the geographer it is sufficient to distinguish this rock as basalt. Basalt differs from granite in having mineral particles which are minute and essentially microscopic. It has also a dark greenish-black or greenish-blue colour. Quartz is less common than it is in granite, but felspar is very important. In addition there are various dark-coloured minerals formed from compounds of iron and magnesium. This assemblage of minerals may be regarded as typical of the sima which, it will be remembered, lies under the sialic rafts and forms the floors of the ocean basins.

Both granite and basalt are known as igneous rocks, and may be regarded as a mass of crystals which have formed from a hot mixture of minerals (molten rock) that has cooled. Various factors, such as the rate of cooling, the pressure, and the original composition of the molten rock, have resulted in the large crystals of granite, with its preponderant quartz and felspars, and in the small crystals of the basalt with its preponderant felspars and dark minerals.

Metamorphic Rocks

Sedimentary and igneous rocks may be altered or metamorphosed by a variety of processes, details of which are largely of geological importance. Metamorphism means, literally, a change of form. It shows itself in rocks in various ways:

1. By foliation, whereby the rock has a distinct grain shown by the alignment of mineral particles, usually resembling stratification, but often in wavy lines.

2. By cleavage, which resembles foliation, although the direction of cleavage may be quite independent of the stratification.

3. By the development of new materials which were not present in the unaltered rock; precious stones and valuable ores may be produced by metamorphism.

4. By the development of a crystalline structure from an originally amorphous rock.

5. By the development of amorphous material from an originally crystalline rock.

Sometimes more than one process may be responsible for the metamorphism. Intense heat (developed by the contact of molten rock), intense strain (from severe earth forces), solutions charged with gases (and even very hot water) may be involved, singly and severally. The physical effect of heat and strain, combined usually with chemical reactions produced by solutions, appears to result in a very profound change in the chemical or molecular structure of the various minerals within the rocks undergoing metamorphosis, so that in some cases one may say that essentially new rocks are formed.

Almost every type of sedimentary rock has a metamorphosed form. Limestone and Chalk may be converted into marble. In Weardale, Co. Durham, the baking of limestone by the injection of basalt in the Whin Sill has caused the rock to become crystalline.

Shales may be converted to slate, which is a more valuable rock, since its cleavage makes it easy to split into uniformly thick slabs (Fig. 1.11). Sandstones and grits may develop a coarse crystalline texture when they are changed into quartzite. Coal is possibly converted into anthracite by metamorphic processes. Igneous rocks may yield veins of valuable ores through metamorphosis, and steam charged with acids may convert crystalline granite into amorphous kaolin or china clay.

FIG. 1.11—Folded Slates with Cleavage

The curved lines represent the bedding planes of folded rocks whilst the straight lines show the cleavage which usually has a direction that is independent of that of the bedding.

These particular changes are fairly localized, although extensive areas of slate are recognized in Wales and elsewhere. Over a large area, such as the Highlands of Scotland, widespread metamorphism has given rocks which are distinguished by the geologist, but which may be regarded by the geographer as granitic, in that the essential features of these rocks are those of granite. Vast areas of the Canadian Shield, the Brazilian and the Guiana Plateaus have suffered from this regional metamorphism, and consist mainly of granitic rocks with local areas of particular value. Such areas are at Sudbury with its nickel ores and at Cobalt with its silver and cobalt deposits in Ontario; at Itabira, in Brazil, there are iron ores, whilst in similar regions there are to be found the gold-mining areas of the world.

Stratigraphical Sequence

One branch of geological investigation is known as stratigraphy, in which an attempt is made to decipher the order in which the rocks were formed. Originally, the sequence of sedimentary rocks was determined by two methods. It was assumed that strata which were in sequence represented successive periods of time. Supposing that three sedimentary rock layers, *a*, *b*, and *c*, are found in the order shown in Fig. 1.12*b*, then *c* was laid down before *b* and *a* was laid down after *b*. In another area of the country stratum *c* might be found above the two other layers *d* and *e* (Fig. 1.12*c*), which could therefore be regarded as of earlier origin than *c*. Let us suppose that in each of three distinct areas there are three strata (Fig. 1.12). In area (i) and area (ii) *a* is common to both, whilst in areas (ii) and (iii) *c* is a common rock. It is reasonable to assume that the complete sequence of rocks is as shown in Fig. 1.12*d*. In the early days of geological surveying, the recognition of this sequence depended upon

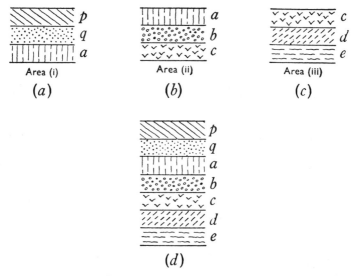

FIG. 1.12.—Sequence of Strata

the identification of rock *a* in two separate areas and so on. Whilst most sedimentary rocks have been laid down in water, it is possible for differences to occur in a given deposit over large distances, since the conditions under which deposition occurred could vary in different parts of the sea. The outward appearance of the same stratum might be very different in two separate localities, thus making correlation doubtful.

A surer method of checking the rock sequence involves the careful study of the fossil content of the rocks. To the layman two related fossils may look almost identical, but to the trained geologist certain subtle distinctions show that they are different. Such minute differences are the result of evolution, which produces marked changes in the structure of an organism over a long period of time. Such changes could hardly be wrought in the period required for the deposition of one thin layer of rock, and so one particular fossil may be used to identify a given stratum, several feet in thickness.

In more recent times the geologist has also made use of igneous rocks as a means of dating the rocks. It has already been noted that there are within the crustal layers of the earth radioactive minerals which apart from creating heat, produce of their own accord new substances by the process of disintegration. The rate of disintegration of each mineral is constant, and the amount of new substances which has been produced is used to calculate the age of the rock.

The stratigraphical sequence is shown in the table below, together with the representative rocks which were laid down at various times and their ages. Each main division in the sequence is known as an era, within each of which there are several systems of rocks; each system has some fairly characteristic rock, although within a system there may be a great variety of rocks.

STRATIGRAPHICAL TABLE

Era	System	Representative Rocks	Age in Million Years
Quaternary	Holocene (Recent) Pleistocene (Glacial)	Sands, clays, and gravels	1
Tertiary	Pliocene Miocene Oligocene Eocene	Sands, clays, and gravels. Some limestones and some areas with coal (lignite) and igneous rocks	70
Secondary	Cretaceous Jurassic Triassic	Chalk Limestones and clays	200
Primary	New Red Sandstone Permian	Sandstones Magnesian Limestone	
	Carboniferous	Coal Measures Millstone Grit Carboniferous Limestone	
	Devonian (Old Red Sandstone)	Sandstones, limestones, and shales	400
	Silurian Ordovician Cambrian	Mainly slates and shales with some igneous rocks	600
Archean	Pre-Cambrian	Mainly igneous and metamorphic rocks	At least 3,000

This stratigraphical table is of geological importance, and each system or group of rocks may include a great variety of sedimentary rocks and, since they have been formed at various times during this long interval, it is necessary to include igneous rocks as well. Without belittling the value of a fairly deep knowledge of the stratigraphical subdivisions, the primary knowledge which a geographer should gain is that of the relationship between the rocks and the landscape. Knowledge of the resistance, or lack of resistance, of certain rocks to the processes of denudation is thus desirable.

For instance, the association of many upland areas of Wales and Scotland with resistant rocks, chiefly shales and slates of Primary age or metamorphic rocks of the granitic type, should be noted. Of course, the upstanding nature of such areas does not depend solely upon the resistance of these rocks, since each area has a structural history which must be understood as well. In parts of south and eastern England, Chalk and limestone suffer little surface erosion by water. With their many joints these rocks are highly pervious to water and thus they form uplands in contrast to the neighbouring lowlands which have developed on less resistant rocks, particularly clays.

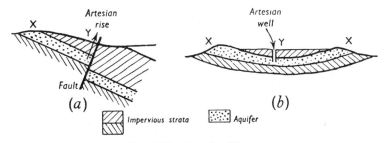

FIG. 1.13.—Artesian Water

In both diagrams the head of water at X in the saturated aquifer is higher than Y, thus permitting a rise of water to the surface along the fault in (a) or by the well which pierces the impervious layer above the aquifer in (b).

Knowledge of the water-bearing properties of rocks is of economic value. Sandstones and limestones, in particular, are usually very pervious in that they permit water to pass freely through their pores and along their joint planes. An abundance of fine pores in a rock may lead to water-logging when the pore spaces become saturated— water cannot pass through the rock which is then impervious as is common with clays and shales. Further discussion of this is given on p. 125. A stratum that bears much water, which is also free to move within the rock, is called an aquifer. Rock structures are of importance in relation to water supply. For instance, a fault may place an aquifer against an impervious stratum and cause underground water to rise to the surface (Fig. 1.13a). This is an artesian rise of water, although artesian wells are more usually associated with downfolds (Fig. 1.13b).

Coal and Petroleum

One other type of rock must be referred to, namely coal. Before coal can form there must have been a production of peat. Peat is derived from vegetation which has decayed under rather special conditions, so that the raw vegetable material has been humified. Further details of the production of humus will be given in a later chapter dealing with the formation of soils. For the moment it is sufficient to note that the plants and trees from which the peat is formed have grown in bogs and swamps, and many areas of the world show the active production of peat today. The Dismal Swamps of North Carolina (see Fig. 9.9) have modern peat layers as much as seven feet in thickness. Ideal conditions are probably found today in such areas as the Ganges delta, where there are forested swamps and a hot humid climate. With humification the plant tissues are converted into a residue which is rich in carbon as well as various hydrocarbons (compounds of carbon, hydrogen, and oxygen). Investigation of coal-bearing rocks shows that there is a succession of seams each of which represents a peat layer. The seams are separated from one another by sand and clay beds. It is probable that the peat formed on coastal flats which, as a result of minor earth movements, sank beneath the sea. On this depressed layer of peat were laid beds of coarse sands and, later, clays which built up high enough to form a new zone of coastal flats. Once again plants flourished thereon and more peat was formed only to sink with a further depression to give another coal seam. The overlying sands and clays pressed down each layer of peat and squeezed out of it both water and gases thus increasing the proportion of carbon in the material which could then be called a coal.

Various types of coal can be identified, and the varieties depend upon the plants from which the peat was formed, and the amount of chemical change which has occurred in the residue. Lignite or brown coal is the least altered form of peat, and has a relatively low carbon content. Most lignites are of Tertiary age, but the valuable coals, which have a fairly high carbon content, are usually much older, being almost exclusively Carboniferous, or late Primary, in age. The result of greater chemical changes in these coals is to form bituminous types, which grade finally into anthracite, which is almost pure carbon. The removal of so much volatile hydrocarbons in anthracite is due to the effect of very great pressure having been exerted on the coal. These pressures are often related to past earth movements and a probable increase of temperature, so that anthracite may be a metamorphosed bituminous coal. Boghead coal and cannel coal seem to be derived from microscopic forms of vegetation (algæ) which have collected as very fine muds and oozes. They have less carbon than the other coals, but they may yield oil.

In passing it may be of value to draw attention to the precise significance of the strata known as the Coal Measures. These rocks may have a thickness of several thousand feet, and yet only some forty of fifty of these feet may be coal seams. This small proportion of coal is due to the fact that consecutive seams are separated by a varying thickness of deltaic sands and clays as described above. In some areas there are no seams of coal within the Coal Measures. It is important to interpret British geological maps with care since the outcrops of Coal Measures, usually shown in black, may represent such barren coalfields. Large outcrops of Coal Measures do not necessarily coincide with large outputs of coal since the seams may be relatively few in number and considerably worked out. Furthermore much coal is obtained from concealed coalfields where the Coal Measures lie beneath younger rocks and this type of coalfield is not normally indicated on our geological maps. The map of Coal and Iron in the National Atlas (on a scale of 1:625,000) is much more informative in this respect. Incidentally, the Coal and Iron map carries very fine geological sections of many of our coalfields.

Another mineral of organic origin found in rocks is petroleum, which consists of gaseous and liquid hydrocarbons whose source is probably both animal and vegetable. As a liquid, it can migrate through pervious rock. Petroleum is thus found in porous strata, or what are called reservoir rocks, since these are so capped and underlaid by impervious rocks that the liquid is actually sealed off as a pool. But the concentration is always too great to be entirely derived from organic remains in the immediate vicinity. An oil pool, we must realize, is therefore nothing less than a rock, like an aquifer, into whose pores oil has collected by migration from source rocks: some of these may be a considerable distance from the pool. In such concentrations, gas frequently occupies the pore spaces above, and groundwater lies below, the petroleum.

The rock structures associated with oil pools are various—in particular, we may note upfolds and strata that have arched into such forms by salt domes. These domes form when salt, under great pressure rises from depth and distorts overlying strata. They may be likened to laccoliths (see p. 22), except that no igneous activity is involved. Thus in Texas many oil pools are found on the flanks of these domes. Secondly, oil may be trapped in a reservoir rock by a fault that has brought this rock immediately against an impervious one. Here the structure is that of Fig. 1.13a for artesian water, where the aquifer could be regarded as containing the oil pool. However, most oilfields are found in folded rocks of Cretaceous and Tertiary age, which are closely related to the Alpine fold mountains shown in Figs. 4.9 and 4.10.

17

Crust and Mantle

In recent years seismological observations have revealed a more detailed structure of the outer layers of the earth than has been suggested by Fig. 1.1. It will be seen from Fig. 1.14 that the outermost layers of the earth form the crust below which lies the mantle. The division between these two zones is recognized by seismologists, since below depths of about twenty-two miles beneath the continental surfaces and at only six or seven miles below the surface of the oceans, earthquake waves speed up significantly. This boundary of varying depth marks the base of the crust and is known as the Mohorovičić discontinuity. It lies in the zone which is described as being made of sima in Fig. 1.1. It is a matter of speculation at the moment as to why the sima layer should show this differentiation at this level so that its lower parts are in the mantle of the earth. Sufficient to say here that the crust has a base of sima which forms the ocean floors and underlies the continents of sial. There are, in addition, relatively thin skins of sediments on the surface of both continental and oceanic parts of the crust.

Fig. 1.14.—Crust and Mantle

In view of the shallow level of the Mohorovičić discontinuity under the oceans an attempt to bore through the crust at its thinnest part (only three to four miles below the ocean bed) is projected. Geophysicists would then have a sample of the upper part of the mantle and this, it is hoped, would shed new light on many of their problems. It seems highly probable that mantle material is involved in the formation of surface features such as volcanoes and some of the structures within mountain ranges.

The Theory of Isostasy

Evidence obtained from measurements of gravity in many areas of the world has led to the belief that the high parts of the continental masses are balanced by a sial layer which is somewhat thicker than elsewhere. The sial is less dense than the sima, but a balance is struck which may be illustrated as in Fig. 1.15. It has been suggested that the continents are rafts of sial 'floating' in a layer of sima, the substratum. If this view is permissible, then Fig. 1.15 represents a

solid continent floating in a 'liquid'. Hence, at a depth indicated by
the line XY, there should be equal pressures on equal areas of a
plane lying at that depth. In other words, if four columns of equal
cross-section (1, 2, 3, and 4) be considered, then the weight of material
in each column should be the same. Thus the thin, light sial layer of
column 2 must be balanced by a thick, dense sima layer, whilst a
thick sial layer as shown in column 3 must be balanced by a relatively
thin layer of sima and so forth. As it is assumed that there is no sial
on the ocean beds the sima must stand higher than elsewhere in both
columns 1 and 4 in order that the total weight of the light ocean water
together with the dense sima above XY in these columns is equal to
the weight of sial and sima in the middle columns. If this balance

FIG. 1.15.—Isostatic Equilibrium

exists, then the various columns are said to be in isostatic equilibrium
with one another. The word isostasy means 'equal poise', and therefore upstanding surface areas and low-lying areas are adjusted with
regard to one another. This, in brief, is the theory of isostasy.

It is very unlikely that isostatic equilibrium is maintained for very
long. Let us see how it may be disturbed, and then how a readjustment is possibly made. In Fig. 1.16 part of the cross-section shown in
Fig. 1.15 is considered. Let us assume, for the sake of our argument,
that erosion has removed the top of a mountain and spread the rock
waste to a uniform depth over the continental surface at the top of
column 2. This has disturbed the isostatic equilibrium, for clearly
the base of this column is now supporting a greater weight than the
base of column 3 which has now a lighter load. There is too great a
thickness of sial in column 2 and too little in column 3 for equilibrium
to exist. Recalling that the sima may at times become fluid, it is
regarded as possible that some of the sima flows from column 2 to
column 3. The removal of sima from column 2 would correct the
overloading, whilst the addition of sima to column 3 would make up

the deficiency of load therein. This would result in an elevation of the sial below the mountain region and a depression of the sial of the continental surface nearby. Since it is absurd to think of the sial of the continent moving up and down in separate columns, the adjustment is probably effected by a warping or tilting of the sial block, so that one part of its surface rises and another descends. Such warping could be responsible for marine transgressions which have been referred to on p. 7.

Fig. 1.16.—Effect of Disturbance at Surface and readjustment of Isostatic Equilibrium

The 'flotation' of the sial rafts, which is dependent on isostatic equilibrium, as required by the theory of isostasy, may help to explain the theory of continental drift (p. 3). Large-scale movements of the deep sima of the mantle, at the time when isostatic adjustments are taking place, may be responsible for some lateral shifting of the continents. Later, it will be necessary to refer to isostatic uplift and depression in order to explain such phenomena as the formation of mountains from geosynclines (p. 38) and various glacial problems in Chapter 6.

CHAPTER 2

Major Structures of the Earth – (1) Volcanic Land Forms

Introduction

In the ensuing sections the surface features of the earth will be examined in some detail. A description of the lineaments of the earth's surface falls into two parts. The major structures of the continents, such as mountains, plateaus, and plains, must be discussed before attention can be given to the finer details of the picture. In the first category we are concerned with features that are determined mainly by large-scale earth movements, and these range over vast periods of time. The many minor details of the second category are developed from the former group, and depend very largely upon the effects of erosion by water and, in particular areas, by ice and wind. Erosion is a lengthy process when measured against the span of a man's life, but it is relatively speedy in its effects when compared with the time involved in the production of a mountain range. It is frequently necessary to consider the effects of large-scale earth movements as well as the later and more recent effects of erosion when describing the details of a particular land form. In the discussion that follows, the major pattern of the earth's surface will be traced by reference to vulcanicity, mountain building, and plateau construction, with associated rift valleys. The decoration of this pattern by the minor details will be developed later from a study of the work of rivers, ice, and wind.

Vulcanicity

Below the crust there is material which at times becomes liquid and thus may be able to rise to the surface of the earth through conveniently placed fissures and pipes (or vents). Despite the high temperatures at depth this material is usually solid because of the great pressure exerted by the superior masses of rock. At times, a local increase of heat, combined almost certainly with a reduction in pressure causes this material together, in all probability, with the basal layers of the crustal sima to become molten rock or magma. Whilst magma is essentially a mineral aggregate it contains a considerable amount of gas including water vapour. As the magma rises the decreasing pressure releases some of the included gases and when the surface of the earth is reached much of the original gas has been lost. The molten rock is then called lava which unlike the original magma is relatively poorly charged with gas.

Whilst access of magma to the continental surfaces and ocean floors results in volcanic activity the rising magma may penetrate only to a limited extent into the earth's crust, chilling, after engulfing some of the crustal rock, when its movement is arrested. All such activity, whether taking place within the crust or on its surface, is known as vulcanicity. Reference to volcanic activity should imply that only surface vulcanicity is under consideration.

FIG. 2.1.—Forms of Igneous Rocks

When the magma chills inside the crustal layers, it produces several types of rock masses (Fig. 2.1). Great masses known as bathyliths, with domed upper surfaces, may extend upwards from a deep-seated magma reservoir. At higher levels and nearer the surface the molten rock may have been squeezed in between two layers of surface material, and has produced a laccolith on cooling. The supply of magma to a laccolith has possibly been effected by means of a thin horizontal layer of molten rock which was an offshoot of a vertical stream of molten rock. These horizontal and vertical layers of chilled rock are known as sills and dykes respectively. The injection of rock to produce a laccolith has distorted the surface layers above, and gives a dome-shaped mountain or hill mass. Such are found in the Henry Mountains of Utah, in the upper part of the Colorado Basin. Removal of the surface layers by erosion may expose the surface of bathyliths and laccoliths. This has occurred in South-west England, where Dartmoor, Bodmin Moor and associated uplands are the exposed surfaces of bathyliths. Phacoliths are similar to laccoliths, but the magma has been injected into folded structures. If the magma collects on the crest of an upfold, then a saddle reef is formed, which is frequently the site of mineral deposits of value.

When the molten rock flows out on the surface of the earth, it spreads in extensive sheets and, in contact with the atmosphere, chills fairly rapidly to form a congealed lava flow. Extrusion of lava is not infrequently accompanied by explosions, which help to build up volcanic cones. Broadly speaking, the rock which solidifies in depth, in the crust, is coarser in grain than the rock which forms on the surface. The rocks in bathyliths and many laccoliths are akin to granite, with large crystals, having cooled very slowly at depth. A lava solidifies very quickly to produce a fine-textured rock with small crystals, known as basalt. The rocks in sills and dykes are usually not unlike basalt (see p. 11). When weathered and exposed, sills and dykes may give rise to local relief features. Sills may form waterfalls, as at High Force, in Teesdale, whilst part of Hadrian's Wall in Northumberland also lies on the Whin Sill.

To the geographer, surface vulcanicity is the more important, and is represented by:

(*a*) Outflows of lava.

(*b*) Explosive activity.

(*c*) Emission of steam and hot water charged with various substances. Sometimes all three types of surface vulcanicity are active in the same locality, whilst elsewhere only one type may be present.

Lava Flows

Lava in these flows is not usually accompanied by large quantities of gas, so that it represents a relatively gentle form of volcanic activity. Today lava may be seen pouring out periodically in Iceland. It issues spasmodically in great flows from a long line of fissures. Study of such areas as the North-west Deccan of India, the plateaus of the Columbia-Snake rivers in the States of Washington and Oregon, and the Antrim Plateau of Northern Ireland shows that in the past there were several distinct lava flows, each probably separated by a considerable interval of time (see Fig. 1.10). The explanation of this intermittent activity is probably related to the conditions at depth which control magma movements. It is suggested that the rock material becomes fluid in only small quantities at a time. The extent to which lava flows from a fissure, before chilling is sufficient to cause it to become solid, is determined not so much by its initial temperature as by its mineral composition and gas content. If the lava is rich in minerals containing silica, it tends to be viscous, and so its progress is limited. On the other hand, when the silica content of the lava is relatively low and ferro-magnesian minerals are abundant, it is very mobile, and the lava will extend over great distances before

23

solidification occurs. Loss of gas from a lava tends to increase its viscosity.

Some lavas flow gently, producing relatively smooth surfaces which are, however, undulating like irregular waves. These are known as ropy lavas (in Hawaii—pahoehoe) whilst others have quite irregular surfaces and are known as block lavas (in Hawaii—aa). The blocks are partly the result of small explosions caused by entrapped gases which shatter the congealing crust of the lava. When ropy lava solidifies on the sea floor it may form rounded masses of rock when it is called a pillow lava. Yet another feature is the development of well-jointed vertical columns in lavas as seen in the Giant's

FIG. 2.2.—Basic Lava Cone Volcano

FIG. 2.3.—Section across Hawaii

Causeway in Antrim and in the Isle of Staffa in the Inner Hebrides of Scotland (see Fig. 1.10). Excessively rapid chilling may result in the formation of volcanic glass (obsidian) in which practically no crystalline structure may be discerned.

Lava Cones

Not always does the lava find its outlet by a fissure of great length. Eruption of lava is often confined to a small vent, and it is then that a cone develops. Usually this restricted vent is responsible for encouraging explosive activity, since it may become sealed by chilled rock, which must be blown away before further activity is possible. There are various types of cone, and each is determined by differences in the lava and by the presence or absence of vigorous explosive activity. Some cones are built almost exclusively by lava, which flows out from a crustal vent. A very mobile lava will develop a low cone, which is little more than a series of lava flows, but which is higher in the middle and radiates in all directions from the vent (Fig. 2.2). Such are known as shield volcanoes.

Successive outpourings of lava will tend to build up the cone to a certain extent, but such cones invariably show a base which is broad in relation to the height. The island of Hawaii is formed from the higher parts of such basic lava cones. In the south-west of the island is the largest cone, the active Mauna Loa with Kilauea on its south-eastern flank. To the north are the inactive cones of Mauna Kea, Kohala and Hualalai. The section (Fig. 2.3) reveals that the base of Mauna Loa is about 120 miles across at a depth of some 17,000 feet below sea level whilst the summit is about 6 miles above the sea floor.

On the other hand, a viscous lava will produce a dome-shaped cone, since the congealing of the lava in this case is quite rapid and the most elevated part has a height which is great in proportion to the breadth of the base. Further additions of lava in such cones develop from inside, and the earlier-formed layers are heaved

FIG. 2.4.—Acid Lava Cone Volcano

up (Fig. 2.4). Extinct cones of this type are to be found in the region of Auvergne in Central France, where they help to build the characteristic landscape of the area (puys d'Auvergne).

Explosive Activity

As the magma rises towards the surface, there is expansion of its included gases, and this may give explosive activity. This causes a fragmentation of the lava much in the way that air bubbles shatter the surface of boiling water. It has been noted that a sealed vent must be blown free by renewed activity, so that explosions may give a shower of fragments consisting of both new lava and previously formed rock. The fragments which are ejected by these explosions may be fairly massive, volcanic bombs as large as big boulders, but, in general, they are smaller, and are called volcanic ash. The larger fragments usually fall around the top of the vent or the crater, and assist in building the cone upwards, whilst smaller fragments are responsible for developing the cone outwards, since the latter are thrown farther and fall on the sides of the cone. The finest of this fragmentary material is known as volcanic dust, and often remains suspended in the atmosphere for a long time after the eruption has occurred. This dust is usually carried away by air currents and gradually settles on areas of the earth's surface or on the ocean floors which are remote from the volcano. Some fragments are cooled so rapidly that they form volcanic glass. When large quantities of this dust are disseminated through the atmosphere, particularly vivid sunsets are common. After eruptions of great magnitude cool weather may be a feature of the ensuing months, due, it is thought, to the interception of the sun's rays by the fragments in suspension in the air and the consequent reduction of insolation at the earth's surface.

The alternation of lava flow and explosive activity creates a composite volcanic cone which is typical of most volcanoes. The structure of a composite cone is shown in Fig. 2.5. It will be observed that the

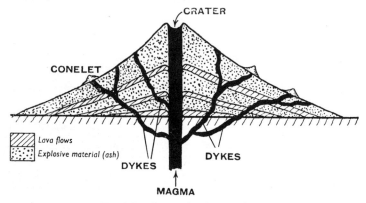

FIG. 2.5.—Composite Cone Volcano

cone is high compared with that of a basic lava volcano. The sides of the cone have a slope of about 30°–40°, this being determined by the angle of rest of the fragmentary material. Lava has, at certain stages in the history of the volcano, issued sideways from the vents, with the formation of dykes which have strengthened the cone. Sometimes active conelets are established on the flanks of the main volcano; these are known as parasitic cones. Vesuvius is an excellent example of a cone built of lava flows and fragmentary material. In some instances eruption has been exclusively of the explosive type, so that the cone is composed entirely of fragmentary material. These cones are lofty, and resemble in appearance the composite cones. Monte Nuovo, near Naples, is an example of such a cone, also El Misti, in Peru (Fig. 2.6).

Catastrophic explosions which probably disrupt a congealed plug in the vent of a quiescent volcano may result in a radical modification of the cone. The upper part of the cone is weakened to such an extent by the explosions that it subsides, the crater at the top of the vent becoming much wider and so a caldera is formed. Fracturing of the sides of the caldera is quite common (Fig. 2.7). Kilauea, in the Hawaiian Islands, is a caldera on the flanks of Mauna Loa. Krakatoa, in the Sunda Straits, was converted from an island volcano into a great caldera which is now largely occupied by the sea as a result of

James Sawders—Combine

FIG. 2.6.—El Misti, Peru

A volcanic cone of fragmentary material, showing the crater from the air.

a very violent eruption in 1883. The cone of Vesuvius was wrecked by the explosive eruption of A.D. 79, when Pompeii and Herculaneum were overwhelmed by very hot ashes and hot mud, respectively. Frequently a new cone arises within a caldera. The modern cone of Vesuvius is placed inside the older caldera, and in this century Anak Krakatoa (the Child of Krakatoa) has appeared in the sea area which occupies the site of the earlier island.

FIG. 2.7.—A caldera

Volcanoes may be distinguished by the rhythm and intensity of their explosive activity. The fairly regular and moderate explosions which are characteristic of Stromboli, in the Lipari Islands of the Tyrrhenian Sea, are replaced in the case of Vesuvius by irregular and violent activity, accompanied by a towering cloud of fragments. Sometimes the upward release of gases is impossible on account of a plug of chilled lava which seals the vent, and then the gases and hot ashes issue sideways as a blast of hot fragments. These blasts are made very mobile by the abundance of gas, which helps to reduce friction between the moving fragments. Montagne Pelée, on the island of Martinique, erupted in 1902 with such *nuées ardentes*.

V. C. Browne

FIG. 2.8.—Mount Egmont, North Island, New Zealand

A typical volcanic cone showing both radial and dendritic drainage.

This type of eruption is probably the most dangerous of all, since nothing which is in the path of the erupted material is likely to escape destruction. The town of St. Pierre, which lay below Montagne Pelée, was therefore literally smothered in hot dust.

On the other hand there is the quiet emission of lava as generally displayed by Kilauea. In recent years the caldera of this volcano has been little more than a lake of bubbling lava whose level rises and falls, reflecting changes deep down. Occasionally Kilauea may be explosive and at times there are spectacular fountains of incandescent lava which fill up the lava lake after its level may have fallen particularly low. Such fountains have on occasions, as in the 1958–60 eruption, risen to heights of some 2,000 feet.

Land Forms produced by Volcanoes

Volcanoes may form quite notable elements in the structure of the continents, and many significant mountain peaks in the Andes, the western mountains of North America, the islands off eastern Asia, and in many other localities are volcanic cones (Fig. 2.8).

Chilled lava in the vent of a volcano may extend down as a solid plug below the base of the cone and produce either an extinct or a dormant volcano. Dormancy may be ended, when the chilled plug is forced out or disrupted by renewed activity, as in the case of Montagne Pelée, described above. In extinct volcanoes there has been no activity over long periods of geological time. The result is that the cones of such volcanoes have been reduced by erosion so that their conical shape is either much modified (see p. 79, radial drainage-planèzes) or largely destroyed. The almost complete reduction of an extinct cone is seen in the volcanic crags, such as those of Arthur's Seat and the rock on which the castle is situated, at Edinburgh. Here the outer parts of the cone have been removed, but the solid plug which sealed the volcano has been more successful in resisting erosion, so that it remains as a conspicuous feature of the landscape (Fig. 6.26). In the craters of some extinct volcanoes there are lakes today. Several of these are found near Naples, in the Phlegrean Fields, and others are located in the Eifel district of the Rhineland of Germany. The most famous example is that of Crater Lake in Oregon. A crater lake is shown in Fig. 2.9.

The distribution of the outstanding active volcanoes in the world today is given on the maps (Figs. 4.9 and 4.10).

Hot Springs and Geysers

A relatively mild form of vulcanicity is the emission of steam, derived from magma, as well as from atmospheric water which has seeped down, and hot water charged with various minerals. Fumaroles and solfataras are points of issue, on the sides of volcanic cones and on lava flows, for such emanations. Around these springs are deposited multi-coloured layers (sometimes in the form of terraces) of siliceous sinter and travertine, the latter formed of calcium carbonate. Geysers are found in areas of waning vulcanicity such as Iceland, New Zealand and the Yellowstone National Park in U.S.A.

The Aircraft Operating Co. of Africa (Pty.) Ltd

FIG. 2.9.—Crater Lake, near Lake Kivu, Zaïre

Part of the fault scarps of the western East African rift valley is seen in the background.

At no great depth the pressure is so increased that water will not boil until its temperature is raised much above the normal boiling point. A sudden decrease of pressure on such super-heated water will cause a paroxysmal release of steam which hurls the water from relatively shallow reservoirs to heights of 100 feet or more into the air. The ejections of a geyser are intermittent, since intervening quiescent periods are required for the critical temperature to be reached.

CHAPTER 3

Major Structures of the Earth – (2) Mountains

Mountains

Every continent has a variety of structural features which give it a distinctive pattern. A relief map of any continent will show very clearly the contrast between highlands and lowlands, so that the recognition of many mountains is relatively simple. From the point of view of the geologist and the geomorphologist, a mountain region is not determined solely by its superior relief, but also by its structural characteristics. It may happen that regions which display these structures are relatively lowland areas today. The predominant features which may therefore be regarded as typical of mountains are the product of certain geological processes.

Simple Folds	Asymmetric Folds	Overfolds
(*a*) Equal dips	(*b*) Unequal dips	(*c*) Dips in same direction

In each part → Dips, ➡ Forces

FIG. 3.1.—Types of Fold

Folding

Compressional forces acting horizontally along the surface layers of the earth will produce simple folds (Fig. 3.1*a*). Although such simplicity of structure may be seen occasionally in mountains, it is much more common to find complex folds. The folding forces which are opposed to one another will rarely be equal and furthermore the resistance to these forces will vary not only from one rock to another but also along a given stratum. Thus irregularities will occur as in Fig. 3.1*b* and *c*, where two other types of folding are shown. The varying dips on the several limbs or sides of the folds help to distinguish them. Overfolds may develop still further into recumbent folds whose limbs are more or less horizontal (Fig. 3.4).

31

As an upfold is formed there is tension or stretching in the rocks on its crest so that joints are developed there. These joints assist in the fairly rapid erosion of the upfolds whereas the rocks in a downfold are compressed, giving them strength to resist rapid erosion. Not uncommonly in areas that have been folded extended erosion may lead to inverted relief in that the upfolds become valleys with intervening ridges formed by remnants of the downfolds.

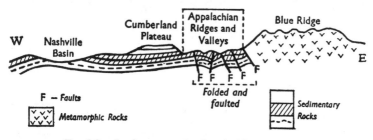

FIG. 3.2.—Section across the Appalachian Mountains

Faulting

Faulting which results in the vertical displacement of rock masses is caused by forces which are essentially radial to the surface of the earth and at right angles to those producing folds. Nevertheless it is feasible that lateral forces create tension in the surface rocks thus forming cracks that permit vertical movement of the rock masses —downwards by gravity and upwards by pressure, the latter caused possibly by deep-seated movements of magma. Reference to Fig. 3.2 will show fault patterns in the Appalachian Mountains. The faults are seen to cut across the folds which suggests that faulting must have come after folding in the development of this mountain structure. Other effects of faulting are discussed in Chapter 4.

Thrusting

Thrusting refers to the lateral displacement of rocks by faulting and folding. Faulting may result in nearly horizontal movements of rock masses. Forces act along thrust planes and result sometimes in movements over very considerable distances. Within many mountain zones several thrust planes have developed together with intermediate minor thrust planes which are usually inclined to the major oness This is called imbricate structure (resembling the overlapping tiles on a roof) and it is associated particularly with the North-west Highlands of Scotland (Fig. 3.3). Thrusting, without faulting, may convert an overfold into a recumbent fold (Figs. 3.4 and 3.5). Recumbent folds piled up on top of one another (like a folded tablecloth) form nappes. Such overthrust masses of rock are a particular feature of the Central Alps (Fig. 6.11). In many instances recumbent folds will fracture under the intense forces and then the folding passes into thrust faulting (Fig. 3.4*b*).

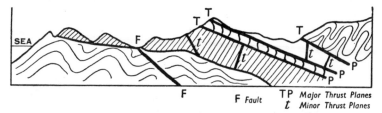

FIG. 3.3.—Imbricate Structure in North-west Highlands of Scotland

Stages in Mountain Formation

There is clearly a relationship between these various processes, since they all tend to produce a reduction in the surface area of the rock masses. This shortening of the surface is regarded as an essential feature in the building of mountains, and the sections of various mountain regions shown in this chapter demonstrate that singly or

FIG. 3.4.—Recumbent Folds. Both these structures are typical of nappes
(a) with almost horizontal dips on limbs.   (b) part of fold has been displaced by thrust faulting.

in combination these processes produce a contraction of part of the earth's surface. Investigation by geologists has shown that much of a mountain region is built of great thicknesses of sedimentary rocks, often very considerably metamorphosed. Where a particular group of sedimentary rocks can be traced throughout a mountain zone and beyond it into the adjacent lowlands, it frequently happens that the thickness of these layers varies considerably. For instance, certain strata are 25,000–40,000 feet thick within the Appalachian Mountains, and yet the same group of rocks in the Mississippi Basin, to the west, is only 4,000 feet thick. Such a thickness as 40,000 feet represents a long period of accumulation, and it would appear that the mountain zone has been derived from the section of the deposits which was thickest.

Intense folding and thrusting, together with faulting in depth, have given access to molten rock from below. Thus the mountain

Yugoslav National Tourist Office

FIG. 3.5.– Fold Structures in the Durmitor Mountains, Yugoslavia

structures are ramified by masses of igneous rock which have resulted from widespread vulcanicity. In some mountain regions active volcanoes are found, and a good many mountain areas are characterized by the remnants of basaltic lava flows and volcanic cones, whilst within the cores of the intensely folded structures are granitic masses which represent the exposed upper surfaces of great bathyliths (see Fig. 3.8). Metamorphism of both sedimentary and igneous rocks has been inevitable, because of the great strain resulting from thrusting combined with the heat produced by the contact of the molten rock. With such regional metamorphism there is a close association between valuable mineral deposits and mountain structures.

Patterns of Mountain Regions

Mountains may be grouped according to their geological age. Some mountains are 'young' whilst others are 'old'—the terms 'young' and 'old' are used in the relative sense since even 'young' mountains may be several million years in age. Clearly the presence or absence, within a mountain area, of rocks of a known age gives a clue to the time when the mountains were built. Admittedly such dating is a more involved process than has just been suggested but, with other evidence, this is the main approach to the problem.

Obviously 'older' mountains have had more time to be affected by denudation, so that although the typical mountain structures are present there are substantial differences in the appearance of these mountains as compared with 'younger' mountains. Although 'young' mountains have been denuded they are usually higher than 'older' mountains. Furthermore prolonged erosion has reduced 'older' mountains to peneplains (almost level surfaces at low elevation), or they stand out as plateau regions, which are peneplains that have been elevated by more recent uplift. In fact, most 'older' mountains have probably experienced several episodes of reduction to peneplains followed by uplift and further erosion so that only the lower parts of the original mountain structures are visible—these are often referred to as the roots of the mountains.

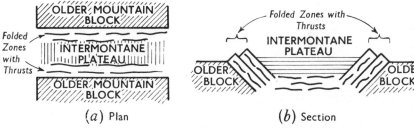

(a) Plan   (b) Section

FIG. 3.6.—Pattern of Fold Mountain Region

It is sensible, then, to examine the pattern of 'young' mountains, since they are more likely to show the ground plan of what may be regarded as a typical mountain zone. This pattern is related to 'older' mountain areas that are represented by plateaus bordering the 'younger' mountain region. The simplified pattern may be shown by a diagram (Fig. 3.6a). Highly folded (Fig. 3.7) and thrusted zones of sedimentary rocks lie between areas which are remnants of 'older' mountain blocks. The mountain zone is invariably longer than it is wide and included within the folded region is an area of relatively undisturbed rocks which are recognized as intermontane plateaus (Fig. 3.6b).

The plan, as shown in Fig. 3.6, is matched in most of its details in many of the present-day 'young' mountains. Perhaps, the nearest approach to this ground plan is afforded by the extensive systems of mountains which cross the great land mass of Eurasia, including the Alps and their associated ranges, as well as the Himalayan region. Fig. 4.10 will show the two border regions of plateaus which are 'older' mountains. These are represented by most of northern Africa, Arabia, and the Indian Deccan on the south side, whilst on the northern side is the series of plateaus and plains in Central and Northern Europe and in Central Asia. The folded and thrusted zones are shown in Fig. 3.6 by sinuous lines enclosing such intermontane plateaus as Tibet, Iran, Anatolia. Farther west in the Alpine region these plateaus are not represented, but in their place are the basins of the Mediterranean Sea which have been produced by extensive faulting followed by foundering of intermontane areas. The great western mountains of the Americas (Fig. 4.9) exhibit a similar, if

The London Electrotype Agency, Ltd.

FIG. 3.7.—Allegheny Ridges and Valleys, United States of America

Denuded fold structures in the Appalachian Mountains. Note the trellised drainage which is exhibited.

apparently less complete, plan. In North America the eastern folded and thrusted zone of the Rocky Mountains and the western zone of the Cascade Mountains, Sierra Nevada, and the several coast ranges are separated by the intermontane plateaus of Arizona and the Great Basin of Nevada, with the adjacent lava plateaus of the Columbia-Snake River basin. In Central America the outer folded zones are literally one, although an intermontane region is found in Mexico. South America has in the Andean region only one extensive plateau area which is restricted to parts of Peru and Bolivia; elsewhere the two folded zones have coalesced to form one, although smaller intermontane areas are recognized in the northern parts. These American mountains have bordering blocks of 'older' mountains in the east of Canada and the United States and in South America, but elsewhere in the west and to the east of Central America these blocks have foundered, and in all probability lie in the Pacific and Atlantic ocean basins.

The ground plan of some mountains shows a series of mountain arcs. These are very characteristic of the folded mountains which thread the islands off the eastern coast of Asia. The trend of a mountain range in one island may be clearly traced into an adjacent island. The arcs are convex towards the Pacific Ocean and similar curves are noticed in the Himalaya Mountains and on the south side of the Iranian Plateau (see Fig. 4.10). It is possible to trace similar arcs in the mountains of other continents; some of these may be convex towards the continental interiors (i.e. the Rocky Mountains in North America and the main Alps as well as the Carpathian Mountains in Europe—see Figs. 4.9 and 4.10). It has been suggested that these Asiatic arcs are the surface outcrop of great thrust planes which extend inwards from the surface of the earth and towards the interior of the continent of Asia. Each arc may be related to a 'pole', and it has been shown that the poles of the Asiatic arcs align themselves along parts of two great circles.

The Process of Mountain Building

In the preceding pages a description of the structure, rocks, and the ground plan of mountain regions has been attempted. Many theories have been advanced to give an adequate explanation of the piling of rock masses into a mountain system. Early attempts were concerned with the contraction of the surface layers of the earth as cooling down proceeded through long periods of geological history. Jeffreys computed the loss of surface area which would occur as the result of a calculated contraction of the earth. Unfortunately, a re-examination of his calculations showed a great discrepancy between the shrinkage that Jeffreys allowed and the reduction of surface area required by the geologist to produce all the older and younger mountains which were recognized. Joly developed a theory which turned upon the accumulation of radioactive heat within the rocks of the sima. He argued that periodically sufficient internal heat accumulates in the sima to make it plastic, and thus allows the sial rafts to subside to a certain extent. This subsidence leads to an extension of the oceans, whose waters would in time cause a dissipation of this heat, and then the sima gradually returns to a more rigid state. The contracting sima would compress the sial rafts from the sides and also thrust them upwards. The combined effect would, in Joly's opinion, develop the structures of folded mountains. Neither of these two theories, which have been merely outlined, is acceptable today, although each may contain an element of the truth. No satisfactory explanation has yet been given of the forces which are required to build mountains, but although modern theories are very divergent in many of their details, there is general agreement that a geosyncline must be formed prior to mountain development.

The geosyncline is regarded as a long and narrow depression which developed in the sialic crust, and was occupied by the sea. In it sedimentary rocks, derived from continental areas, were laid. It will be remembered that observation has shown that parts of the Appalachian Mountains are built of rocks which are some ten times thicker than they are outside the mountain region. Accumulation of such a thickness of rock would only be possible if the bottom of the geosyncline was steadily sinking throughout the very long period of deposition. Forty thousand feet of sediments in the Appalachian zone were accumulated over a period of the probable order of 200–300 million years. After a certain stage of deposition had been reached, the geosyncline would be overweighted, and thus, according to the theory of isostasy (p. 18) adjustments in the load of the column of rocks below the geosyncline would occur. It is thought that the sial layer bends downwards beneath the geosyncline and sima is displaced. To compensate for this disturbance of the sima it is conceivable that the continents would be slightly uplifted. Continuation of this overloading of the geosyncline leads to the development of forces which act from the sides of the trough of sediments towards the centre (Fig. 3.8). In time the sediments are literally crushed between the continental blocks, which resemble the jaws of a vice, and intense folding of the rocks occurs. At the same time an uplift of the sediments, with thrusting (Fig. 3.9), results in the development of the other features which are common to mountains, such as the overthrusting of nappes, vulcanicity in its various forms, and the formation of inter-montane zones which are parts of the geosynclinal deposits that have been relatively undisturbed by these forces. In addition, some of the basement rocks or sial may be incorporated in the mountain structure.

An elaboration of this theory of mountain building from a geosyncline suggests that the sialic base of the geosyncline becomes so strained with down-warping that it fractures, and a great mass of sial sinks into the underlying sima. The gap which is thus produced permits the movement of the continental blocks on either side of the geosyncline with consequent folding. At the same time this gap gives molten magma easy access to the folded mass. Fig. 3.8 shows the stages of development of the Alps, based on such theories as have been outlined. It should be emphasized that in the stages which follow the crushing of the geosynclinal sediments, the elevation of the folded structures inevitably upsets isostatic balance and further adjustments are necessary. Since the sediments are relatively light, there is probably a tendency for sima to move back beneath the geosyncline and buoy them up. This uplift is no doubt responsible for the forces which develop thrusts, and the outward facing thrust

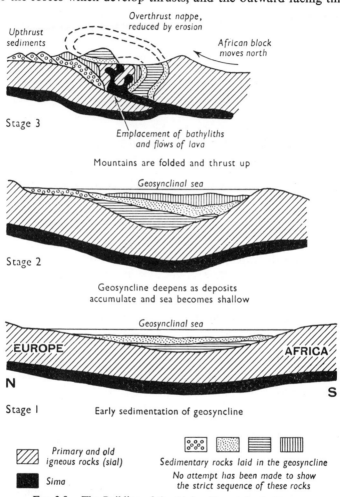

Upthrust sediments

Overthrust nappe, reduced by erosion

African block moves north

Stage 3

Emplacement of batholiths and flows of lava

Mountains are folded and thrust up

Geosynclinal sea

Stage 2

Geosyncline deepens as deposits accumulate and sea becomes shallow

Geosynclinal sea

EUROPE

AFRICA

N

S

Stage I   Early sedimentation of geosyncline

Primary and old igneous rocks (sial)

Sima

Sedimentary rocks laid in the geosyncline

No attempt has been made to show the strict sequence of these rocks

FIG. 3.8.—The Building of the Alpine Mountains in Europe.

planes, shown in the cross-section of the Himalaya Mountains (Fig. 3.10), are probably due to this process. Geosynclines take a very long time to develop, and since there is a very considerable geological interval between mountains of different ages, it would seem that

Literary Services Mondiole Ltd.

FIG. 3.9.—Part of the Swiss Alps to the east of Zürich Lake

Upthrust sedimentary rocks are seen on the northern edge of the fold mountain zone. The view is taken looking eastwards.

there are periods when geosynclines are absent from the surface of the earth. Today there is only one region which has some of the characteristics of a geosyncline, and it lies in the area of the East Indies and close to some of the mountain arcs which have been mentioned. Off-shore to the south of Java and Sumatra the force of

FIG. 3.10.—Cross-section of Himalayan Zone

gravity is much less than normal. This observation has been interpreted as an indication of a down-warp in the sial which must be occupied by lighter rocks, presumably sediments. If this is true, then the mountains of the Asiatic arcs are very young indeed, and may, in fact, represent the earliest upfolded structures to emerge from a geosyncline.

40

Holmes has developed a theory which seeks to explain the down-warping of the sialic crust more satisfactorily than perhaps the earlier theories do. He envisages the development of radioactive heat in the sima layer which sets up currents in the plastic sima that are analogous to convection currents in a liquid. These may become so forceful that they drag the base of the sial downwards and create a geosynclinal depression (Fig. 3.11), in which eventually the

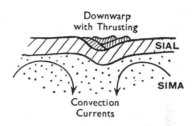

FIG. 3.11.—Downwarping of a Geosyncline

sediments are crushed. Like Joly, he insists upon the dissipation of this heat after considerable time has elapsed. Then the convection effects wane and the sima chills and produces uplift in the mountain zone.

CHAPTER 4

Major Structures of the Earth – (3) Plateaus and Rift Valleys: Conclusion

Fault Structures

In the preceding sections it has been necessary to refer to the effects of both folding and faulting, together with thrusting, which have worked severally to produce mountain structures. It will be recalled that the major movements that are involved in such developments are developed by forces which act more or less horizontally, and these may be called collectively, orogenetic, or in other words, they create mountains. In some areas the present structures may show that the predominant forces which have operated on the surface layers of the earth have been at right angles to the direction of these orogenetic forces, and the main effect is not to reduce the surface area by crumpling, but to produce a relative uplift or depression of adjacent areas in conjunction with large-scale faulting. The units of surface relief which are thus developed are known as horsts and rift valleys. Figs. 4.1 and 4.2 will show these two units in perspective. The

Fig. 4.1.—Development of a Horst

classic explanation of the development of these features, which are almost inversions of one another, suggests that they are due to uplift or depression, or to both these processes acting simultaneously (the arrows in Figs. 4.1 and 4.2 show how upward and downward movements can account for these features). Whilst a horst may stand out above relative lowland on either side, a rift valley (or graben) is largely defined by the two horsts which are its margins. In both cases the boundaries of these features of relief are steep edges which are known as fault scarps (Fig. 2.9). Fault scarps may be reduced by erosion, but it is possible for the scarp feature to be re-established by the wearing of the weaker rocks along the fault. Such a scarp may be almost indistinguishable from a fault scarp but, as it is an erosional feature, it is better described as a fault-line scarp.

Some of the most perplexing problems have been involved in the explanation of the uplift of great blocks of the surface layers of the earth and the subsidence of sections of the crust to account for the formation of a rift valley. It will be noted, from Fig. 4.2, that the depressed block which has formed the floor of the rift valley is comparable to the keystone of an arch, but it has sunk, despite the wedging effect of the horsts on either side. It has been suggested that

FIG. 4.2 —Development of a Rift Valley

the collapse of the crust forced the horsts apart. On the other hand the descending block may have become tilted to adjust itself to this construction. Often vulcanicity has occurred at the site of the faults at the foot of the fault scarps, although this is by no means an inevitable consequence. At one time this collapse was considered to be a result of the contraction of the surface of a cooling earth. It has also been suggested, however, that tension in the earth's crust pulled the horsts away from the rift block which was then able to sink.

Plateaus

Since horsts, which may be extensive enough to produce great plateaus as major features of the earth's surface, can be regarded as products of uplift, the forces which are responsible for them are known as epeirogenetic. The expression 'epeirogenetic' refers to the formation of the continental masses. It will not have escaped notice that one stage of mountain building involves extensive uplift, with the production of intermontane plateaus. Many of the 'older' mountains may be regarded as upland features that have been raised by epeirogenetic forces which operated much later than the orogenetic forces. European massifs, such as Bohemia and the Central Plateau of France, as well as the North and Central Pennine Uplands, have been produced by such uplifts, although they may contain within their limits folded structures dating from earlier episodes of

Royal Canadian Air Force

FIG. 4.3.—Plateau of Devon Island, Northern Canada

The horizontal Silurian rocks of this plateau have been little disturbed for some 400 million years. It has been dissected by rivers and by ice. Note the fjord in the middle distance and the braided river entering a delta in the foreground.

mountain building. All such plateaus have been modified after uplift as a result of the dissection of their surfaces by the forces of erosion (Fig. 4.3).

The 'older' mountains have been called block mountains by many writers, but it is more suitable to apply this term to more restricted uplands which often show a distinct tilt and which are bounded by distinct fault scarps. Tilted blocks of this type are found in the North and Central Pennine regions. The north part of this zone is bounded on its northern and western sides by faults, the latter giving the bold fault scarp of Cross Fell Edge. In section this region is seen to be tilted eastwards towards Co. Durham (Fig. 4.4). This tilted plateau of northern England is a small-scale example of more extensive areas, such as the Deccan of India, the Arabian Plateau, the Brazilian

Plateau, and many others. When faulting is complex and dislocations of the surface are unequal, basin and range structure is developed as in the intermontane zone of the west of the United States of America. Surface patterns of faults are very intricate, and since both upward and downward displacements have occurred (although the

FIG. 4.4.—Tilted Block Plateau of North Pennine Uplands

main effect has been one of uplift), a series of plateaus or longitudinal flat-topped ranges are found in juxtaposition to depressed areas or basins (Fig. 7.3). Most of the ranges are individually somewhat like the tilted blocks of the North Pennine region. Observe that this section, across the basins and ranges, in Fig. 4.5, is from west to east and only shows tilting in those directions. In most cases the floors of

FIG. 4.5.—Section across Basins and Ranges
Region (U.S.A.)

the basins and the tops of the ranges will be tilted towards the north or south. Fault developments, at right angles to one another, may subdivide a basin area into a series of minor basins each at a different level. Quite frequently tilts are so varied that certain basins are 'land-locked' by fault scarps on all sides, and have, in consequence, no

FIG. 4.6.—Section of the Rhine Rift Valley

outward drainage. These areas may be quite elevated and shut in by even higher mountains, so that they are largely deprived of rainfall. Such flows of surface water as may occur are inadequate to fill the basins and so produce lakes which could spill over the edges of

45

Over 1500 feet above sea level (approx)

─·─·─ Sea level

More than 600 feet below sea level (approx)

Contours interpolated at 450 and 900 feet approximately

SCALE

0   5   10   15   20 miles

By Courtesy of the 'Department of Geography, The Hebrew University, Jerusalem

FIG. 4.7—Jordan Rift Valley

the basin. Thus these basins are characterized by internal drainage with salt lakes and playas (Fig. 7.8). Similar enclosed basins, such as that of Tarim, are found amongst the plateaus of inner Asia.

Rift Valleys

It will be noted from Fig. 4.6 that a series of parallel faults may form something like a stairway of faulted blocks. Such faults are known as step faults. Rift valleys are not infrequently developed within a zone of step faults although usually the series of fault scarps is not seen because more recent deposits have filled in the lower part of the trough and thus conceal the steps, as is true of the Rhine rift valley. The rift valley of the Jordan in Palestine shows from a relief map that a series of fault scarps is quite usual. Fig. 4.7 shows the inner trench, which is more than 600 feet below sea-level, with the Jordan flowing between fault scarps. Nevertheless, the rift feature is apparent in other scarps set at a considerable distance from the Jordan plain and at an elevation of between 600 and 1,000 feet above sea-level. Outstanding rift valleys include:

1. Central Scotland, bounded by the Grampian Mountains and the Southern Uplands.

2. The Rhine Rift Valley, bounded by the Vosges Mountains and the Black Forest and their northward extensions.

3. The Torrens Rift Valley in South Australia.

4. The Jordan Valley of Palestine.

5. The great African rift valleys (Fig. 2.9).

The Rhenish, Scottish, and other isolated valleys of this type are relatively insignificant in comparison to the great African rifts which are far from simple structures. These rifts, which extend from Syria in the north to the Zambesi River in the south, are nearly 4,000 miles in length (Fig. 4.10). Most of the several sections of these rift valleys are bounded by a series of fault scarps rather than by a single scarp. There are several points of interest in regard to most of these African rifts. Each valley is uniform in width - although some are only twenty-five miles wide, others may have twice that width. The valley floors vary considerably in height - some are well above sea-level, whilst those supporting Lake Tanganyika and Lake Nyasa are 1,000 or 2,000 feet below sea-level. The adjacent horsts are of unequal elevation and tend to slope down and away from the edge of the rifts. Gravity measurements on the valley floors are very low whilst on the horsts gravity values are fairly normal.

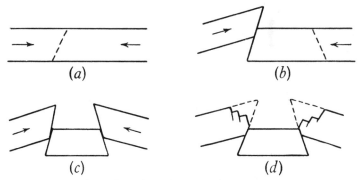

FIG. 4.8.—Origin of a Rift Valley through Compression

Various theories, which have been developed during this century to explain rift-valley formation, discredit the possibility of a collapse of a wedge of the sial rocks between two faults. The most satisfactory recent theory is one which demands compression rather than an uplifting force from inside the crust of the earth. It may be compared to the force which crushes the sediments in a geosyncline to form mountain structures but it is operating upon a rigid block of sial in this instance. It is argued that compression in the surface of the crust will cause a rigid block to weaken so that thrusting occurs as shown in Fig. 4.8. These thrusts result in the formation of two opposed fault scarps which override the rift block. Later, step faulting will take place on the edges of the trough so produced, whilst some folding of the strata lying on the floor of the valley may be observed. The low-gravity observations in these rifts indicate a depressed block of relatively light sial. If this block was free to rise it would regain isostatic equilibrium but, of course, it is held down by the overthrust horsts. Calculations based on the estimated thickness of the sial layer show that it would break down under great stresses to give troughs whose width would correspond to that of many of the African rift valleys. Over-thrusting would also tend to tilt the horsts away from the edges of the valleys as observed.

World Survey of the Major Earth Structures

Mountains, such as have been described as 'young', cover a considerable portion of the surface of the earth today, but there remains a much larger area which is developed on a foundation of 'older' mountains. The history of most 'old' mountains is still incompletely known. Whilst they have almost certainly originated from geosynclines of the past they have been much altered by erosion to peneplains (see p. 74) followed by uplift to plateaus on several occasions. Even 'young' mountains are old enough to have suffered in this way although to a less extent.

The surface relief of many areas of the world today is that of plains or plateaus. Here the underlying structures are obscured by relatively recent deposits of rock. However, it is not entirely unreasonable to say that such lowlands, as those of Amazonia or of Northern Europe and Asia, rest on a foundation of very old rocks which probably show evidence of having been high mountains in the past. Other areas may be 'old' but are now plateaus (or elevated plains) in consequence of fairly recent uplift; the mountains of Scandinavia are a good example. Many of these plains and plateaus have been relatively undisturbed for a long time, apart from being eroded (Fig. 4.3).

Four distinct ages of mountain building may be related to the stratigraphical sequence (see p. 14). The earliest phase is known as Laurentian (named from the Pre-Cambrian rocks of Canada to the north of the River St. Lawrence) but there were undoubtedly several episodes of orogenesis during the very lengthy Pre-Cambrian period. The two maps (see Figs. 4.9 and 4·10), which should be consulted at this stage, show that each continent is built in part of these very 'old' mountain structures. They form the regions of shield lands which encircle the Arctic basin in the northern hemisphere. They are nowhere of great elevation, but they form large zones of ancient stable rocks in the form of peneplains. They resemble shields in their shape. The 'old' mountains form the more elevated plateaus of Brazil, Africa, and Australia, together with Arabia and the Indian Deccan, whilst Antarctica is essentially another shield. These several southern plateaus and parts of Asia may be regarded as portions of a single continent of the past. They have been displaced to their present locations as a result of continental drift (see p. 3).

Somewhat 'younger' mountains than the 'very old' mountains were developed in mid-Primary times, and these are known as Caledonian, since North Scotland is built of mountains of this age. Fig. 3.3 shows the complex structure of parts of this region in the Highlands

Fig. 4.9.—Structure of the World — I

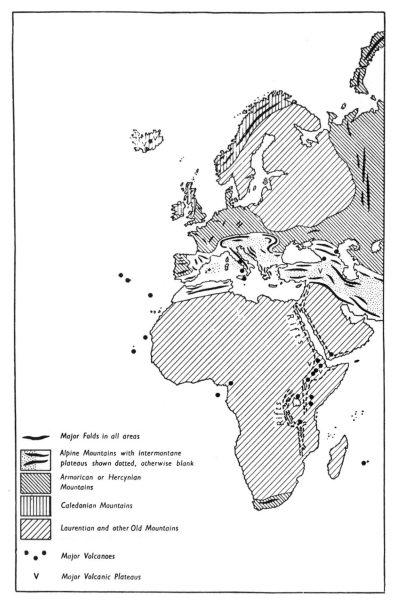

Major Folds in all areas

Alpine Mountains with intermontane plateaus shown dotted, otherwise blank

Armorican or Hercynian Mountains

Caledonian Mountains

Laurentian and other Old Mountains

Major Volcanoes

V   Major Volcanic Plateaus

FIG. 4.10.—Structure

of the World — II

of Scotland. There is little, if any, resemblance to the pattern of 'young' mountains in this section of the Highlands. Again, all continents show some evidence of this period of mountain construction. Most of the north-western part of Europe is Caledonian, whilst, to the east of Norway, lies a shield land of Pre-Cambrian rocks. To the south of these two zones lies the third, or Hercynian, mountain region of Southern Ireland, South Wales, and Southern England (where it is overlain in the south and east by younger rocks but exposed in Devonshire and Cornwall), with much of Western and Central Europe. The Hercynian mountains (alternatively, Armorican or Variscan) are late Primary in age. There are no very elevated mountains of this age in Europe, although some areas have been uplifted to form plateaus, such as the Central Plateau of France and the Bohemian block. In North America the Appalachian Mountains show evidence of both Caledonian and Hercynian developments.

Finally there are the 'young' mountains of the world known collectively as Alpine mountains. These have been formed over a very long period of time indeed. Some were elevated in early Secondary times (Jurassic age) and have been reduced and uplifted at least once and probably many times; whilst others were folded as recently as Tertiary times, and some are probably in the process of formation today, as in the case of the mountains of the East Indies. It will be noticed, from a study of the two maps already referred to, that the Alpine mountains are marginal to the continents. They form a circum-Pacific girdle, with island mountains in arcs on the Asiatic coasts, and with a local extension into the Atlantic basin in the region of the West Indies. Probably the most remarkable feature of all is the great train of east-west Alpine folds which runs from northern Africa, through southern Europe, to eastern Asia. It would seem that the build of Euro-Asia, at least, shows a fairly orderly arrangement, with the 'oldest' mountains in the north, the 'middle-aged' mountains aligned centrally, and the 'young' mountains on the southern fringe of the continental mass.

The rift valleys of East Africa and their northward extensions, together with that of the Rhine, are structural features which were formed concurrently with the building of the Alpine mountains, that is, in Secondary and Tertiary times. The Scottish rift valley was developed, however, much earlier and was associated with the Caledonian orogenesis. When the Alpine-Himalayan folds were thrown up there was an inevitable effect on some of the rocks in the great land blocks which crushed the sediments of the geosyncline. The Jura Mountains were subsidiary ripples to the main folds of the Alps of Europe, whilst still farther north the Wealden upfold in Southern England was also developed. Similar minor structures may be identified in marginal areas of other 'young' mountains.

Closely related to the 'young' mountains are most of the present-day active volcanoes, although exceptions occur in Iceland and in the African rift valleys which are not in zones of Alpine mountains (see maps, Figs. 4.9 and 4.10). The vulcanicity, which has given rise to lava plateaus in India, Washington and Oregon, Northern Ireland, and elsewhere, was as early as Jurassic times in some cases and as late as Tertiary times in others. The areas of the 'young' mountains are also characterized by earthquakes which are not infrequently related to major fault lines that have developed in the mountain structures.

We may regard the Alpine mountains as unstable—in the sense that many are still active as regards volcanic and seismic disturbances. 'Older' mountains are almost invariably inactive as regards vulcanicity but sometimes seismic disturbances are associated with them. For instance, minor earth tremors are felt today near the faulted edges of the rift valley of Central Scotland. The NE–SW trend of this rift indicates that it was probably developed in Devonian times at the end of, or not long after, the Caledonian orogeny. Nearby lava flows and volcanic crags give evidence of past vulcanicity which occurred in Carboniferous and Permian times.

Plate Tectonics and Orogenesis

In recent years much attention has been given to the oceans in relation to the mid-ocean ridges and their median rifts, the island arcs and the ocean trenches, the latter often adjacent to the arcs (see Fig. 21.2). Concurrently, there has arisen the concept of plate tectonics which embodies the theory of ocean floor spreading and has led to new accounts of orogenesis and to a reappraisal of continental drift. The evidence for these new concepts belongs properly to the study of geophysics and, in a textbook of this nature it is only possible to state the beliefs which are now held widely by various authorities.

The ocean features, referred to above, are described in reasonable detail at the beginning of Chapter 21. It is believed that basaltic magma, derived from the upper mantle, ascends into fissures opened along a mid-ocean ridge by the sideways spreading of the ocean floor or crust. The speed of such outward spreading is of the order of 1–6 cm per annum—as this movement occurs on both sides of the rifts, a maximum increase of width of the ocean floor by 12 cm per annum is possible. Further, it is known that no ocean floor consists of rock which is much older than 250,000,000 years. Thus, assuming an annual increase in width of an ocean by 5 cm, in 250,000,000 years an ocean basin could develop as wide as some 8,000 miles or 12,900 km, which is about the equatorial width of the Pacific Ocean. Ocean floor spreading from a median rift is believed to be opening a new ocean along the axis of the Red Sea (see Fig. 21.2). It is important to realize that ocean floor spreading must be compensated for by the eventual

53

consumption or compression of the ocean floor in order that a more or less constant surface area of the earth be maintained. In other words, whilst some oceans are widening, as is the case of the Atlantic Ocean, others, such as the Pacific Ocean are contracting. This contraction is accomplished by the consumption of ocean crust in the vicinity of the ocean trenches. Fig. 4.11 shows a great thrust zone, descending into the mantle, down which crust consumption, by melting, is taking place. This thrust zone is known as the Benioff zone and is an important source both of earthquakes and of magma which may rise to form volcanoes at the surface adjacent to the ocean trenches, as seen in the East Indies.

According to the concept of plate tectonics the earth's crust is composed of six major and many minor units or plates. Each plate may

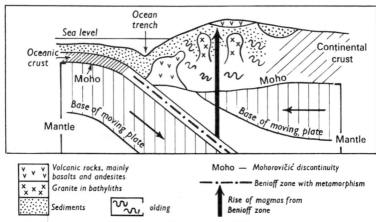

FIG. 4.11.—Orogenic Belt

consist of either, or both, continental and oceanic crust materials (p.18). From Fig. 4.11 it will be seen that these plates probably consist of oceanic or continental crust with a basal layer, below the Mohorovičić discontinuity, consisting of part of the upper mantle. Plates may move away from one another in which case the common plate margin is a mid-ocean ridge and rift system where new crustal material is being formed. Plates may slide past one another, so that the common margin is a transform fault—such as the San Andreas fault system (see Fig. 21.2 and p. 343). A third possibility is that plates may converge on one another and, in this case, one of the plates is forced to descend below the other. Orogenesis is essentially the consequence of plate convergence and collision. Where both convergent plates are composed of oceanic crust, a trench and island arc system is established, as in the East Indies. If there is oceanic crust converging on continental crust at a plate margin then a trench and mountain system is developed, as on the western side of South America such is illustrated in Fig. 4.11. However, if the convergent plates are both composed of continental crust a mountain range is formed in the collision zone. The Himalaya Mountains are believed to have resulted from a collision of the Indian sub-continent with Asia.

It will be seen from Fig 4.11 that as oceanic crust spreads from a mid-ocean ridge crest it is slowly covered by sediments largely derived from the erosion of volcanic peaks formed on the flanks of the ridge—ashes, from eruptions of these volcanoes, and organic deposits may accumulate as well. These deposits thicken as spreading proceeds and they may be quite deep on the outer margins of the ocean floor. When the oceanic plate descends into a trench these sediments are swept off by the outer edge of the continent, thus providing the equivalent of geosynclinal deposits as envisaged by earlier writers. Sediments from the continental slope may also be included. The basaltic material of the oceanic plate descends along the Benioff zone and with the development of great heat as the plates slip past one another, melting and metamorphism of the adjacent plate margins occurs and various magmas are produced; some of these are andesitic (although basalt is involved as well), whilst others are granitic. (Andesite is named from Andean volcanoes and is a more acid lava than basalt.) These magmas, on rising from the Benioff zone, produce lava flows and granite bathyliths in the sediments, when the latter are folded and uplifted to form mountains on the edge of the continental plate.

The energy required to maintain plate movement is probably the heat generated by radioactivity in the earth's interior (see p. 2). This heat may induce convection currents, rising below the mid-ocean ridges and sinking below the ocean trenches. Between these two zones the convection currents probably move the plates away from the ridges. It must be emphasized that there is much uncertainty concerning the cause and mechanism of plate tectonics.

The permanence of the ocean basins, throughout geological time, has long been accepted but, in the light of plate tectonics, this belief must now be abandoned. It would seem that cycles of opening and closing of oceans must be considered as a part of earth history. It is thought that the continents were initiated as island arcs, by the conjunction of oceanic plates, in an original and continuous ocean on the earth's surface. It is believed that these early continents evolved, during geological time, by successive phases of orogenesis, following plate collisions on their margins. Successive episodes of mountain building, in relation to continental growth are hinted at in p. 52. The concept of plate tectonics has obviously made the theory of continental drift more readily acceptable.

Part II   Earth Sculpture

CHAPTER 5

The Work of Rivers

Introduction

In a previous chapter, various processes by which the surface of the rocks is weathered were discussed. Whilst weathering does not result in the removal of material it may be regarded as an essential preliminary to the dynamic action of erosion or denudation. Once weathering has produced small fragments of rock, then it is the turn of other agents to remove these by transportation to other positions. Although ice, wind, and the sea are powerful agents of erosion it is unquestionable that a very large proportion of the land surfaces of the world is affected by running water. Much of the transported fragments, which constitutes the load of a river, is used for further erosion—thus rivers are most important agents in producing earth sculpture.

The Longitudinal Profile of a River

An examination of the courses of many rivers will show that they have a longitudinal profile which matches fairly closely that shown in Fig. 5.1 (it must be made very clear that the vertical scale of this profile is much exaggerated compared with its horizontal scale).

Fig. 5.1.—Longitudinal Profile of a River Course

This 'ideal' curve is seen to be concave upwards so that the gradient of the stream bed decreases towards the sea. However, whilst it appears that the speed of the river should, therefore, slacken downstream, it must be realized that, at intervals along its course, the main river receives tributaries which successively augment its

56

volume of water. Thus, the bed of the stream becomes both wider and deeper in its lower reaches compared with that of the headstream zone. This enlargement of the stream bed is accompanied by a significant reduction of friction between the flowing water and both the bed and the banks of the river. This is more than sufficient to offset the effects of decreasing gradient so that, on the average, a stream flows fastest near the sea.

The course of a river is frequently regarded as having three sections:

   (i) The upper tract—with steep gradients along the river bed and a narrow steep-sided valley, with little or no development of a plain. The cross-section of the valley here is characteristically V-shaped.

  (ii) A central section, with a plain and much less steep valley sides. The river gradient has decreased from upstream but it is by no means insignificant.

 (iii) The lowest part of the course is essentially a plain with very gently sloping sides that form a very flattened V-shape. In the case of many large rivers the stream bed lies above this plain (Fig 5.20). The gradient of the stream in this plain is very slight.

Cross-sections, typical of each of these three tracts, are shown in Fig. 5.2. However, it is important to note that individual sections of the valley in any of these divisions may show features which depart considerably from the descriptions given above. Generally, these differences are related to the resistance of the rocks. A very hard sandstone

Fig. 5.2.—Progressive widening of the Valley

may cause an otherwise wide valley to be constricted in the form of a gorge whilst a weak shale may permit the enlargement locally of an otherwise narrow valley.

River Erosion

A river is primarily concerned with the transport of rock fragments which have been collected from its valley sides. It uses this load of fragments to erode and deepen its channel. The load is introduced into the river by such agents as rain wash, soil creep, gravity, and occasionally by landslides. In the river, collisions between moving rock fragments of the load and the rocks forming the bed of the river will produce further erosion. The largest fragments may be rolled along the river bed or, in some instances, they may only move intermittently (by saltation) as circumstances permit. The finest particles are carried in suspension in that they are swirled along in

57

J. Hardman

FIG. 5.3.—The Dry Bed of a Stream in Langdale, Westmorland
This shows some of the load carried by a river.

the water. This suspension load may be increased as comminution proceeds. In addition to the solid load, there is dissolved rock material which is carried in solution by the river.

Large fragments are not readily moved far but must await comminution—thus it is fairly obvious that, in general, only relatively fine fragments will constitute the solid load in the lower reaches of the stream. It is possible that this solid load may increase to such an extent that it becomes too great for all of it to be moved continuously—unless there is an increase in the carrying power of the river—so that deposition of part of the suspended load must occur somewhere along the river's course.

Erosion by running water, or corrasion, is by no means constant throughout the length of a stream. The velocity and the volume of the river will determine very largely the capacity of the stream to move rock fragments and this will vary from point to point along the river profile. Also there will be seasonal fluctuations in the volume of the stream and these will control the load which is carried. The amount of material transported also depends on the nature of the load. A stream which is supplied mainly with fine rock waste will be able to carry a very large load whereas if most of the rock debris supplied to the river is coarse the same stream will probably find it difficult to transport the material (Fig. 5.3).

Development of the River

Initially, then, a river erodes by cutting down its bed in an attempt to produce the profile of Fig. 5.1 as rapidly as possible. This is known as the graded profile where each section of the river course has a gradient which is sufficiently steep to enable the transportation of all the load supplied to it (this gradient is maintained so long as controlling conditions remain unchanged). Such a state of affairs must be considered as 'ideal' and is obviously rare, if not non-existent.

Such a graded course would be easily disturbed by alterations in the flow of the river. For instance, a temporary influx of storm waters may result in an increase of down-cutting which will flatten locally the graded curve—thus producing degradation. Yet this same down-cutting will increase the load of the river and almost certainly there will be deposition farther downstream, where the capacity of the stream becomes too small to carry all the load. At such points of deposition aggradation occurs with a local steepening of the graded curve—however, in time, this will probably be further degraded to re-establish the graded curve at this point.

FIG. 5.4.—Early Stages of Degradation

To make these facts more readily understandable a simple case of river development will be discussed. Let it be assumed that the course of a river is developed on a land surface which was irregular at the time when streams started to flow on it (Fig. 5.4a). Clearly the gradients are very varied along the river profile. At first, the river will enlarge its channel and cut its valley more deeply and in a relatively short time, geologically speaking, the profile will appear more or less as shown in Fig. 5.4b. Three changes in the profile have occurred. Firstly, there has been a general lowering of the stream bed from the original XY to ZAY. Secondly, the lower part of the course is graded from A to Y. Thirdly, there has been an extension of the head region of the course to Z. Normally progressive development of the lower, graded section will proceed in an upstream direction so that, in time, an approach is made to the graded profile of Fig. 5.1.

Frequently, in the early development of a river, its course may be divided into two or more sections, each of which is practically graded. A band of resistant rock may lie across the course and produce such a division, marked by a waterfall or rapids in the river bed (Fig. 5.5). The removal of the fall in the course of time will result in the merging of the two curves, so that one continuous curve is produced. In Fig. 5.5 horizontal lines are drawn which are called base levels. Every graded curve is related to such a level, which is a horizontal plane passing through its lowest point. The base level of a completely graded stream coincides with sea-level. A tributary stream will be graded to a base level which passes through its confluence with the main river.

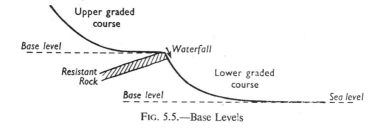

FIG. 5.5.—Base Levels

Immature Valleys

The immediate effect of down-cutting in the initial stages of the development of a river course is to produce narrow valleys with V-shaped cross-sections. Whilst such cross-sections were common throughout the course of the river in the earliest stages of its development, with the establishment of a graded profile in its lower sections there has been considerable modification of the cross-section of the valley, as will be seen later, with the widening of the valley and the flattening of its floor to form plains. Even where river valleys are well developed throughout most of their length there are usually some sections, commonly at the head-stream area, which show the characteristics that are typical of this early development. Such tracts are often called youthful, but this is a somewhat misleading description since most of the river course must be regarded as of the same age. It is more sensible to regard such sections with their narrow, V-shaped valleys as not having reached the advanced stage of development shown elsewhere in the course. Obviously, such less mature sections may be found anywhere in the course where resistant rocks have retarded the opening up of the valley or where some other process is at work, such as rejuvenation (p. 84).

The chief features of such relatively undeveloped tracts in the course of a river are as follows. The stream has a fairly small volume of water but a fairly high speed, because of its considerable gradient, and has a valley which is steep-sided with a deep, V-shaped cross-section. As has been said, the primary work of the stream is downward corrasion so that the initial valley would have almost vertical sides but these would be very rapidly modified as a result of slumping so that a V-shaped cross-section would be produced. Sometimes such ravine-like valleys are more permanent when they are formed in very resistant rock by pot-holes. The swirling action of the flowing water causes a boulder to drill a deep hole as it mills around in a cavity

FIG. 5.6.—
A Ravine

in the river bed—the boulder is eventually smoothed and resembles a cannon ball. A series of pot-holes may unite to form a valley which is like a slot in the land surface whose width may be very much less than its depth (Fig. 5.6). The Strid, on the River Wharfe in Yorkshire, is an example of such a slot-like ravine.

The contour diagram in Fig. 5.7 shows a section of a river course in this immature stage. The average gradient of the stream is about

FIG. 5.7.—Upper Valley Tract (Kingsdale, near Ingleton)

Based on the Ordnance Survey Map with the sanction of the Controller of H.M. Stationery Office

1 in 10, but at A the close spacing of the contours indicates that for a few yards the gradient is very much greater, possibly marking small waterfalls. To some extent the bends of the river are seen to fit into a series of interlocking spurs. These bends in the river were, in all probability, caused originally by local irregularities of the surface. The spurs make it difficult or impossible to see far up or down the river course at stream level (Fig. 5.8); and between each spur side streams form gullies which develop in time into more open amphitheatres. The bed of such a stream would be characteristically littered with boulders and large fragments of rock which must be reduced in size before they can be moved downstream although, in times of flood, boulders may be transported short distances.

Waterfalls and Lakes

Waterfalls are very common in the upper section of a river's course but they may occur at any point where an outcrop of resistant rock obstructs the flow of the river (Fig. 5.9). The life of such falls is short, as measured by geological time, since the stream proceeds with all speed to remove these obstructions by down-cutting. In

61

The Aircraft Operating Co. of Africa (Pty.) Ltd.

FIG. 5.8.—Kafue River Valley, Zambia

An immature valley showing V-shaped cross-section and interlocking spurs. The valley slopes are covered with dry forest.

some cases the fall is determined by a horizontal stratum which acts as a protective capping to layers of less resistant rock, as shown in Fig. 5.10. It is, of course, possible for a fall to develop at a later stage in the history of the river, as for instance where a sill of igneous rock which was originally below the surface of the land is reached and

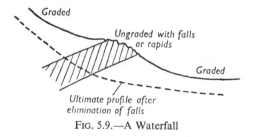

FIG. 5.9.—A Waterfall

exposed by the downcutting of the stream. Falls recede in an upstream direction, and in the case of the Niagara Falls the recession has produced a gorge nearly seven miles long on the downstream side of the falls which are 160 feet high. This state of affairs will persist until the falls are completely reduced and a graded stream will then take their place. The recession is now at the rate of 2½–4 feet per annum, and eventually the gorge will extend back to Lake Erie. However before the falls reach the lake they will decline in height, becoming rapids which, in time, will disappear.

FIG. 5.10.—Niagara Falls

Even more spectacular than the Niagara gorge is that of the River Zambezi below the Victoria Falls (Fig. 5.11). Here the water plunges 360 feet from a basalt plateau into a gorge which is sixty miles long. The falls have left a zig-zag course to the upper part of this gorge since the recession has been controlled by a series of faults which have shattered the basalt so much that erosion has inevitably followed these lines of weakness. Some of the highest falls are located in South America, where the ancient and resistant rocks which form the Brazilian Plateau and the Guiana Highlands interrupt the courses of streams as they leave these uplands. Two of these are the Iguassu Falls, on the Parana, and the Kaieteur Falls, in the Essequibo basin.

Lakes, like waterfalls, are often produced by some barrier that obstructs the flow of a stream although, in many cases, lakes are developed as a result of the occurrence of some hollows which contain their water. In the latter cases it is feasible to regard the lake as being produced, in part, by a barrier. As with waterfalls so lake barriers may be reduced or cut through by the outlet stream and thus in a relatively short time the lake is drained. However, lakes may be eliminated in another way. The still water of the lake will check the

63

The Aircraft Operating Co. of Africa (Pty.) Ltd.

FIG. 5.11.—Victoria Falls, Rhodesia

Part of the zig-zag gorge of the R. Zambezi is seen below the falls.

speed of the river as it enters the lake on its upstream side, resulting in the settlement of part of the load of the river so that eventually the lake is filled in. Sometimes deposits from side streams may sub-divide a lake (p. 71). Various types of lake are discussed in other parts of this book and page references will be found in the index.

Valley Widening

Throughout its course in its early development a river is presumed to have cut down as rapidly as possible in an attempt to attain a state of gradation. A glance at the graded profile in Fig. 5.1 will show that a river cannot cut down into the land surface below its base level (this is, in general, sea-level). Long before the curve of

FIG. 5.12.—Change of Cross-section of Stream Bed
with Side Cutting

64

the longitudinal profile has been lowered to the position indicated in Fig. 5.1, the down-cutting process will have been replaced, in part, by side cutting. Initially the stream, as well as its tributaries for that matter, is rarely straight, and at all the bends, associated with interlocking spurs, side cutting is likely to commence. This side cutting results in a change in the cross-section of the stream-bed (Fig. 5.12). Apart from lateral currents, there are also vertical movements in the stream which hasten the widening and deepening of the minor bends into meanders (see Fig. 5.12b). This produces a distinct shift of the stream course, and visual evidence of this is afforded by the gentle, crescentic

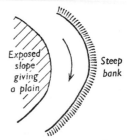

FIG. 5.13.—The Beginning of a River Plain

slopes that are exposed on the inner banks of the meander curves, whilst on their outer banks there are steep, undercut slopes. The

Aerofilms Ltd.

FIG. 5.14.—The Beginning of a River Plain, Wye Valley, Monmouthshire
Note the crescentic areas in the foreground where spurs have been reduced with the widening of the valley.

gentle, crescentic slopes are the beginnings of a river plain (Figs. 5.13, 5.14 and 5.19), and they may be built up by storm deposits after the river has been in full spate. With the appearance of these plains the river is often considered as having entered its mature stage of development. These features are to be seen in the majority of river

(a) Interlocking spurs

(b) Shift of river—start of meanders

(c) Spurs are reduced on up stream sides

(d) Spurs are almost completely reduced— meanders have increased in amplitude and shifted downstream

p – Plains
s – Spurs
≋ – Steep banks

(e) Valley side Valley side

Meander Plain between Bluffs

FIG. 5.15.—Development of Meanders and River Plains

valleys and, on a miniature scale, in brooks of quite modest proportions.

Development of Plains

Further development of this plain is effected by the removal of the valley spurs which are eventually set back in lines of bluffs (or river cliffs) which mark the sides of a wider and much more mature valley. A meandering stream tends, at first, to cut into the spurs on their upstream sides but as meandering streams shift their courses downstream this helps to blunt the spurs. This process is advanced still further by the fact that meanders increase in amplitude and thus widen the valley floor. The various stages in the development of the plain are illustrated in Fig. 5.15. It must be remembered that downslope movement of rock debris will also help to set back the valley sides.

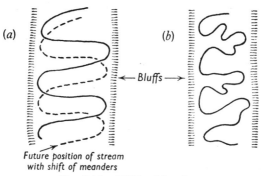

FIG. 5.16.—Shifting Meanders

The valley is now relatively open and visibility upstream and down is vastly improved compared with that in an immature valley. Inevitably some irregularities of relief remain on the valley floor but these are relatively insignificant. The migration of the meanders planes thoroughly the lowland over which the stream flows between the two sets of bluffs (see Fig. 5.16a). The meandering river shows one other feature in that it increases its length within the limits of the plain by becoming very sinuous (see Fig. 5.16b). A well-developed river plain is also demonstrated by the map (Fig. 5.17). Here the gradient of the stream is slight as it falls only about thirty feet in approximately ten miles. Whilst emphasis has been placed on side-cutting in the development of meanders, it should be realised that down-cutting has not ceased and this produces an additional load to be deposited in the plain.

Such plains may be found almost anywhere in the course of a river, with the probable exception of the headstream zone. If a river course is divided (as in Fig. 5.5) into at least two tracts with independent base levels, then an upper and a lower plain are likely to be present.

With the acquisition of more and more tributaries the plains are increased still further. As the valley sides of the main stream and its feeders are more or less completely reduced these several plains merge into one very extensive lowland. The relief of these ultimate plains on either side of the rivers is so slight that an increase in the volume of the water, consequent upon excessive rainfall or, perhaps, a sudden melt of snow upstream, will inevitably lead to their flooding. Hence this lowland is frequently known as the flood plain

Based on the Ordnance Survey Map with the sanction of the Controller of H.M. Stationery Office
FIG. 5.17.—The Plain of the River Stour, near Wimborne, Dorset

(Fig. 5.20). The plain which is nearest to the sea is likely to increase in area more than any other, since the available load for deposition, together with the planation by the meanders, is usually very great in the lower tracts of rivers.

Meandering lower courses of large rivers are easily identified on atlas maps, and it is of interest to note that the name 'meander' is derived from Meanderes, a river of Asia Minor. Amongst other rivers with pronounced meandering courses are the Mississippi, the Forth, and the Seine. Another feature, developed from meanders, is the oxbow, a type of lake. Oxbows are formed when a meander

FIG. 5.18.—An Oxbow

loop is breached by storm waters and then sealed off by the deposition of the excess load which is carried at such times by the river (Fig. 5.18). An oxbow is a form of lake which, in general, has but slight importance. An alternative name is 'mortlake', and a suburb of London near the meandering Thames has this name, since it lies near a drained oxbow. Deposition consequent upon the excessive load of the stream may cause it to build up its bed, thus confining itself between natural levees of mud and silt (Fig. 5.20). The Po, the Hwang-ho, and the Mississippi afford good examples of this process at work in their plains. A breach of a levee is disastrous, since flooding is very extensive over the plain.

The natural levees may be artificially reinforced to obviate such floods as have swept the Mississippi lowlands in certain years of this century, although local success has come by tackling the problem from outside the flood plain region in the upper basin of the Tennessee River, an important tributary.

Ray— Delvert

FIG. 5.19.—Meander Course of the R. Lot. at Luzech, France

Several meanders show the plains on one side of the river and the steep slopes opposite. The valley is probably entrenched (see p. 85).

The natural levees may divert tributary streams so that they flow parallel to the main stream until some local advantage permits an entry into it (Fig. 5.17). There may also be formed a braided course through the choking of the water channel by a dropping of a considerable part of the river's load which produces a bifurcation of the

River
Flood plain   Levee ↓ Levee   Flood plain

FIG. 5.20.—The Levees of the Flood Plain

stream (see Figs. 4.3 and 5.35). This may become widespread, and there are quite a number of local names for these several branches of a braided stream. Anabranch and billabong (from Australia) are two terms applied to such branch streams.

Estuaries and Deltas

A river enters the sea at the end of its course through an estuary or a delta, the latter often being a seaward extension of the lower plains. A river has an estuary or mouth if tidal scour is strong enough to clear much of the load which is likely to be deposited in this last part of its course. The mixing of salt sea water and fresh river water helps to precipitate the load, as it causes the finest particles to coagulate. An estuary is much wider than the true river—at high tide it is filled with sea water whilst at low tide the river swings in a braided course through extensive banks of mud and sand which are exposed at that time.

If, on the other hand, the sea into which the river is flowing has weak tides, then a delta may be formed. The lack of tidal scour does not adequately account for the formation of a delta, since some rivers entering tideless seas have no deltas, whilst some deltas are built on the shores of seas with moderately large tides. A river which has a relatively ungraded upper course is likely to carry a big load which will result in deposition in the lowest part of the plain on a scale that is adequate for the formation of a delta. Choking of the river channel will lead to braiding and the formation of distributaries near the sea. Distributaries are distinguished from tributaries in that they lead water away from the main stream. Each distributary disposes of its load by extending the natural levees into the sea, so that the initial form of most deltas is lobate (Fig. 5.21a). The delta of the River Nile, which was the classic example of the Greeks, represents a further development from the lobate type. The natural levees projecting seawards along the sides of the distributaries are converted into curved spits of silt according to the prevailing long-shore drift in the sea immediately offshore (Fig. 5.21b). These spits eventually unite and enclose areas of water which are known as coastal lagoons (Fig. 5.21c). The Rhône delta shows this stage of development today. Lastly, the area of the delta is increased laterally by further deposition, particularly by longshore drift, thus creating the more typical arcuate form, as exemplified by the Nile delta (Fig. 5.21d). The resemblance of this outline to the Greek letter Δ (delta) has given the term which is so widely accepted (see Fig. 4.3).

Locally, sea action may produce somewhat unusual outlines to deltas, but the essential features will be present. Atlases of the nineteenth century may be compared with modern editions, and it will be seen that there has been a considerable change in the last fifty years in the outline of the Mississippi delta. An outstanding example of the diversion of a stream by the blocking of distributaries is given by the Hwang-ho. Since the middle of the nineteenth century this river has entered the sea both to the north and south of Shantung at various times.

Small deltas may be produced by side streams entering lakes. In some instances, such deltas, extending from opposite shores, may eventually divide the lake into two. For long it was believed that Buttermere and Crummock Water, in Cumberland, had been formed in this fashion from one large lake. However, recent investigations have shown that, in fact, each lake is in a distinct rock basin. The delta, which appears to separate them, has very largely obscured a rock bar which divides the two basins. In Switzerland, Brienzersee and Thunersee are probably separated by a delta at Interlaken.

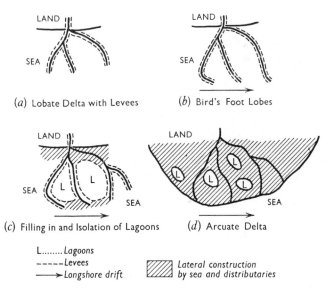

(a) Lobate Delta with Levees (b) Bird's Foot Lobes

(c) Filling in and Isolation of Lagoons (d) Arcuate Delta

L........Lagoons
-----Levees
———▶Longshore drift

Lateral construction by sea and distributaries

Fig. 5.21.—Development of a River Delta

Examples of River Courses

Students are recommended to attempt analyses of river courses based on the foregoing account by reference to large-scale maps. The map in Fig. 5.22 is of the basin of the Glenariff River in Co. Antrim, Northern Ireland and it will be seen that this stream has a valley which widens progressively towards the sea. This is shown very well in the photograph (Fig. 5.23). In its course from just upstream from the waterfall (W in Fig. 5.22) the stream descends in about a mile from just over 1,000 feet to about 650 feet at V. In a further mile and a quarter from V the river falls 550 feet to P where, at about 100 feet above the sea it may be said to enter its plain course. According to the map the river takes a course of $3\frac{1}{4}$ miles to the sea from P but the photograph shows that the lower course has been straightened. This explains the absence of meanders, in the picture, which helped in the past to develop this plain. Thus, the upper, immature

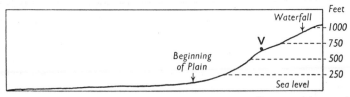

FIG. 5.22.—River Glenariff, Co. Antrim, Northern Ireland.
Relief Map of the Valley (above). Approximate Profile of the River (below).

valley ends at V, from V to P is the middle section of the whole river course, where valley widening is in progress, and this leads at P into the lower plain course, as shown by both the map and the section.

A relief map of the British Isles in an advanced atlas will show the salient features of the course of the River Severn, which is one of considerable interest. Not far from its source area in Plynlimmon the river enters an upland plain between Llanidloes and Newtown, centred on Caersws, but below Newtown it flows through a narrow

Aerofilms Ltd.

FIG. 5.23.—The Valley of the R. Glenariff, Co. Antrim,
Northern Ireland

The waterfall (**W** in Fig. 5.22) is seen at the bottom right. The scarps on the valley sides are formed by lava flows (see Fig. 1.10)

valley almost as far as Welshpool. East of the latter town is the wide plain of the Camlad, a tributary stream. Below Welshpool the main river enters a very extensive flood plain, across which it meanders until it has passed Shrewsbury. From Buildwas to beyond Bridgnorth it flows once again in a gorge-like valley with steep tributary valleys entering from either side. Below Stourport the Severn enters its lower plain leading to the estuary. It is, perhaps, unfair to cite this example without additional comment. The Severn is a river that has suffered diversion by glacial damming which helped to produce the upper plains (these were the floors of glacial lakes) and the intervening gorges. Further discussion of the Severn will be found on p. 107. Other causes than glacial damming may produce similar variations in the width of the valley in different sections of the course of a river —some of these are discussed in another part of this chapter.

FIG. 5.24.—Dendritic Drainage in Borden Island, Northern Canada

It is possible to trace several watersheds in this view.

The Cycle of Erosion

The work of rivers will eventually lower the land surface to an almost level plain not very much above the level of the sea. There must be, even at this stage, some slight slopes to enable rivers to maintain their flow. The final form of the land surface is known as a peneplain, but there will be a few residual hills of low elevation which will represent remnants of the land surface that has been reduced. Such residual hills are known as monadnocks, after Mount Monadnock, in New Hampshire, which is of this type. The complete process of reduction from the initial uplifted land surface is known as a cycle of erosion. It is questionable whether such a cycle is ever completed. It would seem that long before the time required for absolute peneplanation has elapsed, some interference with the land surface will have occurred. Usually the cycle of erosion is cut short by an uplift of the eroded land surface, with a consequent rejuvenation of the rivers, as will be explained later (p. 84). The concept of the cycle of erosion may be applied to erosion of arid areas, limestone regions (where special characteristics arise), and to coastal erosion—these are discussed in later chapters.

Drainage Patterns

A study of fairly detailed maps will show that a pattern is discernible in the streams of most river basins. A river basin is an area which is drained by one complete set of streams whose waters reach the sea by a common main stream. The basin is enclosed by a line that follows the crest line of the highland margins—this line forms the main watershed of the basin. Streams within a basin will show one of two patterns which are called dendritic and trellised, the latter being sometimes referred to as gridiron. The former type is characterized by a series of streams which resemble the branches of a tree as they converge to its trunk (Fig. 5.24, also Fig. 2.8). With the second or trellised pattern, the main stream is usually well defined throughout the basin, and its feeders join one another and eventually enter the main stream approximately at right angles to it. The resultant pattern is thus more regular in appearance than that of the dendritic type (Fig. 5.25, also Fig. 3.7). The two patterns are produced by different circumstances. With the dendritic type the direction of river flow is largely determined by original irregularities in the land surface whereas trellised patterns are very considerably controlled by geological structures. Rarely does a river basin exhibit one of these patterns throughout, and not infrequently a mixture of the two may be observed. If the whole basin is worked out in the same

FIG. 5.25.—Trellised or Grid-iron Drainage Pattern

type of rock or similar rocks, then the dendritic pattern will almost certainly be dominant, particularly if the rocks offer uniform resistance to erosion by running water. If, on the other hand, the basin has rocks in parallel outcrops which are of varying resistance, then the chance of the development of trellised drainage is considerable.

Trellised Drainage and Escarpments

Trellising is often developed as shown in Fig. 5.26, where in (*a*) an initial stream which is flowing fairly directly towards the sea crosses alternate outcrops of weak and resistant rocks. At the resistant bands, side streams are largely absent and the valley is

75

narrow, whilst upstream and down from this point the development of side streams is evidently easy along the bands of less
resistant rock. These side streams tend to flow parallel to the edge
of the resistant rock (Fig. 5.26b). Obviously all the side streams
continue to cut downwards in order to grade their respective valleys,
but whereas they have lowered the level of the less resistant rocks
over a wide area, the more resistant rock bands will not be so
reduced except at the points where the main streams cross them
This results in the isolation of an upstanding band of resistant
rock known as an escarpment, which has a relatively deep, narrow,

FIG. 5.26.—Development of Trellised Drainage with Escarpments and
Gaps

Note (i), (ii), and (iii) in (d) refer to north-south sections in (a), (b), and (c)
respectively.

and steep-sided gap cut into it at the point, where the main stream
passes. The development of escarpments and their river gaps is
shown in Fig. 5.26c. Examples of such river gaps are innumerable.
The relation of the more gentle slope of the escarpment to the dip of
the resistant rocks is reflected in the name of dip slope which is
given to it. The steeper slope is called the scarp slope or edge (see
Fig. 5.26d and Fig. 5.27). Escarpment development is a local feature,
although lines of scarplands may persist for several hundreds of

miles where a resistant outcrop is so disposed. Whilst an escarpment may appear to be a very significant element in the landscape, it is destined to be reduced. In Fig. 5.26c it will be seen that the feeders of the main stream have acquired their own tributaries, some of which descend the steep scarp slope. These streams must reduce this slope, and eventually a recession of the whole scarp occurs. This recession leaves greater space for the development of side streams flowing parallel to the chief feeders, and thus the trellised pattern will be extended still further. The limestone escarpment of the Cotswold Hills shows that recession has occurred near Winchcombe, but there remain isolated parts of the previous scarp front in Bredon Hill and its neighbouring summits—these may be seen in some atlas maps.

Aerofilms Ltd.

FIG. 5.27.—Limestone Escarpments, near Wenlock, Shropshire

Looking N.E. along Wenlock Edge (left) and a parallel escarpment (right) which are separated by a narrow clay vale. Note scarp edges and dip slopes. See also Fig. 9.17.

Trellising is also a possible consequence of drainage in folded structures where parallel streams may flow in the downfold valleys, and at certain weak places in the upfolds gaps may be formed with connecting streams at right angles to the general trend of the drainage. The drainage of south-western Ireland is controlled in this fashion, as shown by the map given in Fig. 9.11. This pattern may also arise where faults or joints control the drainage lines. Two areas which show trellised drainage very well are the Wealden area of south-eastern England and much of the Appalachian valley region of the United States of America (see Fig. 3.7, p. 36).

The development of trellised drainage has called into being a nomenclature for the various types of stream. The initial drainage in consequence of the general slope of the land surface towards the sea produces consequent streams (C) as shown in Fig. 5.28, whilst the later tributaries, more or less at right angles to these streams, are called subsequent streams (S). Usually these subsequent streams follow outcrops of weak rocks or are controlled by lines of weakness, such as may be produced by faulting. The rôle of these streams is clearly a major one in escarpment formation. Later still the pattern is enriched by more streams, which are, in general, short and act as feeders to the subsequent streams. These are relatively minor streams, and tend to flow at right angles to the subsequent rivers. Some are known as minor consequent streams (MC) and others as obsequent streams (O). These flow therefore nearly parallel to the original consequent rivers, the former like the consequent rivers in a seaward direction, although they never reach the sea as independent streams, whereas the latter are opposed to this direction in their flow. The rôle of the obsequent rivers is a fairly important one, since they are largely responsible for the reduction and recession of escarpments. The drainage pattern of the Weald shows all four of these types of river. The upfold of the Weald has given rise to two sets of streams each having developed from a series of consequent streams which flowed respectively northwards and southwards from the crest of the upfold that ran east and west, the remnant of which is marked by the Forest Ridge today.

FIG. 5.28.—Consequent, Subsequent, and Obsequent Streams

The height of a scarp edge is determined by the dip of the stratum of rock which produces the escarpment. With strata of equal thickness a steep dip will give a relatively low scarp edge whereas a gentle dip will result in a much higher edge being developed. Thus, the height of the scarp face of the North Downs decreases westwards with the increasing dip of the Chalk. The dissection of horizontal strata results in tabular land forms known as mesas (see Fig. 7.5).

Radial and Superimposed Drainage

The drainage of some areas is radial (Fig. 5.36). This is not necessarily entirely distinct from the more widespread dendritic or trellised patterns; frequently this radial drainage pattern shows elements of both the other types. The chief characteristic of radial drainage is largely dependent on the structural features of a dome. Usually upfolding produces such an upland region which is comparable to a domed roof or cupola, in that its surface slopes downwards in all directions from the summit. Another cause may be the injection of a laccolith into the crustal layers so that the surface is raised into a dome. Erosion may expose the surface of a granite boss such as forms Dartmoor. Drainage on such domes tends to be divergent in

FIG. 5.29.—Superimposed Drainage of the
Lake District

Based on the Ordnance Survey Map with the sanction of the Controller of H.M. Stationery Office

all directions from its higher levels. Perhaps, the most perfect example of this type of drainage is to be seen on a volcanic cone which is only slightly denuded (Fig. 2.8). In Central France, in the region of the Cantal (a much dissected volcanic cone), the radial drainage has isolated a series of triangular plateaus known as planèzes. Cotton, the New Zealand geomorphologist, has suggested that these may be regarded as a distinct type of land form. The radial pattern is often developed on a surface which consists of homogeneous rock, although in the Lake District of England, where this type of drainage is found, the streams are flowing over rocks of various kinds. It is considered by geologists that the area was formed as a dome with a surface of Secondary rocks that covered both igneous and sedimentary rocks of Primary age. On the former surface an almost symmetrical pattern of radial drainage must have been established, but once the streams had removed the whole of this layer, they cut into the underlying rocks and maintained the pattern which was thus superimposed upon these older rocks. Minor modifications have occurred, such as are produced by faults in the older rocks, and local control of the superimposed streams has followed. Thus, in places, it is possible to discern a rectilinear pattern, as may be seen on the map, Fig. 5.29.

Superimposed drainage is not necessarily a subsequent development of radial drainage. In the area of the South Wales coalfield the eastern valleys show a remarkable alignment from north to south. The drainage, as in the case of the Lake District, was initiated on a surface of younger rocks, which has now disappeared, but the drainage lines have persisted, despite the general east-west downfold axis of the coal basin which might have produced a main axial stream flowing parallel to this trend. However, the earlier down-cutting has been strong enough to overcome the structural controls of the downfold on which the relatively simple north-south pattern of drainage has been superimposed. To the west, however, faulting has produced a shatter belt which gives the north-east to south-west drainage typical of the River Neath.

Fig. 5.30.—River Capture

River Capture

A very important modification of drainage patterns may result from the process of river capture or river piracy. This is quite common in areas in which trellised drainage has been developed, although it may occur with dendritic patterns. The capture of a stream is most easily described by reference to the series of diagrams in Fig. 5.30. In (a) two consequent streams are seen in relatively close proximity to one another, each having two tributary subsequent streams whose heads are separated by some distance at X. Now it is possible for a stream to increase its drainage area by the development of minor feeders in the headstream region. This process of extension of the drainage may produce a dendritic pattern in such areas. These additional minor feeders increase the erosive power of one of the subsequent streams, and it encroaches upon the other stream. Thus in (b) the distance at X is reduced. It should be realized that one stream must have greater erosive power, and will therefore have lowered its bed in relation to that of the adjacent shorter subsequent stream. Thus in (c) the more powerful stream has reached the head

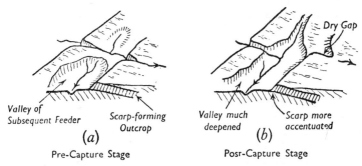

Valley of Subsequent Feeder *Scarp-forming Outcrop* *Valley much deepened* *Scarp more accentuated*

(a) *(b)*

Pre-Capture Stage Post-Capture Stage

FIG. 5.31.—Formation of Dry Gap by River Capture

After Davis

waters of the other stream, and has lowered the head region of this stream sufficiently to divert its flow. It must be emphasized that throughout this process all the rivers have been cutting down continuously, but that this diversion depends upon the much greater opportunity which one river system has compared with the other. This may be better understood by reference to Fig. 5.30d which shows the head stream profiles near X at various stages and levels in the sequence, corresponding to (a), (b), and (c). Immediately after capture has taken place, the successful stream becomes even more powerful through the addition of water derived from the other river. It therefore lowers its bed very rapidly, so that at Y in Fig. 5.30c not only does a gap occur, but in a relatively short time this gap is standing at a higher level than the beds of the streams which have been diverted by capture. This gap is usually without drainage and is called 'a dry gap' (Fig. 5.31). Often there is a reversal of stream flow when capture occurs, and at Y (Fig. 5.30c) there arises what is essentially an obsequent stream, although of different origin from those referred to above (p. 78), since it arises from a reversal of drainage following capture.

Gaps in Escarpments

The lower part of the drainage basin of the captured stream is arrested in its further development, so that it may have relatively steep slopes on its sides (representing a less mature valley), for effective erosion is well-nigh impossible, since it can only draw upon a very limited surface area for its supply of water. In fact, the river is receiving so little water in comparison to what it had at its disposal in pre-capture days that it appears to be too small for its valley, and so it is called a 'misfit'. In some escarpment areas which have been formed in limestone and Chalk the perviousness of the rock permits this meagre misfit stream to sink underground, and so there is literally no surface drainage and the valley becomes 'dry'. Only when the water-table in the rocks is elevated temporarily by seasonal rains do surface streams appear. The Winterbourne villages in the various dry valleys of the Chalk area of the Marlborough Downs are aptly named, in that they lie near to streams which flow only in

FIG. 5.32.—Gaps in an Escarpment, Generalized Profile of South Downs viewed from the North

the wetter periods of the year. Dry valleys may be produced in other ways than by river capture, and the reader is referred to pp. 130 and 133.

An escarpment may be modified very considerably by such stream developments, and there is obvious evidence of these changes to be found on maps of such land forms, and also by direct observation in the field. Fig. 5.32 shows a typical crest line of part of one of the Chalk escarpments in the South Downs of England. Two types of gap are shown, and each is of value in that it assists and controls communication by road and railway. Even the dry gaps, sometimes known as 'wind gaps', despite their relative height in comparison with the deeper-cut water or river gaps, ease the gradients which must be encountered in laying a route across an escarpment. Once again the Wealden area is a very good one for the examination of these capture features (Figs. 8.9 and 8.10).

Examples of River Capture

On the maps of an elementary atlas the student may discern the considerable river capture which has produced the system of the Yorkshire Ouse. Here there has been a succession of river captures by a powerful stream of the past which entered the sea by a mouth which corresponded to the present-day Humber. This stream captured first one and then another river on the north side of its course which was roughly eastwards to the sea. Remnants of the captured rivers may be seen in the relatively short coast streams of the Esk and Rye, although today the latter flows into the River Derwent, which goes southwards out of the Vale of Pickering. Reversed drainage may be identified on the map in the district of the Hambledon and Cleveland Hills (Fig. 5.33). The pattern of the River Derwent is not

Note:—Reverse drainage of the feeders of Wiske and Leven

Fɪɢ. 5.33.—River Capture in Northern Part of the Basin of the Yorkshire Ouse

Based on the Ordnance Survey Map with the sanction of the Controller of H.M. Stationery Office

explained on these lines, since its history is complicated by the effects of glacial diversion, which is discussed in Chapter 6, p. 106.

Furthermore, there is, without doubt, widespread evidence that there were numerous rivers flowing from north-west to south-east across the area of Wales, the Midlands, and South-east England, which by various river captures, assisted by local warping of the surface, have developed into the present-day patterns. It would seem that the headstreams of these rivers (which presumably fed, in the past, a river that is represented by the modern River Thames) were diverted in different areas to form the Lower Severn–Warwick Avon drainage, the Trent drainage, and the Wash drainage. In order that the reader may envisage this process more clearly and that he may accept this suggested history more readily, he should remember that the surface on which such a series of streams was first developed lay at a much higher level than the present surface level of this part of the British Isles. There is evidence to show that there are clearly defined surfaces of planation throughout this wide area which give testimony of earlier river plains that have now very largely disappeared as a result of the general reduction of much of this surface by river erosion.

Recent investigations have revealed the probability of several major streams flowing from west to east in the past which have been severed in much the same way as suggested above. It is possible that an early Trent flowed from North Wales to the east coast of England and part of its course may be represented by the valley, between Corwen and Llangollen, followed by the present-day River Dee. The Tweed, Forth and other rivers in Scotland may be further examples.

Rejuvenation

Two other features of many valleys are the entrenched meander course and the appearance of terraces on either side of the valley at

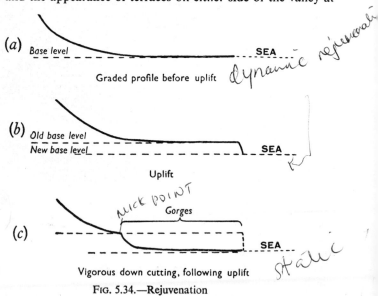

FIG. 5.34.—Rejuvenation

The stream may have two sections with their own base levels.

various levels. These represent the effect of rejuvenation on the stream concerned. The details of the cycle of erosion have been given earlier. All streams are attempting to produce a graded course, and ultimately this would be achieved on one condition, namely, that no appreciable change in the relative levels of land and sea occurs. It is exceedingly doubtful whether a cycle of erosion is carried to its final stages because of the disturbances of level which are likely. Slight oscillations of the mean levels of both land and sea occur more frequently than those which cause large-scale marine transgressions, and it is possible to consider a localized change of level which may affect merely a section and not the whole of a river basin. The effect of uplift on a stream is to destroy its grade, and this often encourages the stream to resume the down-cutting which was typical of its youth. With the onset of fresh down-cutting the stream is said to be rejuvenated. The effect of such rejuvenation on the profile of the river is shown in Fig. 5.34. Some slight rejuvenation may occur in the upper parts of a river's course with an increase of rainfall there.

V. C. Browne

FIG. 5.35.—Part of the Canterbury Plains, South Island, New Zealand

The rejuvenated valley of the River Waipara is entrenched in glacial deposits. Note the braided course of the river as well as the bars along the shore, enclosing lagoons, and the shore flats, leading inland to low cliffs.

Entrenched Valleys

The lowest section of a river course is usually in the form of a wide and low-lying plain, across which the main stream meanders on a grand scale. There are, however, rivers whose lower tracts are in quite elevated country with steep-sided valleys that resemble the immature upper tract. For instance, the River Wye, in southern Herefordshire and Monmouthshire, enters such a gorge-like valley after passing through Ross-on-Wye, and it does not leave it until reaching Chepstow at its entry into the estuary of the River Severn. The Wear and Tyne Rivers of northern England have similar. if less spectacular, gorges at their seaward ends.

The lower Wye has an entrenched or incised valley which is as tortuous as was the course of the river over its flood plain before local uplift disturbed its grade and caused it to be rejuvenated. The valley sides descend to the river precipitously in some sections, as for

Paul Popper Ltd.

FIG. 5.36.—An Abandoned Meander Course, River Ebro, Spain

The central area, surrounded by the dry meander bed, shows radial drainage.

instance at the Yat Rock, near Symond's Yat, giving a difference of level of almost 300 feet between the floor and the shoulders of the valley. Above Ross-on-Wye towards Hereford the river shows somewhat similar features, but here the valley never appears to be gorge-like, as it does farther to the south. Here a steep slope on one side of the valley is paired with a much more gentle slope on the opposite side showing that side cutting has played its part, but the cross-section of the valley is not typical of the lower tract of a mature river. Such features of rejuvenation, as in the Wye valley (Fig. 5.14), may be seen in many other valleys (Fig. 5.19). On the east side of the Wye valley, south of Monmouth, there are arcuate valleys at a higher level than the present river. These channels have been abandoned by the meandering river after rejuvenation, in much the same way as oxbows are left when a meander loop is cut off in a flood plain. In this case, however, a short circuit has been made through a valley spur, thus leaving an isolated hill. The bed of the abandoned channel may be dry but usually it carries some drainage near each end. Fig. 5.36 shows an example on the side of the Ebro valley in Spain. It is possible for such short-circuits to be caused by glacial diversion (see p. 107). Entrenched valleys may be found in areas where glaciation has left in its path a thick mantle of drift that has

FIG. 5.37.—Site of Durham

elevated the land surface, and thus caused the rejuvenation of the streams so that deep-cut valleys have been excavated in post-glacial times (Figs. 5.35 and 6.17).

The strategic positions afforded by the steep sides of an entrenched valley have been utilized by man. The older part of Durham City is enclosed within a great entrenched meander loop of the River Wear, so that its site was impregnable in the past apart from the narrow isthmus of land on the northern side of the town. On this side of the old settlement a castle and wall have guarded the northern approach (Fig. 5.37). The core of Berne, the capital city of Switzerland, is likewise enclosed within a bend of the River Aar.

It is clear that in some instances the local uplift which led to rejuvenation was so gradual that the river, with its renewed power for cutting down, was able to retain its grade whilst carving a gorge. Such was the case with the middle Rhine between Bingen and Bonn. There is a distinction between the two processes of entrenchment, as illustrated by the Wye and the middle Rhine, but the resultant valleys are essentially the same. Drainage which is successful in maintaining grade during a period of uplift is called antecedent. It will be seen that antecedent drainage is a form of superimposed drainage consequent upon local uplift. The Brahmaputra is considered to have maintained its flow across the rising Himalaya Mountains as these were formed so that the river is entrenched in remarkably deep and narrow gorges.

Terraces

Terraces are marked by distinct breaks in the slopes of valley sides, and they are often paired, in that they lie at the same level on either side of the valley above the stream bed. On the other hand, it is possible for such a correspondence of level between opposite terraces to be absent. The distinction is shown in Fig. 5.38. The longitudinal profile of some streams may exhibit a considerable diver-

(a) Paired Terraces   (b) Unpaired Terraces

FIG. 5.38.—River Terraces

gence from the perfectly graded state. This lack of grading may be due to structural differences, as has been explained in a previous section, but rejuvenation may also be responsible. Fig. 5.39a shows a valley profile with two sections each of which has an independent base level of erosion. An examination of the cross-section of such a valley in conjunction with its longitudinal profile will show that this change of slope in the profile is reflected in the terraces on the valley sides (Fig. 5.39b). These terraces are products of rejuvena-

FIG. 5.39.—Knick Point and Terraces

tion, since they are remnants of an earlier flood plain of the river. Uplift leads to fresh down-cutting, and the inner section of the previous flood plain has been removed. It is possible to trace terraces on each side of a valley until they converge at some point on the stream course which is known as a knick point (see Fig. 5.39). There may be several terraces with their associated knick points in one stretch of valley, each pair representing a remnant of a distinct flood plain of the past and, of course, a distinct episode of uplift. This results in what is sometimes known as a 'valley-in-valley' cross-section. Knick points will migrate upstream as the river restores the

graded curve of erosion after each uplift, with its consequent rejuvenation. These successive uplifts were in all probability separated
by considerable intervals of time, when down-cutting attempted, not
always with success, to restore the graded profile which had been
disturbed. The geomorphologist regards each of these intervals as a
distinct cycle of erosion, and each cycle is thus marked by a particular terrace line. The persistence of a terrace for great distances
along a valley side is unusual, because of the breaching of the terrace
by tributary streams, and in certain cases the swing of meanders in
the development of a plain may destroy the terraces.

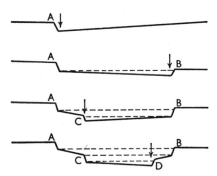

FIG. 5.40.—Development of Terraces by a Meandering River

Terraces may be produced by other means than rejuvenation. It
has been noted that terraces on opposite sides of a valley are not always coincident in level. The reason for this may be that the terraces
have been produced by a meandering river as it swings across the
flood plain and migrates downstream. It is essential to accept the
possibility of some down-cutting by the river, even when meandering is well developed, in order to explain the formation of unpaired
terraces. The composite diagram (Fig. 5.40) attempts to show the
development of unpaired terraces in this way. The arrow in each
stage of the diagram marks the position of the river as it moves with
the progression of its meanders to different parts of the floor of the
plain. The terraces have been formed with down-cutting in the order
A, B, C, and D. A series of terraces is a common feature in post-
glacial valleys, where the work of the stream is concentrated in
largely unconsolidated rock. Terraces are of considerable importance, because they are often the sites of settlements (their gravels
and sands are frequently water-bearing), and some are valuable as
lines of communication above the flood-plain level.

CHAPTER 6

Glaciation and Glacial Land Forms

Glaciers

During the recent geological past, ice from the north spread over much of Canada and the northern states of the United States of America, whilst from Scandinavia it moved south to cover the north of Germany, and from the Scottish Highlands and Scandinavia it was dispersed over much of Northern and Central England. In this Ice Age the northern world was not continually covered with ice. Four times at least the ice advanced southwards, and four times did it retreat polewards. One obvious condition which promotes an advance of ice is that the prevailing temperatures of the air must be low, yet it would appear from geological evidence that over this period of a million years the temperature fluctuated so that at times the climate was relatively mild. Today we live in a northern world which witnessed the start of the last retreat of ice about 20,000 to 25,000 years ago. This is a small fraction of the 1,000,000 years which are allocated to the whole Ice Age, and it is possible that our mild climate of today is a mere interlude, and that in time it will deteriorate and there will be a fresh advance of ice from the north. In the northern world there is therefore abundant opportunity for observing the effects of an ice cover which has so recently been withdrawn. The last retreat of the ice sheets may be regarded as ending about 9,000 years ago in this country.

Today glaciers are of two types, those which start from mountain snowfields and follow valley routes as in the Alpine regions of France and Switzerland and, for that matter, in parts of most high mountain regions of the world and those which are continental and cover the whole surface of the land to its sea margins in the form of extensive ice sheets as in Greenland and Antarctica. The former or alpine type is usually found in temperate latitudes so that the descent of the ice along pre-existing river valleys brings the glaciers to levels within the mountains where melting occurs so that, in general, these glaciers do not reach the sea. The latter group is essentially arctic in regard to climatic conditions, since low temperatures prevail throughout the year and the ice does not melt until it reaches the ocean—in Antarctica some of the ice spreads out on the sea in the form of ice shelves (Fig. 12.14). Irrespective of the relief of the land below these ice sheets in both Greenland and Antarctica the ice surface rises from the coasts inland to heights of the order of 7,500–9,000 feet within 200 miles of the sea. The general form of these ice sheets is that of a dome or lens. Here and there in coastal regions of both areas ice-free mountain surfaces project as nunataks between which the ice tends to be discharged more or less as large valley glaciers (Fig. 6.4). Nunataks are common with alpine or valley glaciers as in the case of the Trugberg (see Fig 6.1 and Frontispiece).

Formation of Glaciers

As a glacier moves it must be fed with ice at its head in order that it may persist, and it must be realized that low temperatures alone are insufficient; they must be accompanied by adequate precipitation of snow to maintain a constant supply of ice. In fact, estimates suggest that temperatures in Britain during part of the Ice Age were approximately 20° F (11° C) lower during most of the year than they are now—North Scotland must have had temperatures in summer not far above freezing point. The speeds at which glaciers move are very varied. Some may move more than fifty feet in a day, but the majority travel less than five feet in this time. It is clear that a glacier, while losing ice at its lower end by melting or by calving into the sea where large fragments float away as icebergs, must eventually disappear unless it gains at its head the equivalent amount of ice which is lost at its lower end or snout.

Glacier ice is produced from snow which falls during the year on the high parts of mountains or the inner regions of continental areas. Some of this accumulated snow may melt in summer, or it may evaporate and be lost as an effective agent for the production of ice. Even in sub-Arctic regions, such as Spitzbergen, there is a distinct loss of snow by summer melt, and the surface layers of glaciers turn to melt water. This ablation of snow is a factor which must be more than balanced by accumulation of sufficient snow to give an adequate supply of permanent ice to maintain the glacier. The alternation of accumulation and melting is shown on mountain slopes by the variation of the snow level or line which descends in winter and rises with the warmer conditions that prevail in the summer months.

An examination of large-scale maps of alpine areas which possess glaciers today will show the frequent use of the word 'firn' (Fig. 6.1). This word is applied to the snowfields at the very head of a glacier and has entered into geographical literature. This German word means 'of last year' but 'firn' is also used technically to describe the intermediate or transitional state between snow and compact glacier ice. There is a French equivalent in the term 'névé'.

The firn zone is the surface of several layers which extend downwards to the solid compact ice that forms the main glacier. This upper part of a glacier may be regarded as stratified, and the layers are shown in Fig. 6.2, which represents, not to scale, a section from the surface of a snowfield down to the compact ice region. The two upper zones of snow and firn respectively are each subdivided by

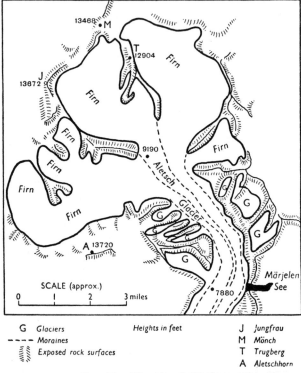

FIG. 6.1.—The Aletsch Glacier
(Reference should be made to the frontispiece)

thin crusts of ice, and these represent annual banding which could be used, to a much more limited extent, in the way that tree rings are employed to date the age of a tree. The snow is much interspersed with air, and each ice crust marks a layer of snow which has melted in summer after the winter accumulation and has then frozen to ice with the onset of the following winter. Progressive layers have accumulated with successive years, and in the deeper layers the individual snow crystals have lost their feathery tips, and have apparently grouped themselves to form particles of firn which in turn become coarser with increase of depth. There is a considerable amount of enclosed air in the firn, but the proportion of solid content increases with depth. The weight of the superior layers plays its part in compacting the lower layers, and eventually a solid ice layer is formed at varying depths from the surface. In one investigation[1] it was found that with increasing depth the specific gravity of the layers increased. Firn changed to solid ice when the specific gravity had risen from 0·6 at the surface to 0·82–0·84 at depth.[2] Even in the glacier ice there is still some enclosed air, but the crystals have massed together so as to exclude any possibility of inter-communication by means of fine air passages. Thus, whilst firn

FIG. 6.2.—Vertical Section of Firn Zone (not to scale)

may be quite porous to melt water, which forms at the time of the summer heat, glacier ice is literally impervious.

Examinations of firn and glacier ice have shown that in the firn zone lateral movements of individual masses of ice crystals may occur within a given layer, but there is no comprehensive movement of the whole firn. On the other hand, glacier ice moves *en masse*, or, at least, in distinct layers. There appear to be thrust planes within the ice which permit differential movement of the several layers (Fig. 6.3). It is still impossible to render a full account of the movement of ice in a glacier, but it would appear that older theories concerning this movement are not completely overthrown by more recent investigations, which have confirmed to a certain extent the possibility of movement of crystals under stress in a liquid which

FIG. 6.3.—Lateral Movement of Ice.

After May

Screws, arranged vertically in the line AB, will tend to show a differential movement, and after an interval they will assume fresh positions as indicated by the line CD

---

[1] Made in 1938 by a Cambridge University expedition on the Jungfraujoch in Switzerland.

[2] The Antarctic firn has a density of 0·3–0·4 gm per cc at the surface whilst solid ice is found at depths varying between 150 and 300 feet with a density of about 0·82.

is saline and derived from melt water. Sliding or shearing of adjacent layers is also very probable.

Expeditions Polaires Françaises; Photo J. Languepin

FIG. 6.4.—Glacier on the East Coast of Greenland

Note the tongue of the glacier, the crevasses and lateral moraines. The foreground shows some of the outwash sands and gravels (see p. 110).

Surface Features of Glaciers

In alpine areas the firn lies in masses which are separated by exposed rocks in the form of sharp edges or pyramidal peaks. However, many firn areas are found to coalesce at lower levels and give rise to a valley glacier (Figs. 6.1 and 6.7) which extends down-slope to its snout that is usually convex in front. The snout represents the level at which the rate of melting of the ice just equals the forward movement of the glacier and the melted ice disperses from it as a stream of water. The surface of the glacier is rarely smooth; it is usually fretted by deep cracks or crevasses which are largely created by strains that develop in the moving ice. The convex snout and the crevasses are largely due to the fact that the ice moves or slides downhill more rapidly in the centre than at the sides of the glacier, where frictional effects cause a retardation. The snout protrudes in the middle to accord with this effect. Crevasses develop at right angles to the direction of the strains which arise from the more rapid progression of the medial part of the glacier (Figs. 6.4 and 6.5).

A longitudinal profile of a mountain glacier indicates that a very large crevasse, known as a bergschrund,[1] is formed near the head of the glacier in the firn zone; this particular feature is more obvious in the summer season (Fig. 6.6). The profile section also shows the crevasses and the depth of the glacier ice below the firn zone from which the glacier is fed. Glaciers in high latitudes, such as in Greenland and Antarctica, possess crevasses, but there is much greater continuity of the ice surface, since in these areas the whole land surface is literally buried by the deep ice cap and there is little friction at the upper surface of the ice. However, marginal areas of these continental ice covers are liable to stresses, since the ice is descending from inland, which result in the production of a large number of transverse crevasses, and, in ad-

Glacier movement

— — — Lines of strain
C——C Crevasses

Valley side

Fig. 6.5.—Crevasses

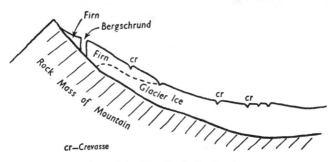

Fig. 6.6.—The Head of a Glacier

dition, there are longitudinal crevasses lying approximately parallel to the direction of the ice flow (Fig. 6.4). When these arctic glaciers reach the sea, they form extensive cliffs of ice from which icebergs

[1] Also known as a 'rimaye'.

detach themselves. However, in some cases, they move down valleys to the coast and resemble valley glaciers with snouts (Fig. 6.4).

The Work of Ice

In areas from which a previous ice cover has retreated it is possible to estimate the work that has been done by glaciers. Glaciation has left in highland regions, such as those of North Wales, Scotland, Scandinavia, and elsewhere, sharp-angled ridges or arêtes, and pyramidal peaks such as the Matterhorn in the Alps of Switzerland. These two features may be regarded as developments from the precipitous-sided concave hollows known as corries or cirques (Fig. 6.7), which are almost ubiquitous in these glaciated uplands.

Widerøe's Flyveselskap, Oslo

FIG. 6.7.—Glacier in Svartisen, Norway

To the right are seen shallow corries which hang into the main glaciated valley. The glacier has retreated recently as shown by the light-coloured, bare rock surfaces. Probably a bergschrund can be seen at the foot of the rocks near the head of the glacier.

In addition, there are to be found the U-shaped valleys (Fig. 9.13), with relatively level floors but almost precipitous sides, into which tributary valleys enter at high levels and thus form hanging valleys (Fig. 6.7). Very often extensive sections of these U-shaped valleys exhibit a longitudinal profile which is scalloped (see Fig. 6.14), with present-day rivers following courses in narrow ravines and plunging over waterfalls at the points marked X in the diagram.

In the earliest days of glacial study it was considered that great ice masses acted like a chisel, or more probably as a gouge, scooping out or scalloping the landscape. It is clear, from the study of existing glaciers, that on the margins of the ice mass there is much weathering of the nearby rock surfaces. The action which produces this weathering is often referred to as sapping, and is consequent on the melting and freezing of ice by day and night respectively on the margins of cavities in the ice, such as a bergschrund or crevasse. Rock debris so produced, together with frost-shattered rock waste that falls by gravity from the slopes above, forms long trails of rock fragments, known as moraines (Fig. 6.8). Those which lie along the outer margins of the glacier are known as lateral moraines (Fig. 6.4), but where two or more glaciers unite, the confluent lateral moraines of each produce a series of inner moraines. These are called medial moraines from their positions (see Frontispiece).

FIG. 6.8.—Moraines

The base or sole of a glacier is a zone in which, possibly, similar sapping takes place and large fragments of rock are enclosed within the ice of the glacier. As these fragments move with the ice, they erode very powerfully and give the action which is likened to gouging. Issuing from the snout of a glacier is a stream of water which is not fed by the melt of the snout ice alone, but is, in fact, a subglacial stream which deposits in front of the snout its burden of rock fragments. These rocks, together with additional material from the lateral and medial moraines which are carried to the snout end of the glacier and there deposited on melting of the ice, form a third type of moraine known as a terminal moraine. Recession of the glacier by prolonged melting, with a warmer climate, leaves the land surface, which is thus exposed, littered with rock fragments, and these constitute a ground moraine. It is this moraine which lies over such extensive lowland areas adjacent to glaciated highlands, although much may be found on the floors of the mountain valleys.

Despite the erosive power of the enclosed fragments of rock in the sole of a glacier, many geographers have been sceptical of the potency of ice erosion, since ice can be deformed by the irregularities of the surfaces over and against which it passes. Some geographers have argued that ice has acted as a protective cover to the land surface, and that it was the areas not so covered which were actively eroded in the Ice Age by running water. The outstanding forms of glacial landscape will now be discussed more fully, and regard will be paid to the fact that some authorities believe in the effectiveness of ice erosion, whereas others consider that water erosion outside the ice-protected areas has been the more important agent.

Corries

In many of the Welsh mountains and in many parts of the Scottish Highlands the outstanding peaks are surrounded by quite deep hollows or corries which have arcuate margins enclosing areas that are almost circular in plan (Fig. 6.9). These hollows have

FIG. 6.9.—Cader Idris Region, North Wales

Based on the Ordnance Survey Map with the sanction of the Controller of H.M. Stationery Office

precipitous walls that may tower as much as a thousand feet above the floor of a depression, which is not infrequently occupied by a lake whose outlet is into a typical U-shaped valley (Fig. 6.10). The summit of Cader Idris in North Wales is thus surrounded by several corries. These depressions were probably initiated by the process of nivation. Nivation depends upon the collection of snow in a hollow, or at a valley head, and on its margins there is thawing and freezing in turn which has the effect of sapping at the adjacent rock surfaces, with the result that there is developed a very powerful form of mechanical erosion. The alternating thaw and freeze may exhibit a seasonal as well as a diurnal rhythm. Long-continued action of this kind results in a recession of the inner walls of the hollow. With greater accumulation of snow as in the firn areas of the Alpine peaks and with the formation of a marked bergschrund, the sapping would be much accelerated. Later, with the formation of glacier ice and its enclosed rock fragments, the hollow would be deepened. It is possible that sliding and shearing of adjacent layers (p. 94) could result in a rotational movement which might account for the deepening of the corrie. There are, however, many views regarding the mechanics of corrie formation.

FIG. 6.10.—Corries and Arête

Arêtes and Cols

Knife-edge ridges may be developed when the walls of two back-to-back corries have met after sapping from both sides. Fig. 6.10a, shows a north to south section of the summit region of Cader Idris. Clearly it would involve very little more erosion to produce a knife-edge ridge or arête. Striding Edge, on Helvellyn, in the Lake District,

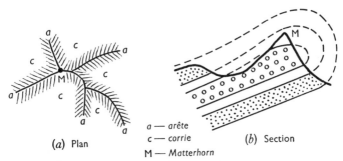

FIG. 6.11.—The Matterhorn

The Matterhorn has been derived from a recumbent fold which has been partially reduced by ice action, leaving a pyramidal peak.

is a fine example—a section is shown in Fig. 6.10 (b). Several corries whose walls have receded by erosion on various sides of a mountain summit in time create a pinnacle which is pyramidal in shape, with a series of arêtes rising to a culminating 'horn' as shown *par excellence* by the Matterhorn and many other Swiss peaks (Fig. 6.11). The reduction at a later stage of an arête gives rise to a col, one of the most important features in high-mountain terrain since it often provides the only means of inter-communication in such areas (Fig. 6.12). It must be noted that a col may be formed in other ways and does not necessarily depend upon glaciation.

Fig. 6.12.—Development of a Col by the Intersection of Two Adjacent Corries

(a) Just before intersection of walls.
(b) Immediately after intersection.
(c) Further erosion produces a col.

U-shaped Valleys

The U-shaped valley is regarded by some authorities as wholly the product of ice erosion. Through a V-shaped river valley of preglacial origin a glacier has forged its way almost as a gouge, so that the profile of Fig. 6.13 was developed (see Fig. 6.7). The erosion was accomplished partly by sapping and partly through planing by the ice, armed with large rock fragments. The scalloped floor, already referred to, can be explained by differential erosion, and the steps in the longitudinal profile (at X, Fig. 6.14) are interpreted as zones where the rocks were more resistant to erosion than those above and below these points. In this respect the steps in the valley floor may be compared with the un-graded sections of the immature tract of a river's course. On the other hand there is a strong likelihood that at these points ice from confluent glaciers joined the ice of the main valley glacier so that there was a great increase in the

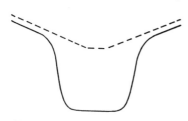

Fig. 6.13.—A Glaciated Valley. U-shaped Valley imprinted into V-shaped Valley

Fig. 6.14.—The Scalloped Floor of a Glaciated Valley

erosive power of the glacier, resulting in these irregularities in the floor of the U-shaped valley.

From the point of view of ice protection the U-shaped valley was formed in the following way. The upper part of a pre-glacial river valley became occupied by ice at the onset of cold conditions, whilst down valley, below this ice cover, normal water erosion proceeded. On the retreat of the ice, the valley would show two distinct sections, an upper one which, owing to ice protection, would be relatively un-graded compared with the lower part that had been continuously developed by running water. Upon the resumption of water erosion in the upper part of the valley, vigorous down-cutting would take place, and a deep V-shaped valley would be developed. Advance of the ice at a later stage would again give protection to the upper section of the valley, although it is likely that some modification of this valley would result from the movement of the glacier ice, so that its floor would be widened to a certain extent at least. Repetition of this advance and retreat of the ice with alternating periods of water erosion and ice protection would result eventually in a deep U-shaped valley which had not depended solely upon ice erosion for its excavation. The scalloped floor of the U-shaped valley would be almost inevitable, since complete grading by successive periods of water erosion in front of the ice cover would be virtually impossible. Each halt of the ice would be marked by a relatively graded section of the valley downstream from the ice front (Fig. 6.15).

FIG. 6.15.—Development of a Scalloped Valley Floor

In many of the exposed glaciated valleys of the northern world there is evidence of valley spurs on the higher slopes. At lower levels these spurs have been reduced at the time when ice moved through the valley and widened it by planing off irregularities on its sides. Consequently, the basal sections of such spurs are truncated, and they fall in line with the markedly rectilinear walls of the glaciated valley, which are unbroken, save where today tributary streams enter through V-shaped notches that are being cut down with great rapidity by very youthful streams (Figs. 6.16 and 6.7). The remnants of the spurs, above the valley walls, are proof of previous water erosion, and, whilst the ability of ice to clear the sides of such a valley is admitted, many hold the view that its depth has been determined primarily by rivers, and not by ice. At the head of such glaciated valleys the steep walls form an amphitheatre, known sometimes as the trough end, lying below several corries.

101

Hanging Valleys

The hanging valley is one of the other interesting features in glaciated regions. Usually a tributary river joins its main stream at the same level, in other words, the two valleys are accordant. It is only in the ungraded mountain tract of a river valley that it is possible to have a tributary plunging into the main stream over a waterfall. In mountain valleys of glaciated regions it is very common to find a tributary stream descending by falls and cascades for several hundreds of feet down the valley sides before it enters the main stream (Figs. 6.16 and 6.7). Neighbouring tributary valleys do not

T   Truncated Spur
HV Hanging Valley
W   Waterfall

FIG. 6.16.—Truncated Spurs and Hanging Valleys

necessarily show the same amount of discordance between their floors and the floor of the main valley; in fact, some may be quite accordant. This discordance has exercised the minds of geographers and there is a variety of explanations. Those who believe in the effectiveness of ice erosion attribute the discordance to the unequal excavation by a major glacier and its more shallow, and therefore less effective, tributary glaciers. Those who believe in ice protection maintain that most of the deepening must be fluvial and that it has occurred in inter-glacial periods. To explain fully the hanging valleys, it is suggested that in a period of ice retreat the main valley was unoccupied by ice, whilst the higher parts of the tributary valleys still carried an ice cover and could not be eroded by water. These tributary valleys remained ungraded while the main valley was undergoing active erosion. The various streams that enter the valley and lake of Tal-y-llyn from the southern slopes of Cader Idris in North Wales hang in varying degrees (see Fig. 6.9). Since the final retreat of the ice, a river has cut into the floor of the upper part of

Judges Ltd.

FIG. 6.17.—Tal-y-llyn Pass, Merionethshire

Here is seen a U-shaped valley with the post-glacial development of a V-shaped valley in its floor. Tal-y-llyn Lake can be seen in the distance with its deltaic flats (see Fig. 6.9).

the U-shaped valley of Tal-y-llyn and produced a V-shaped ravine, but the side streams are far from being graded (Fig. 6.17).

Roches Moutonnées and Erratics

Within a glaciated region it is usual to find rock surfaces which are grooved and scratched. These striations have been made by angular rock fragments enclosed within the soles of glaciers, and they give some indication of the direction of ice movement, a matter of geological importance. Some of these rocks are known as roches

FIG. 6.18.—Roche Moutonnée

moutonnées. In section a roche moutonnée shows two distinct aspects of surface: (*a*) a smooth surface with a slight slope, and (*b*) a relatively irregular surface with quite a steep slope (Fig. 6.18). The two surfaces represent different actions of moving ice, the former indicating the planing action, combined with scratching, whilst the latter slope is the result of the plucking and sapping action similar to that which may be observed in the bergschrund zone of a glacier. Fig. 6.18 shows how the ice has moved over these rocks and that the plucked surfaces are on the down-flow sides.

Erratics may also be found lying on the uplands, and for that matter in the lowland areas beyond the mountains over which ice has moved. For instance, boulders of granite, unmistakably derived from a granite mass in the Criffel district of the Southern Uplands of Scotland can be found in fair abundance in the South and Central Pennine regions of England. These fragments have been transported by the ice of a glacier that moved at some time from Scotland in a southerly or south-easterly direction. By tracing erratics back to their source it is possible to ascertain the direction in which the ice flowed, and where erratics have been found to contain valuable ores of metals it has sometimes been possible to locate the ore body.

Glacial Lakes

Throughout glaciated regions there are innumerable lakes of various types which owe their origin, largely, to glacial action of one sort or another. The base of a corrie is hollowed out by ice erosion, so that there is very often a rock rim at its foot which holds a corrie lake or tarn (Fig. 6.9). Many of the very small tarns which are dotted about the surfaces of glaciated mountains occupy very minor depressions that have been scooped out by ice.

Tal-y-llyn Lake (Fig. 6.9) has a somewhat different history. Immediately below the lake is a low ridge through which the stream draining the lake has cut its way by a ravine. The ridge is a terminal moraine which lies across the main valley at this point where at some time a glacier moving from the north-east had its snout. Such a lake is moraine-dammed, and there are many examples to be found throughout all glaciated regions. Tal-y-llyn lake was probably much longer at one time, for its upper end has been filled in with deltaic deposits (see Figs. 6.9 and 6.17).

Long narrow lakes, which are also of very considerable depth, may occur in conjunction with the scalloping of a glaciated valley. Such over-deepened basins are frequent in Northern Europe and in particular in the Swedish mountains, where almost every valley which descends from the Kiolen range to the Baltic Sea possesses one of these lakes, often referred to as a glen lake. The majority of the Cumbrian lakes are of this type.

Lakes dammed by Glaciers and their Outflows

There are valley glaciers which arrest the flow of a side stream and produce lakes. The Märjelen See, on the east side of the Aletsch glacier in Switzerland, is of this type (see Fig. 6.1 and Frontispiece). Such present-day lakes have suggested that there must have been quite extensive lakes of this type at the time of the greatest extension of the ice sheets in the northern world, although the lakes are no longer in existence. Evidence of such lakes is available in the region of Glen Roy and its associated valleys, off Glen More and some distance north-east of Ben Nevis in Scotland. The lower ends of various pre-glacial valleys were choked with ice, and lakes were formed in the

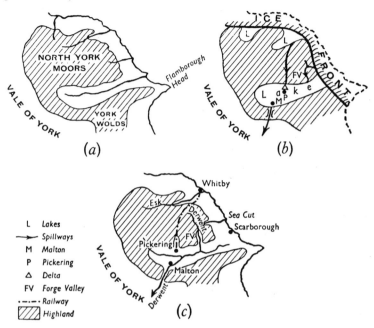

Fig. 6.19.—Glacial Lakes and Spillways in the North York Moors

upper parts of the valleys. The level of each lake rose until a height was reached which permitted its water to flow through a col in an intervening ridge and so obtain an outlet through a valley which was not affected by glacial damming. It will be remembered that the ice cover fluctuated considerably during the Ice Age, and such a system of lakes would be modified as the ice shrank with a change of climate; the level of the lakes fell, and when the ice halted in its retreat, a new outlet or series of outlets was established. In this area of Glen Roy there are no less than three significant levels on the valley sides which are occupied by beach deposits of the pre-existing lakes; they are known as the 'parallel roads' of Glen Roy. The levels of these deposits coincide with the heights of well-defined cols or spillways through which the lake waters found an outlet at various times.

In North-east Yorkshire there is abundant evidence of such glacial damming. The probable pre-glacial relief is shown in Fig. 6.19a. Ice advanced from the north, and was arrested by the Yorkshire Wolds and Moors, so that several lakes were formed by streams that had flowed eastwards to the sea. These lakes, like those in Glen Roy, spilled over at convenient levels, and the outflowing streams cut channels which remain today, one of which is followed by the railway between Pickering and Whitby (Figs. 6.19*c* and 6.20). The small northern lakes probably had a common drainage through the Moors into a larger lake which spilled southwards into

Aerofilms Ltd.

FIG. 6.20.—Newtondale, North Yorkshire
A section of the glacial spillway to the north of Pickering (see Fig. 6.19).

the Vale of York (Fig. 6.19*b*). Today all the lakes have disappeared, but the south-eastern part of the York Moors is drained southwards by the Derwent, which flows through Forge Valley, yet another spillway, and then across the drained bed of the largest lake, now represented by the Vale of Pickering, and finally into the Vale of York by way of the Malton gorge (Fig. 6.19*c*). It may be noted that Pickering stands on a delta constructed by a stream which entered the large lake of the past (Fig. 6.19*b*).

Other examples of such diversions may be found throughout Northern England and the Midlands. The Ferryhill gap between Darlington and Durham has been cut in the Magnesian Limestone escarpment which once separated two glacial dammed lakes. The lower Wear has a gorge-like valley near Sunderland which the river cut when its earlier course into the Tyne near Gateshead was obstructed by ice. Ice from the Irish Sea deflected the Severn (which flowed in pre-glacial days northwards into the sea near the present Dee estuary) to the east, where the ridges of the Wrekin and Wenlock Edge caused a large lake to form in the Shrewsbury area; this spilled southwards and thus the Severn gorge was cut between Buildwas and Bridgnorth and consequently the lake was drained, leaving a plain. Near Llangollen the River Dee has abandoned some earlier-formed meander loops as a result of glacial action. The loops were plugged by ice and glacial deposits, but the Dee was able to cut a new and straighter course, which in post-glacial times it has retained.

It is possible for diversions of glaciers to occur with the creation of spillways. The movement of a glacier may be impeded by some cause, such as a larger glacier or a narrowing of the valley down which it is moving. The ice may build up behind such a barrier and reach high enough to pass through a nearby col—this it has scoured, deeply enough, to divert the river drainage in post-glacial times. This is called glacial diffluence. It is probable that this process explains more adequately several examples of unusual drainage patterns which have in the past been attributed to river capture. Examples from the Cairngorms region of Scotland may be quoted. They include the remarkable deep trough of Lairig Ghru and the watershed zone between the upper Feshie and Geldie rivers just south of the main Cairngorms region.

Lakes formed by Glacial Warping

At the time of the maximum ice cover it is estimated that the thickness of the ice was in some places 6,000 feet, although, as with the cover in Greenland today, it was probably lens-shaped, and therefore tapered considerably towards the margins (Fig. 6.21a). Nevertheless, it is clear that a great weight was imposed upon certain areas which was of sufficient magnitude to create a down-warping of the crustal layers of sial. This down-warping may be compared with the depression of a geosynclinal area (as envisaged in the formation of mountains), but on a much smaller scale. There is evidence that Scandinavia and the Baltic basin, as well as the Canadian Shield, are rising as a result of the restoration of isostatic equilibrium following the unloading by the ice melt at the end of the last glaciation. This elevation of the areas in question is still in progress, partly because the unloading is incomplete (on the highlands of Scandinavia there are remnants of the ice sheets which are still shrinking) and partly because the uplift has not kept pace with the melt of the ice.

At the time of the main retreat of the ice at the end of the Ice Age, land surfaces were exposed, but these remained sufficiently downwarped to encourage the formation of fairly large lakes. Some of these marginal areas were flooded by the sea. It was under such circumstances that the Great Lakes of North America had their origin,

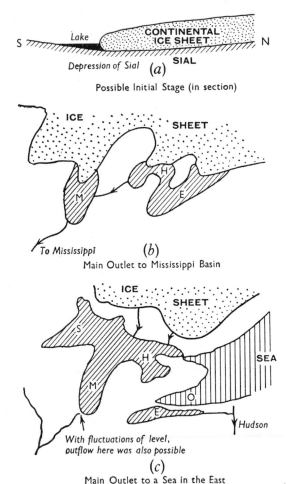

Fig. 6.21.—Stages in the Development of the Great Lakes of North America

although there is evidence that the hollows, created by down-warping, were also scoured, to some extent, by ice. The lake basins were undoubtedly formed on the margins of the ice sheet that covered northern North America. The earliest of these lakes were able to spill southwards towards the Mississippi basin, but as the ice receded northwards the lakes increased in size and found outlets in various directions. At different times the lakes drained towards the

108

Mississippi, the Hudson valley and into an arm of the sea, which occupied an area corresponding to the lower St. Lawrence valley of today (Fig. 6.21*b* and *c*). Of great interest is the fact that the modern Great Lakes are just able to maintain their eastern outlet because of the existing controls of uplift consequent upon the ice melt, but if the present trend of isostatic adjustment persists, then uplift on the northern side of the lakes may permit Lake Michigan to drain southwards once again into the Mississippi basin. It is believed that this could happen in less than 2,000 years from now. However, warping does not account entirely for the formation of the Great Lakes, since they are partly dammed by moraines.

Lowland Glaciation

At the time of the most intense glaciation in the Pleistocene period it is probable that many areas were completely covered by thick ice sheets. Clearly valley glaciers occupied many highlands of the northern world, and these extended to the lowlands nearby, where they spread out and joined with one another to form great piedmont glaciers. Such glaciers had little opportunity of gathering much surface moraine, since at the time of the maximum glaciation most of the land surface in the mountains was buried by ice. However, such continental ice sheets did create on their under surfaces what are known as ground moraines, which have been left as a cloak over the pre-glacial land surfaces. At the same time there was a continuous outwash from the margins of these ice sheets where melting was helping to form plains of glacial deposits (see Fig. 5.35).

There remain in many areas of the European and North American lowlands great east-west terminal moraines which are the melt deposits that accumulated in front of the ice sheets when they remained stationary for a fairly long period of time. These moraines indicate that there were several prolonged halts during the final retreat of the ice. The North German plain is crossed by many parallel, arcuate lines of moraines, and similar groups occur in other lowland regions such as those which lie both east and west of the Pennine Uplands in England over which ice was dispersed. Most of these deposits are clays with enclosed rock fragments which vary in size and quantity from locality to locality. The names of boulder clay, glacial drift, and till are applied to these formations which in parts of Eastern England are of such a depth that if they were stripped from the underlying rocks they would cause the present coastline of East Anglia to recede by many miles. A study of these deposits is of importance to the geographer because, usually, these clays give soils of great fertility and thus influence farming to a high degree. Many of our soils in Britain have been developed from glacial deposits which form the parent rock.

Ground Moraine

In front of most of these terminal moraines which lie in the lowlands there are very extensive outwash plains of clays and gravels, whilst behind each moraine it is quite common to find a group of hummocky low hills, known as drumlins, and winding low ridges, known as eskers and kames (Fig. 6.22). The outwash plains are made of sands and gravels, often interbedded with boulder clay. The

FIG. 6.22.—Ground Moraine and other Deposits

gravels represent, in general, material that has been carried forward either by melt water dispersing from the ice or by rivers which have affected these regions in post-glacial times. The term 'fluvioglacial' may be applied to these deposits. The boulder clays are ground moraine deposits, and may sometimes lie above gravels, in which case the latter have been overridden by a later advance of the ice. Unfortunately, it is not always easy to distinguish the clays and gravels, since both may be modified locally to such an extent that the boulder clay is largely a deposit of boulders and stones without clay and the gravels may be intermixed with clay.

In Eastern England large level drifts of boulder clay form dissected plateaus of no great elevation, and it is considered that these deposits were derived from ice which remained stationary after its final advance. The clays contain boulders from distant areas, but also much local rock, such as Chalk in the areas of North Essex, whilst London Clay (a rock of pre-glacial formation),[1] lying farther to the south and nearer to London, is incorporated in the drift.

In other areas the boulder clay regions exhibit very different land forms from these low plateau lands. Parts of Central Ireland, the

[1] Of Eocene age.

110

Tweed basin, and several areas in north-eastern U.S.A. have what is known as drumlin landscape. The glacial clay remains today in these regions in the form of elongated hillocks or hills which form a peculiar and unmistakable pattern. In some instances where these ridges rise to more than fifty feet above the level of the surrounding land, it is possible for the pattern to be discerned on the large-scale maps of the district by almost elliptical contours (Fig. 6.23). These

FIG. 6.23.—Drumlins

ridges are usually found behind terminal moraines and it seems that they have been developed in the ice mass and left upon its retreat. The map shows that they are arranged longitudinally with their longer axes in parallel lines, and this is in sympathy with the direction of ice-flow movements which affected the region. The drumlins are not in alignment when viewed transversely, which suggests that they were affected individually by the moving ice. Possibly they are great masses of ground moraine which were engulfed by the lower layers of the glacier ice and yet remained practically stationary despite the movement of the ice in general.

Eskers and Kames

Here a brief reference must be made to eskers. These are sinuous gravel ridges which run across country often quite regardless of valley lines or hills. They are clearly of river origin, and are thought to represent the deposits of subglacial streams which threaded their ways in tunnels under, or in, the bottom of the ice sheets. Many valley glaciers of today show outlet tunnels of this nature with an issuing stream. It is also likely that eskers may be deltaic fans that were formed at the mouths of such tunnels where they had an outfall into a lake which was marginal to the ice front. On the recession of the ice sheet the delta extended backwards in the form of a narrow band of deposits, since it had little opportunity to spread out into a fan. A halt in the recession of the ice caused an increase in the deltaic deposits which is shown by a swelling

111

in the otherwise narrow ridge. Several halts of the ice are marked by a series of such swellings, and the esker is then said to be beaded (Fig. 6.24). Kames may appear in the same areas as eskers. They may be isolated masses of deposits, or they may be clustered in the form of a winding ridge. It is probable that kames are also of deltaic origin. They may, in fact, represent the coalescence of several adjoining lake deltas.

FIG. 6.24.—The Formation of an Esker

The eskers and terminal moraines may be of value to man where they form slightly elevated ridges in a lowland region, as they are usually high enough to escape both damage and interference from river floods. Consequently routes may follow the crest of an esker or a moraine. In the Central Plateau of Finland eskers which wind across lake basins, with sufficient elevation above the water-level, are invaluable in that region as lines of communication. One of the finest examples of this use of an esker is afforded by Punkaharju

Paul Popper Ltd.

FIG. 6.25.—Punkaharju, Finland
Esker ridges, above a lake surface in Finland, covered with coniferous forest.

(Fig. 6.25). The town of York has grown up by the River Ouse on either side of a shallow gap that has been cut by the river in an east-west morainic ridge which crosses the Vale of York and gives a relatively dry causeway in time of floods. Some of the North German rivers have been diverted by the arcuate terminal moraines which cross the northern plain and the outlet of the River Elbe has been diverted from the Baltic to the North Sea. Closely-spaced drumlins may produce a type of trellised drainage (p. 75) as shown by the minor tributaries of the River Tweed to the north of Coldstream.

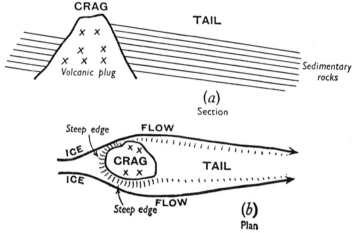

FIG. 6.26.—Crag and Tail

Crag and Tail

A rather special feature of glacial landscape is known as 'crag-and tail'. Reference has already been made to volcanic crags (p. 29), and in the case of some such crags in the Lothian area of Scotland, particularly that on which Edinburgh Castle stands, there is a 'tail' to the crag. Fig. 6.26a and b will help to explain the origin of this combined feature. The crag has been an obstacle in the path of ice which has moved over the area, causing the ice to pass over and round the crag. The tail is built of local sedimentary rock which was largely protected from the ice by the crag, but not sufficiently to prevent some glacial planing and some deposition of boulder clay, mainly on its upper surface. The sides of the crag which were exposed laterally to the ice flow are excessively steep, and give an almost impregnable position to Edinburgh Castle. Today the 'tail' carries the street of Canongate, which leads from the Castle to Holyrood House, lying at its end.

CHAPTER 7

Erosion in Arid Regions and Desert Land Forms

Introduction

Large areas of the continental surfaces have desert or semi-arid climates and their surface features are quite distinct from those of more humid regions. However, there is evidence, in the abandoned towns of considerable size that are found within desert areas of today, that unquestionably these areas have been more humid within historic times. Whilst wind is the most important agent of erosion in these regions it is impossible to overlook the work of running water although its effects are abnormal and intermittent compared with river erosion in wetter areas. The most effective and extensive erosion in these areas is that of deflation whereby the land surface is lowered by wind action. Deflation is the blowing away by wind of weathered rock fragments. Thus both transport and accumulation of rock waste within and beyond arid regions may be almost exclusively æolian. Furthermore, evaporation and the lack of vegetation are other factors which affect the land forms of these regions. Most arid regions have no external drainage to the oceans. De Martonne, the great French geographer, has shown that nearly a third of the land surfaces of the world is characterized by internal drainage, but it must be realized that this type of drainage is by no means restricted to areas with a desert climate.

Deserts

Since the major areas of aridity are deserts, it is desirable to classify their various surface features. The desert surface may be of bare rock as in the hammada of the Sahara, where deflation is predominant. On the other hand, the erg or sandy desert represents a surface of deposition (Fig. 7.3). There is yet a third type of surface consisting of gravels and stones, and this is known as the reg in the Sahara. Some desert areas, such as those in western parts of the United States of America and in Tibet and Mongolia, are deserts largely because of tectonic movements which have resulted in the formation of great depressions within the mountain zones (Fig. 7.3) that are characterized by low rainfall (because of the sheltering effects of the surrounding mountains) and by inland drainage. Although abrupt relief features of tectonic origin are found in the tropical deserts, more often these latter deserts coincide with structural units of plateau character, as in Western Australia and the Sahara.

Wind Erosion

Deflation is, in a sense, the end of a series of processes and wind erosion is preceded by mechanical weathering of rocks although, since in deserts the air can be quite surprisingly humid, chemical weathering also occurs. Nevertheless, it seems quite clear that the initial comminution of rock depends mainly on the effect of expansion and contraction of rocks and their individual minerals through temperature changes, assisted at times by frost. The wind, thus armed with small fragments, can proceed to abrade and reduce large fragments of rock to small dimensions. As with a river so with wind, the load it carries must be adjusted to its speed.

The size of fragments which can be carried in suspension by wind is of the order of less than 0·2 mm in diameter—larger fragments can only be moved by saltation or by slow surface creep which is induced by the impact of smaller fragments as they fall to the surface against the larger fragments. Whilst abrasion may extend as high as twenty-five feet, significant wind erosion is usually limited to heights of the order of six feet. The very fine fragments in suspension, many feet up in a sandstorm, produce relatively little erosion. The most spectacular effects of wind erosion are seen in the tabular zeugen and the under-cut, parallel ridges, known as yardangs—the latter may reach heights of twenty-five feet (Fig. 7.1).

(i) Zeugen   (ii) Yardangs

Fig. 7.1—Wind-carved rocks

Sand blast may cause some pebbles to be converted into dreikanter, with distinct facets, which have been smoothed by the wind in turn as the pebble has been turned over several times, thus exposing one face after another to the wind blast. In some cases, the polishing effect of continued sand blast produces a smooth, shiny surface on pebbles—such is sometimes called desert varnish.

Dunes

Of considerable interest is the way in which sand accumulates in deserts. Apart from the formation of sand dunes the development of relatively small-scale sand ripples and ridges deserves mention. In both cases saltation, produced by the impact of small wind-driven fragments, causes coarse fragments to creep and according to the inevitable irregularities of the surface these pile up and may result in ridges, two feet in height and separated by distances of as much as 60 feet. The ripples are on a much smaller scale and may be only a few inches apart.

The deposition of sand is usually in the form of dunes. It is possible to study dune formation on the sea coasts of humid lands, but there the dunes are somewhat peculiar in that they are readily fixed by vegetation. In addition they are usually on a small scale, since they have only a limited supply of sand. However, coastal dunes do show some of the features which are typical of desert dunes and these may be studied wherever they occur in Britain and elsewhere. Desert dunes may be divided into two groups. Firstly, there are the barchans which are nearly always transverse to the prevailing wind direction—in fact, most barchans depend on the constancy of the direction of the prevailing wind. The windward side of the dune is convex, but its leeward side is concave, with two crescentic ridges or horns curving away and sloping down from the crest at C (Fig. 7.2a).

Fig. 7.2.—Form and Development of a Barchan

Barchans may measure a quarter of a mile in length and be 100 feet high. The profile of these dunes shows a relatively gentle windward slope and a leeward one which is quite steep and concave as a result of wind eddies (Fig. 7.2b). Secondly, there are seif dunes[1] which form long chains that are parallel to the wind direction. Many of these seem secondary developments from barchans which have become unstable as a result of the more or less constant wind, referred to above, becoming variable in direction (Fig. 7.4b). Nevertheless, some of these long dunes undoubtedly develop without the previous formation of a barchan and, in some instances, when they extend to the leeward of a marked ridge or scarp they may in turn break down to give isolated barchans. Seif dunes can rise to heights of 300 feet and may extend for many miles. Fig. 7.3 shows dunes in part of the Basins and Ranges region of the United States of America.

The barchans in true desert areas will move or migrate, so that the surface of a sandy desert may be compared to that of the sea with its progressing waves, except that the propagation of the dunes

[1] Seif is an Arabic word meaning 'sword'.

Fairchild Aerial Surveys, Inc.

Fig. 7.3.—Sand Dunes near Delta, Utah, United States of America

Various types of dune can be seen—the wind blows, in general, from the left. Note the sparse vegetation on the ridge in the foreground. The area is on the eastern fringe of the Basins and Ranges province.

is much slower. But even in the very arid deserts there is rarely a complete absence of either plant life or of a water table. Thus certain barchans may become fixed at their horns by plants or by water which is near the surface. The water makes it impossible for the sand to be lifted (sand must be dry before wind can move it) and the plants act as a wind break. It is only possible for such fixation of dunes to occur at points where the sand has no great depth. Elsewhere the sand is so deep that both plants and water are buried by an overburden of sand whose upper layers can still be moved. After fixation a barchan may be blown inside out by the force of a constant wind when its original concavity is converted to a convexity, facing down-wind. A blow-out may then occur when the centre of the dune is breached and its sand is strewn out in the form of longitudinal dunes separated by bare rock surfaces (see Fig. 7.4*a*). With changes in the direction of the prevailing wind barchans may be distorted and eventually become elongated to form seif dunes as shown in Fig. 7.4*b*.

The Qattara depression in North Africa shows on a large scale the effects of deflation. It is over a hundred miles in width, and in parts

117

it is over 1,000 feet below the level of the surrounding limestone plateau and has been excavated largely by wind, although it is probable that chemical solution has occurred as well. The prevailing winds are northerly (Etesian winds from the eastern Mediterranean Sea), and south of the depression are longitudinal dunes that have been built of sand supplied by the deflation and which extend for scores of miles separated by wide strips of bare rock. Neighbouring depressions have been lowered in this manner to the level of the water table of the area, so that a series of oasis populations has been maintained by a water supply by wells and springs.

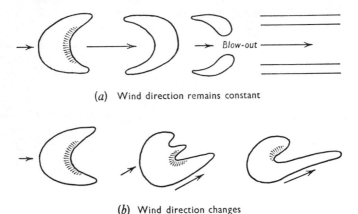

(a)   Wind direction remains constant

(b)   Wind direction changes

Fig. 7.4.—Transformation of Barchans into Seif Dunes
Arrows show direction of wind.

Water Erosion in Arid Areas

There are other characteristic land forms in arid regions which must be reviewed in brief. These show the effects of both regular and intermittent fluvial erosion of the past and the present day respectively. In discussing these features it is necessary to make some distinction between those in plateau areas and those in the tectonic or intermontane basins.

Fig. 7.5.—Mesas

Plateau surfaces in arid regions are scored with numerous ravine-like valleys, some of which show the interlocking spurs that are so typical of youthful river valleys in other regions, and the surface is thus dissected into the land form known as 'bad lands'. When a particularly resistant and horizontal layer of rock has capped a plateau its remnants may be tabular and steep-sided, in the form of mesas (Figs. 7.5 and 7.6). The sides of the intervening ravines (known as wadis or arroyos) are quite ungraded, although their

Black Star

FIG. 7.6.—'Bad Land' Surface near the Dead Sea, Israel

Here are seen wadis with their ungraded sides, but showing evidence of water erosion. The mesa-like plateau surfaces show the effect of erosion on horizontal strata of varying resistance.

floors may be remarkably wide and fairly well graded. Water transport has been limited, largely because there is so much fragmentary rock to dispose of, and the short-lived streams (since evaporation is so great) soon become overloaded to an extent which gives them the consistency of liquid mud. In the areas with extensive plateau surfaces rain produces a considerable movement of material which is akin to sheet erosion of soil. The main result of water erosion is to develop great alluvial spreads over the floors of the valleys, together with lines of deposits which may be compared in their outward form with the morainic ridges left in front of ice sheets.

Intermontane Basins

In the arid regions of intermontane basins there are additional modifications to this picture. The steep fault scarps on the edges of these basins have remarkable screes and cones, built of the larger rock fragments which have been deposited by streams as their speed has been checked by the sudden change in gradient at a scarp

119

base. Towards the centres of these basins, beyond the marginal cones, other deposits are laid in a sequence which is related to the size of the fragments, the smallest being carried farthest away from the scarps. Thus a fringing zone of piedmont gravels is developed which surrounds an inner region of each basin, where fine material, chiefly sands, and sometimes saline deposits are found (Figs. 7.7 and 7.8). Drainage of the past or the present has produced a pattern which is the inverse of radial drainage from a dome. Streams or dry

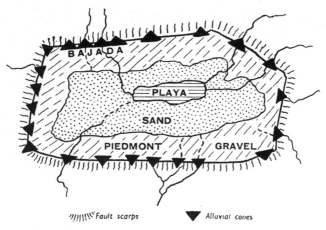

FIG. 7.7.—An Intermontane Basin

beds of intermittent streams converge on the central area which is occupied by a salt lake or a salt plain (or playa),[1] both, of course, resulting from evaporation. Very often the coarser gravels of the piedmont zone have a water table, and this may emerge at the surface or be tapped at the inner margin of the zone.

Sometimes the alluvial fans or cones may coalesce along the foot of the scarp and create what is known as a bajada, which has a relatively gently inclined surface as compared with the slopes of the isolated fans (see Fig. 7.7). On the other hand, the base of the scarp may pass into a pediment of solid rock which slopes out gradually and passes under the alluvial deposits of the inner part of the basin. This pediment probably represents a surface that has been developed by the recession of the fault scarp through weathering and wind erosion proceeding under conditions of aridity, and later this surface has been overlapped in part by transported alluvial material, thus indicating the action of running water.

[1] These plains are also known as bolsons, salinas, and shotts.

Literary Services Mondiale Ltd.

FIG. 7.8.—Playa in Death Valley, California, United States of America

Salinization is evident in the foreground. In the middle ground is the piedmont gravel zone, merging with a bajada.

Inselbergs

The arid areas which have the structural features of plateaus, as distinct from intermontane basins, retain their plateau character after long periods of erosion, since very extensive areas have fairly level rock surfaces which are broken by residual hills, standing above the surrounding plains, whose tops represent an earlier plateau level. Such residual hills may show peculiar forms, and they are known in Africa as inselbergs, from the name given to them originally by the German geographer, Passarge. The typical inselberg is steep-sided and either round-topped or flat-topped. There is a most characteristic change of slope at the base of the steep sides, where a concave

FIG. 7.9.—Inselbergs

slope passes out into a rock pediment (Fig. 7.9). There is still much controversy over the way in which these inselbergs have been formed, but they are probably remnants of a surface, originally plane and level, which has been lowered by erosion under arid conditions. They may, therefore, be regarded as a form of monadnock

121

(p. 74) which has been left when pediments on several sides of an upland have encroached on it sufficiently to leave one of these residual masses. The concave basal slope has suggested to many investigators that erosion by water has played its part in the development of these hills. Round-topped examples are also found in the humid tropical regions as in the environs of Rio de Janeiro. The photograph in Fig. 17.2 shows one of these 'sugar-loaf' mountains in French Guiana.

Cycle of Erosion in Arid Areas

Without attempting any detailed analysis of the probable development of a cycle of erosion, it would appear that the most predominant feature throughout such a cycle is the plateau surface, although it has been doubted whether deflation can lower surfaces to a very great extent unless it is aided by other erosional processes. The probable course of a cycle of erosion in intermontane basin areas is briefly as follows. The filling of the basins and elevation of their floor levels by material derived from the adjacent uplands is the first stage. Each basin is separate in the early part of the cycle, but with the dissection of the intervening ranges, some opportunity arises for the higher basins to drain to lower basins by means of channels, cut by water. The lower basins are then rapidly filled, and reach a stage of maturity. Repetition of this continuous filling in higher basins, together with the reduction of the remaining areas of higher land, results in the final establishment of a rock pediment overlain by sand and sand dunes. Isolated remnants of the high terrain which originally enclosed the basins will form inselbergs. Thus whether the desert region was originally of the intermontane basin type or of the plateau type, the product of prolonged erosion is a plain or a plateau with upstanding highland remnants.

Loess

Under strong and steady winds, it is obvious that some of the product of desert deflation is removed far beyond the scene of its origin. It has been possible to record the extent of the removal of dust and sand by strong winds during great storms. In the United States of America it has been observed that wind has transported material of the soil from Texas to the environs of the Great Lakes. This wind-borne dust, after travelling hundreds of miles, arrives in a more humid region and rain may wash it down from the air to ground level, where it is trapped by vegetation. Such accumulations form loess and are found in steppe regions, marginal to deserts, and also, in fairly close association with northern areas that were marginal to the Pleistocene ice sheets from which the deposits were blown by winds, caused by the high pressure air over the ice. Thus, loess forms an extensive, yet discontinuous, belt across Eurasia from France through Central Germany, Russia, and Turkestan, and ends in the Shansi and Shensi plateaus of China, where it is thickest. In North America it is coincident with parts of the lava plateaus of Washington and Oregon and occupies a fairly continuous zone from Nebraska through the lower Missouri valley and along much of the course of the Mississippi below St. Louis.

Most of these deposits have been derived from glacial deposits, although probably in the Chinese area it is of desert origin. In all cases the loess shows the common characteristics of having been windborne, and the dust, which is yellow, has settled more often than not upon grassland areas. Despite the fact that stratification is absent, there is a columnar structure which, it is thought, is derived from buried grass roots that have decayed and produced fine vertical tubes, lined with calcium carbonate. These vertical tubes have imparted strength to these deposits, so that whilst loess may be eroded the material that remains stands up in the form of almost vertical walls. In China the deposits are so thick that they have been worn into deep 'bad land' areas. Much of this loess provides the alluvium that is dis-

Fairchild Aerial Surveys, Inc.

FIG. 7.10.—Part of the Grand Canyon, Arizona, United States of America

The R. Colorado can be seen (right) in its relatively narrow channel. Note the screes in the foreground.

tributed by the Hwang-ho floods in the Great Plain of Northern China. Elsewhere loess is less thick than in China and, although sometimes it forms low plateaus, it is usually found in plain lands. Whilst, from a geological standpoint, loess is a rock, it is readily converted into a loessic soil.

River Valleys in Arid Areas

Finally, reference must be made to the courses of rivers whose sources are in more humid areas, but which cross deserts or lands that are otherwise too arid to support perpetual river flow. The rivers are able to do little more than flow through these dry zones, and they cannot rely on the help of water from side streams for normal valley development. Thus the valleys are mainly trenched into the surrounding land surface. Down-cutting, where the base level permits, is of supreme importance. The Colorado River has, undoubtedly, produced the most spectacular course of all the great rivers which cross arid regions. The river flows in places over a mile below the plateau surface in an inner gorge of varying width—the stream is of the order of 300–400 feet in width. At the highest levels this great canyon has a width of from five to fifteen miles. The geological history of the region is quite complicated and, in one sense, this canyon represents the effects of rejuvenation with its incised river course, but aridity is responsible for such features as on the sides, where differential erosion of horizontal strata of varying resistance has created fantastic scenery. Side streams are few in number, and there has been little or no reduction of the valley sides other than where spurs have been set back or, in places, isolated, so that they stand out as solitary pinnacles of rock (Fig. 7.10).

CHAPTER 8

Limestone and Chalk Areas

Character of Limestone and Chalk Rock

Limestone and Chalk areas have their own markedly characteristic landscape. Such areas are usually upstanding in relation to adjacent regions, although neither rock is as resistant as granite or many sedimentary rocks. The upstanding relief is related to the pervious nature of the rocks and the effects of chemical solution upon them.

It is important to distinguish between porous and pervious rocks. A porous rock has many very small spaces which may become water-logged, as in the case of a clay or a sandstone, and, for that matter, Chalk. This does not mean that water necessarily moves freely in these rocks, for often it is only along joint planes in Chalk rock that water is readily obtained. Pervious rocks are open-grained or well-jointed, and many igneous rocks are pervious for the latter reason, but the joints in limestone are so numerous that land forms with unusual features are produced. Many limestones are massive, in that normal stratification is absent, the rock having become self-cemented, so that it is but slightly porous. Such limestones are usually fairly resistant to weathering other than by solution along the joints. Thus most running water percolates down joint planes and along bedding planes, so that subsurface erosion is the rule, whereas the surface remains dry and is not readily reduced by weathering and erosion. River water is derived from rain-water that contains carbon-dioxide in solution, and this permits the chemical solution of limestones which are otherwise insoluble rocks. Limestone (and Chalk) may be regarded as insoluble calcium carbonate, but this compound is converted by rain-water into calcium bicarbonate which is soluble.

Chemical studies have shown that there is a much higher concentration of carbon-dioxide in the soil than in the atmosphere. It is therefore probable that a considerable solution of limestone is effected by the moisture and humic acids in the soil in lieu of running water in underground streams. It is possible to see, as in the Buxton area of Derbyshire, the limestone surface after the thin soil layer has been stripped off, preparatory to quarrying. The surface thus

[1] $CaCO_3 + H_2O + CO_2 \rightleftharpoons Ca(HCO_3)_2$.

exposed shows the characteristic clint formation which will be referred to later in this chapter.

The process of solution is very important, since it enlarges the spaces between the many joints and fissures of these rocks, and may encourage the formation of caves, although the latter are not very common in Chalk areas. Both limestone and Chalk hold a very large amount of water, and it can be shown, as in Fig. 8.1, that there is a

FIG. 8.1.—Water Table and Springs in a Chalk Escarpment

water table, as marked by the dotted line, in a Chalk escarpment. However, it must not be assumed that the water can be obtained by sinking a well deep enough below the surface at any point. Water is enclosed in small pore spaces in the rock, and cannot move freely (otherwise it would produce a level water table), and some wells remain dry because they do not happen to strike a joint or fissure, and until a horizontal heading is made to connect with a water-bearing joint, there will be no flow in the well.

Karst Landscape

The land forms of limestone regions have in all probability, been more thoroughly studied in Britain than have those of the Chalk areas, while the most closely studied limestone region of all in the world is that of the Karst of Yugoslavia. Other areas of note which exhibit similar, if not identical, features to the Karst are parts of the Central Pennine region of England, the Causses in the Central Plateau of France, and several American areas, including parts of the limestone plateaus of the Appalachian Mountains in Kentucky and Tennessee, and the low-lying peninsulas of Florida (Fig. 18.7) and Yucatan. Yunnan is yet another region of interest in this respect. Central Ireland, whilst having extensive areas of limestone, rarely shows much more than limestone pavements although, in northern Co. Clare, the Burren district, south of Black Head, shows some Karst features. The Karst of Yugoslavia is a rather exceptional region of limestone, because surface drainage is largely absent, whereas in the other regions which have been mentioned it is usual to find some surface flow of water. Such streams are, however, almost invariably derived from neighbouring areas with impermeable rocks. Let us examine the chief features of the Karst landscape, many of which are common to all limestone regions.

Clints and Caverns

In many limestone areas the surface of bare rock may be fretted into a fantastic pattern of narrow clefts with intervening ridges and pinnacles of rock whose dimensions may be of the order of two or three feet. These are known respectively as grykes and clints in the Pennines. There are equivalent words for the same features in other countries, such as lapiés in France and bogaz in Yugoslavia. The fretting is almost entirely produced by solution along joint planes

FIG. 8.2.—Rectilinear Pattern of Clints

and an almost rectilinear pattern may be discerned, as shown in Fig. 8.2. A very fine exposure of such a surface is to be seen in the Carboniferous Limestone above Malham Cove in Yorkshire (Fig. 8.3).

Geological Survey photograph; Crown copyright. Reproduced by permission of the Controller, H.M. Stationery Office

FIG. 8.3.—Limestone Platform with Clints, above Malham Cove, Yorkshire

Note the vertical joints to the left of the middle view.

127

Swallow holes, which are relatively large, funnel-shaped depressions into which a surface stream may pass, are common, too—they are known as dolines in the Yugoslavian Karst. They may lead into vertical shafts known as ponors in Yugoslavia and avens in France. Gaping Ghyll, near Ingleborough, in Yorkshire, is a fine example of such a shaft. Larger surface depressions, up to half-a-mile across, may be formed by the coalescence of several swallow holes and are known as uvalas in Yugoslavia. In some instances a swallow hole, or more usually a group of these inlets, will lead to a cavern below. The joint or joints below a swallow hole are enlarged by further solution and, where streams persist in their flow, there is a large amount of chemical solution which results in the opening up of a cavern (Fig. 8.4). Limestone caverns form a series of connected

c — Cavern   p — Limestone pillar   pn — Ponor
s — Swallow holes   sc — Stalactites   sg — Stalagmites
⟵ — River flow

FIG. 8.4.—The Solution of Limestone

chambers. Some of these are in vertical planes, related to joints, whilst others follow bedding planes. Frequently caverns show the spectacular development of stalactites and stalagmites. The process of solution is reversible, and calcium bicarbonate yields calcium carbonate by chemical dissociation with the loss of carbon dioxide to the air.[1]

Very slowly but surely the dripping water will form great masses of new limestones. Some are pendant from the roof of the caverns, called stalactites, while similar masses, known as stalagmites, are built up from the cavern floor. It is possible for a downward-growing stalactite and upward-growing stalagmite to join and give a pillar of limestone. Such deposition of calcium carbonate may be observed in Chalk zones, where it occurs as calc-tufa at the margins of springs, issuing from the pervious rock. Nevertheless, much of the dissolved carbonate (or bicarbonate) is removed by river flow to the sea.

$$^{1}\ Ca(HCO_3)_2 \rightleftharpoons H_2O + CO_2 + CaCO_3$$

Poljes

The development of uvalas is probably carried a stage further in the poljes (or polyen) which are found in the Karst. The poljes of Yugoslavia are very large depressions, and although solution has played a part in their formation, it is highly probable that they are partially tectonic in origin. Quite clearly in the late stages of Karst formation there has been a collapse of the cavern roofs, and this has resulted in the growth of the depressions to the size which is

Dorien Leigh Ltd.

Fig. 8.5.—Lake Scutari, Yugoslavia

A polje is seen with residual hills of limestone.

typical of the poljes. The inner parts of these depressions are usually occupied by a group of residual hillocks of limestone which, no doubt, represent remnants of the cavern walls (Fig. 8.5). Although there are some areas in England which appear to have uvalas, it would seem that the poljes are almost exclusively Yugoslavian features. It is not at all certain that truly Karst landscape is present in France, nor, for that matter, in any of the other limestone areas which have been mentioned.

Dry Valleys

Some of the valleys in limestone country are dry, in that they have no surface flow of water in them today. The explanation of the cause of these dry valleys is simplified if it is realized that in the early stages of the development of a Karst landscape there was actually much water flowing on the surface. Until considerable opening up of joints had occurred, there must have been normal valley sculpture in such regions. This would proceed until the mass of limestone rock was sufficiently ramified with a network of interlaced underground channels. At this stage it seems likely that the streams which had cut valleys would plunge underground by way of swallow holes and leave

FIG. 8.6.—A De-roofed Cavern

unoccupied valleys below the points where they disappeared. The valley above Malham Cove in Yorkshire is of such origin (see Fig. 8.8).

With the development of caverns it is possible for a second type of valley to arise by the collapse of the cavern roof. A de-roofed cavern may expose a stream on its floor, but it is also possible, where the water table in the limestone is lower than the level of the cavern floor, for such an exposed valley to be dry. Not infrequently natural arches or bridges cross the valleys at certain places, being obviously sections of the cavern roof which have not suffered the general collapse (Fig. 8.6).

Many limestone areas have rivers which pass through very spectacular gorges, as for instance those followed by the Rivers Tarn and Lot in the Causses region of the Central Plateau of France—in England, Dovedale on the Derbyshire-Staffordshire border and Wyedale, near Buxton, are other examples. These rivers have ap-

Yugoslav National Tourist Office (Photo: Miloš Pavlovič)

Fig. 8.7.—Gorge of the R. Neretva in the Karst of Yugoslavia

parently maintained normal erosion, whilst other features of limestone solution were being developed in the region, because they are fed from outside the limestone areas, and have thus received sufficient water supply to continue as surface flows which have cut down in the limestone and produced the narrow gorges (Fig. 8.7).

Malham District

The base of a limestone is frequently marked by an impervious layer, since most other rocks must be relatively impervious in comparison with limestone. Thus where valleys have been trenched to the level of an impervious rock, it is common to find underground water issuing as springs from the limestone into these valleys. Such issues of water are known as Vauclusian springs. The spring which comes out at the foot of Malham Cove is of this type, although its formation is also due, in part, to faulting. The amphitheatre of Carboniferous Limestone at Malham Cove marks a fault scarp which has receded, for over this, at one time, there was normal river flow. The course of this flow is clearly shown by the dry valley which stretches from the top of the Cove towards Malham Tarn, and also by the dry waterfall which can be seen most distinctly at one point as a notch on the edge of this scarp. The waterfall was almost certainly much wider than this notch at its maximum develop-

131

ment. The base of the scarp is in juxtaposition to impervious Silurian rocks, and it is here that a Vauclusian spring is found. In the dry valley above the Cove are swallow holes into which water may be seen going underground today, near another fault plane. It would appear that this water issues in the spring at Malham Cove, but this is not the case. It has been shown that the spring is supplied by underground drainage through a swallow hole to the west of those shown in Fig. 8.8a. The main Aire drainage which arises in Malham Tarn issues in springs farther down the valley to the south of the Cove. In passing it may be noted that farther west the fault scarp produces the significant limestone edge known as Giggleswick Scar.

FIG. 8.8.—Malham District in the Limestone Region of the Central Pennine Uplands

Cycle of Erosion in Limestone Regions

It is possible to review very briefly a sequence of erosion in limestone terrain as follows:

1. In the earliest stages surface drainage is the rule, and the opening of the limestone along the joints, preparatory to underground drainage is typical.

2. Maturity is marked by the almost complete cessation of surface-water flow.

3. The late stages are indicated by the development of uvalas and poljes. In the Karst this stage has been reached, but it is questionable whether the cycle of erosion is so far advanced in any other limestone region. In the Yugoslavian poljes there are periodical floodings of the floors, which show that the water table is not far below the present surface. Consequently surface drainage might easily be restored as a permanent feature if there was a very slight elevation

of this water table or, on the other hand, if there was a very slight lowering of the general surface level of the floors of the poljes.

Some limestone areas do not show any of these varied features. In some cases it is probable that they have been protected from such erosion until quite recently by the cover of an impervious rock. On the other hand, limestones may be less soluble, as in the case of Magnesian Limestone (dolomite), or the limestone layers may be interbedded with impervious strata which effectively prevent any very deep solution. At Ingleborough and Pen-y-Ghent in Yorkshire cappings of horizontally bedded grits and shales, which are remnants of an earlier cover to the Carboniferous Limestone, protect some of the limestone from solution, thus forming flat-topped, mesa-like uplands which stand above the general level of the surrounding limestone plateaus as monadnocks.

Chalk Areas and their Dry Valleys

Chalk land forms are more subdued than those of most limestone areas. The gorges and the abrupt, steeply inclined edges of limestone country are replaced by more open valleys and by slopes which are both concave and convex, as seen in the rounded spurs and hollows (known as coombes) in Figs. 8.9 and 8.10. There is an absence of fretted surfaces (clints) and caverns are rare since Chalk is a rock with numerous fractures instead of systems of well-defined joints, as in limestone. Also, Chalk is a relatively weak rock and tends to collapse with the result that the many fissures are closed up quite readily. However, swallow holes are fairly common both on the upland surfaces and in the valley floors. The River Mole in its course between Dorking and Mickleham in Surrey, where it uses a gap in the Chalk of the North Downs, disappears at times through swallow holes to reappear lower down the valley. This underground flow occurs when the water table in the Chalk sinks below the level of the normal bed of the river. Some twenty swallow holes are found in a distance of about four miles.

On the dip slopes of Chalk escarpments there are widespread networks of dry valleys (Figs. 8.9 and 8.10)—apart from areas of Chalk which possess a cover of glacial deposits there are very few surface streams. The dry valleys may be fed temporarily in the winter, today, by streams which are known as winterbournes. The word 'today' is used advisedly, since these valleys are evidently the products of previous water erosion. As shown in Fig. 8.1, the Chalk uplands possess a water table which, in general, is below the surface but if this table cuts the surface there will be an issue of water in the form of a spring. The impoverished drainage is clearly related to a depression of the water table, and stream flow would be renewed in the dry valleys by an elevation of this table.

One explanation of the dry valleys correlates the fall in level of the water table with a decrease of rainfall in recent geological times. As there is no substantial evidence of such a decrease in rainfall, this explanation is unsatisfactory.

Aerofilms Ltd.

FIG. 8.10.—Part of South Downs, about 3 miles inland from Shoreham and Hove, looking west towards the gap of the River Arun

The north edge of part of the South Downs is seen, looking west. Reference to the map (opposite) will help to identify several dry valleys and the convex and concave slopes of the rounded spurs and coombes of the scarp slope. The village of Fulking is seen in the foreground. The Devil's Dyke does not appear in the picture.

FIG. 8.9.—(see opposite) Contour map of part of the South Downs about 3 miles inland from Shoreham and Hove

Key to Map

════	Road linking spring line settlements, such as Fulking and Edburton.
====	Track on crest of the South Downs.
A, B	Masts marked in white letters in Fig. 8.10.
C	Dry gap.
D	Point where track appears to end in Fig. 8.10.
	Wooded areas in Fig. 8.10.
	Villages.
300 etc	Contours with heights in feet above sea level.

Based on the Ordnance Survey Map with the sanction of the Controller of H.M. Stationery Office

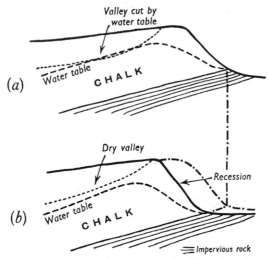

FIG. 8.11.—The Development of a Dry Valley by Recession of a Chalk Scarp

Another argument suggests that in the Pleistocene Ice Age the interstitial water in the Chalk, lying just south of the ice sheets, was frozen, thus making the rock impervious and promoting surface drainage and the cutting of the valleys. Upon the return of a milder climate the Chalk rock was rendered pervious once again and the drainage became subterranean. Although acceptable in the case of dry valleys in the Chalk areas of Britain, this explanation cannot hold for similar, if not identical, valleys in parts of France which were too far south of the ice sheets to be affected in this way.

The third account of dry valleys is rather more complex than the others. The water table in the Chalk is assumed to stand at a fairly constant height above the junction of the impervious stratum (usually a clay) at the base of an escarpment. This junction is marked by springs which are fed by water in the Chalk. Most escarpments possess a series of such scarp-foot springs (see Fig. 8.1) which forms the spring line that is usually marked by a line of settlements. In Fig. 8.11 two stages of escarpment development are shown; in (b) the scarp has receded from the position it held in (a). With the recession of the scarp, the level of the lowland at its foot has been lowered relative to the surface of the Chalk at the crest of the scarp. Thus, in time, the valleys on the dip slopes of the escarpments must become dry downstream from their heads since unless the water table rises it must lie below the floors of these valleys. It will be noted that this explanation calls for no decrease in rainfall, and it accounts for the formation of dry valleys in both glaciated and unglaciated regions of Chalk.

CHAPTER 9

Shore Features and Coastlines –
Coral Reefs and Islands

Introduction

In discussing the action of the sea as an erosive agent it must be realized that the zone of its action is the shore. It is, however, impossible to explain the intricacies of a shoreline without reference to both the geological structure and the history of the coast on which the discussion is centred. Briefly, much depends upon whether the coast (using the term for the margin of the land as distinct from the shore, where the action of the sea is operative) has suffered submergence or emergence (or both alternately) within recent geological times. The work of the sea waves is both destructive and constructive, and the former may be likened to degradation and the latter to aggradation by running water.

Wave Action

In the open sea waves may be regarded as oscillatory movements of the water particles, in that the surface of the water body is deformed into troughs and crests. Long after the wind, which has initiated such waves, has died down the sea shows an undulating surface which is the movement across it of the wave form but not of the water. There is no forward movement of the water as a whole—

Wavelength

● Particle of water   → Direction of motion of each particle

FIG. 9.1.—Wave Motion

the water particles move in circular paths, lying in a vertical plane (Fig. 9.1). Such free waves take a long time to decay as very little energy is required to maintain them and they may travel, literally, for hundreds of miles across the sea. The distance between adjacent crests (or between adjacent troughs) is known as the wave-length.

As free waves and wind-driven waves enter shallow water offshore from land the effect of the decreasing depth of the sea is most pronounced. The paths of the water particles become elliptical, the wave-length decreases, the height of each wave increases, and eventually its crest overrides its base and the wave breaks forward, rushing up the beach as the swash or send. The momentum of this mass of water is in itself sufficient to create a force which has a shattering effect on obstacles lying on the seashore, whilst in caves in cliffs the alternating compression and expansion of enclosed air, trapped by the breaking waves, may cause much loosening of the rocks, particularly if they are well jointed.

The swash is followed by the backwash. In waves of very short wave-length the swash is followed by a strong backwash which removes a great quantity of beach deposits. On the other hand, waves of long wave-length may have a very effective swash on breaking which carries deposits well up the beach, and these are not removed in bulk, as the backwash is relatively weak. The former waves may be regarded as destructive and they have a frequency of over a dozen per minute whereas the latter are constructive and their frequency is about half that of destructive waves. However, the water in a breaking wave is most effective as an agent of erosion when it is armed with rock fragments and the resulting abrasive action is, over a long period of time, more important than the shattering effect. Wave fronts tend to strike the shore normally at all points. Shallow water, lying off a headland, retards the wave in comparison with those parts of the wave which enter far into adjoining bays before retardation occurs. This differential retardation causes the wave front to bend (or to be refracted) so that the wave action is concentrated on the headland, whereas the part of the

FIG. 9.2.—Wave Incidence

wave in the middle of a bay is lengthened and its energy is thus spread along a relatively long front (Fig. 9.2). Thus the headlands are attacked more effectively by wave action, so that they are reduced and the shore is straightened in line with the heads of the bays and not further crenulated, as is often thought. Differential erosion by the sea on rocks of varying resistance may permit irregularities to persist locally on shorelines.

Whilst some parts of a shore are subject to the destructive action of the sea, other parts are being modified by the construction of sand spits and offshore bars. The formation of these has usually been attributed to the action of sea currents and to tidal influences, but today wave action is regarded as of primary importance in forming these features. One very important effect resulting from the breaking of waves on a shore is the production of longshore drift. Although it has been stated that waves tend to advance normally to the shore (Fig. 9.2), this is not possible at all points since a strong wind may give the waves a component which is oblique to the general trend of a particular shoreline. Nevertheless, the retreat of water in the backwash of a wave is always normal to the shore. It will be seen from Fig. 9.3 that material may advance on a zigzag course along the shore, as each successive incoming wave meets a retreating backwash with its load of fragments.[1] Most sand spits have a number of lateral ridges of deposited material on their landward sides, and this suggests that onshore waves, supplied with material from elsewhere by longshore drift, have built these prominences. Tidal influences are incapable of producing deposition on a scale large enough to create a spit, although they may move the smallest fragments of rock. Spits are developed very often at a point where there is a change in the direction of a shoreline (Fig. 9.4).

FIG. 9.3.—Longshore Drift

FIG. 9.4.—Formation of a Spit

Dungeness and Morfa Harlech

Dungeness, on the Kent coast, and Harlech Point, on the shores of Cardigan Bay, have been produced by wave construction. The beak-like Dungeness is in a position where effective wave action from both south and east has developed the two sides of the headland in front of the former shoreline, which is set back today behind Rye and Hythe, as well as being identified by a line of old cliffs on the northern side of Romney Marsh, some ten miles from the sea.

A significant change in the trend of the shoreline near Harlech has

[1] The effectiveness of waves is determined also by the fetch or the length of water surface over which the wind blows. Briefly, a moderate wind blowing over a wide stretch of sea may be capable of creating larger waves than a strong wind with a smaller fetch.

helped to create a spit which extends practically northwards, and behind which the present shore flats, known as Morfa Harlech, were constructed by wave action that carried material over the earlier-formed spit and by wind, producing·dunes. There was also much alluvium deposited by rivers from the landward side. The old cliffs, on which Harlech Castle stands, trend north-eastwards on the inner edge of Morfa Harlech (Fig. 9.5). This development has occurred mainly within historic times, since the castle appears to have a water gate for entry and retreat by the sea which is now at least half a mile from the cliff on which it stands.

Judges Ltd.

FIG. 9.5.—Morfa Harlech, Merionethshire

This shows a constructed shoreline, looking north from near Harlech Castle. The hill in the middle ground is an earlier island.

A depositional feature of interest is the offshore bar. It is probably formed by wave erosion on the offshore bottom, giving submarine deposition some distance offshore. This bar builds up and, in time, rises above the water. Some longshore drift may assist in the production of such a bar. In the earliest stages, offshore bars are completely detached from the shore line but they may be driven by wave action towards the shore and produce spits thereon, or they may be linked to the shore by the development of marshes, on the inshore side of the bars.

Submergence and Emergence

It is now necessary to examine the erosive effects of the sea in relation to coastal areas which have, in recent geological times, been either submerged or elevated. It is possible in each case to trace a cycle of erosion. Let us consider briefly what is meant by submergence and emergence. The level of the ocean depends in part upon the balance between the evaporation of water into the atmosphere and its return as rain, or more indirectly by rivers. Such fluctuations as occur, through the disturbance of such a balance, are normally very slight. However, in periods of great cold, such as in a glacial period, much water is locked up in continental ice sheets and the ocean level is lowered, although the burden of ice will probably depress the land masses by the operation of isostatic adjustment. Even so, it has been estimated that in the Pleistocene Ice Age the level of the ocean surface was 200–300 feet lower than its average level today. In postglacial times the melting of the several ice caps has caused the level of the sea to rise, and transgressions of many tracts of land have occurred. Isostatic adjustments have, at the same time, compensated in part for this rise of the sea-level by the elevation of the land masses which has followed the unloading of the ice burden. To this day Scandinavia, as well as other northern areas, is rising very slightly year by year. Land sediments brought into the open ocean basins must displace water and raise the sea surface very gradually and thus help to produce submergence as well.

In addition, earth movements, such as result from faulting or the tilting of the land surfaces, may affect the level of both the continental blocks and the ocean floors and thus create local elevations and depressions giving similar results. It is perhaps sufficient to summarize these problems by noting that a rise in the level of the sea or a fall in the level of the land will produce submergence of a coastal area, whilst emergence of coastal areas is the result of a depression of the ocean or a rise of the land surface. On any particular coast the features which may be seen are the result, in the majority of cases, of the interaction of these several processes, and it is far from easy to unravel the true sequence of events. Emergence may result in raised beaches which may lie as much as a hundred feet above the present sea level. On the other hand, evidence of submergence may be seen in submerged forests, when at low tide the stumps of trees are visible offshore.

Shorelines on Submerged Coasts

With the submergence of a coastal area the sea is brought into direct contact with relatively high land or former hill slopes. Wave action is restricted to only a few feet above and below sea-level, and the first development on a submerged shore is the cutting of a low cliff (Fig. 9.6a). Then, with the aid of normal sub-aerial erosion, the part of the land edge above this low cliff is reduced. Thus the cliff recedes partly by wave cutting at its base and partly by rain wash from above. It may be noted that the dip of the rocks in relation to the shore is of some importance in regard to the rate of retrogression of the cliff as shown by Fig. 9.7. After a wave breaks, the backwash transports the debris from the cliff and deposits it offshore

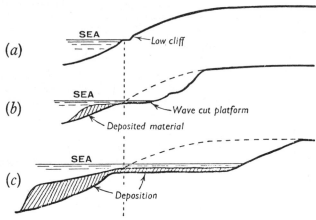

FIG. 9.6.—The Development of a Shore Zone after Submergence

(see Fig. 9.6 *b*) in the form of a submerged bank. Between this bank and the base of the cliff is a wave-cut bench or platform. If very resistant rocks form the shore, this may be seen as a fairly level rock surface which has been planed by the waves (Fig. 9.8); otherwise the bench is covered with shingle and sand. At the base of the cliff is a wave-cut nick, which usually extends slightly above high tide level, since breaking waves will be effective above this. Further

FIG. 9.7.—The Effect of Dip on Shore Cliffs

The seaward dip in (b), combined with the jointing, will help to reduce the cliff more rapidly than in (a).

N.B. Wave cut nick at base of each cliff

stages of this erosion show an extension out to sea of the bank of deposited material and the continued recession of the land margin, and there is a gradual approach to the form shown in Fig. 9.6*c*. This whole process may be regarded as a cycle of erosion, and the late stage corresponds to that of a graded river course.

In addition, it should be observed that originally a submergent

FIG. 9.8.—Chalk Cliffs at Thornwick Bay, near Flamborough, Yorkshire

Note the wave-cut base of the cliffs, the wave-cut platform and the glacial deposits on the top of the Chalk. The change in cliff slope marks the last.

shore will be very irregular and its headlands and bays will be affected as outlined on p. 138. Probably an intermediate stage will include the building of spits, out from the headlands, and these will tend to produce a relatively straight outer shore line as in Fig. 9.9. Even at the most mature stages, as described above, minor irregularities are likely to persist, owing to variations in the resistance of rocks to erosion. The recession of a cliff may also result in minor streams having hanging valleys, such as may be seen in the dry valley mouths between the several Chalk cliffs known as the Seven Sisters, near Beachy Head in Sussex.

Shorelines on Emergent Coasts

With the emergence of a coast the sea is, at first, in direct contact with a gently rising land surface, since the emergence has brought an offshore zone above sea-level. A line of low cliffs is produced by wave action, which may recede fairly rapidly, but the emergence has given a slight rejuvenation of the rivers in the coastal area, and some valleys may hang at these low cliffs. Wave action collects material offshore in a series of bars (Fig. 5.35). The following stages of development are likely. Firstly, the water zone between the inner shoreline and the outer bars is filled in, so that a new set of coastal flats is formed. These in turn are reduced to a line of cliffs in much the same way as has been described in the development of the cycle of erosion on a submerged shoreline.

143

Neutral Shorelines

It is not sufficient to refer only to emergent and submergent shorelines. Some are neutral because there has been no recent change of level, and yet there is a development of the shore which has extended from the land as in great deltaic areas, alluvial plains, and around volcanic islands and, sometimes, coral reefs. Furthermore, many shorelines are compound, in that they have suffered both emergence and submergence within recent times, and have features resulting from both processes. The North Carolina shoreline is largely emergent in type, but some recent submergence has produced the inlets and swamps shown in Fig. 9.9.

FIG. 9.9.—Shore Line near Cape Hatteras, United States of America

Types of Coastline

It is also necessary to discuss coastlines, since they control some of the details of the shorelines. The relation of the coastline to adjacent land structures gives rise to various types of coast, of which two are known as Pacific and Atlantic.

Pacific coasts are so named because many thousands of miles of the coastline of the Pacific Ocean are related to the fold mountain zones which surround this great basin (Figs. 4.9 and 4.10). The coastlines are broadly parallel to the fold trends of these mountains. In general, such coastlines show a remarkable tendency to be very regular or concordant, so that on the western shores of the American continents from Puget Sound in the state of Washington, to Puerto Montt in Southern Chile, there are few large inlets other than the harbour of San Francisco, with the Golden Gate, and the Gulf of Guayaquil.

Despite the fact that the coastlines of both British Columbia and Southern Chile show concordance with the mountain trends inland, there has been submergence with the formation of archipelagos, since the sea has swamped both the earlier valley floors and the lower slopes of the mountain ranges. Thus these coasts are very irregular.

V. C. Browne

FIG. 9.10.—Coast near Picton, South Island, New Zealand

The ridges belong to the fold mountain system at the north of the island. This is an example of a submerged coastline of the Atlantic type.

The island festoons of South-east Asia are obviously related to the fold arcs of that region (see Fig. 4.10), although the separate islands form a discontinuous coastline. Submergence does not explain this broken coast, since there is evidence of recent uplift, and it has been suggested (see p. 40) that the region lies on the northern edge of a modern geosyncline and that these islands are literally the crests of uprising mountains.

Atlantic coasts are very different from Pacific coasts, since their main trend lines are oblique or at right-angles to the structural trends of the adjacent land areas. Such coasts are said to be discordant and are usually very irregular, with alternating peninsulas and gulfs, as exemplified by the coasts of the Maritime Provinces of Canada and those of South-western Ireland. Nevertheless, some Atlantic coasts which are marginal to such continental or sub-continental plateaus as those of Eastern Brazil or of Western Africa are relatively regular. These may be called block coasts.

The terms Pacific and Atlantic, as applied to coasts, are somewhat misleading, since it is far from true to regard the coastlines of the Atlantic Ocean as being exclusively discordant any more than concordant coasts are peculiarly Pacific in their location. Pacific coastlines are evident in the Mediterranean Sea basin in Southern Spain (Sierra Nevada), Northern Africa (Atlas region), and Dalmatia (Dinaric Alps), whilst many of the coastlines of the Indian Ocean are Atlantic in nature, being marginal to such continental plateaus as

145

those of East Africa, Western Australia, and to the sub-continental plateaus of Arabia and the Deccan of India.

Rias

There are several types of coastline' which owe their significant characteristics not only to submergence but also to regional structures which have been impressed upon the coastal pattern. Drowning of river mouths by submergence creates the coastal inlets known as rias (Fig. 9.10). The word 'ria' is derived from the coast of Spanish Galicia where the westward-flowing rivers have submerged mouths; the coasts of Brittany and South-west Ireland are very similar. Fig. 9.11 shows the coasts of Kerry and Cork, where the very straight bays, with their intervening peninsulas, are typical of the west. These coasts are related to a series of east–west upfolds and downfolds, the former giving parallel ridges and peninsulas and the latter carrying the main river valleys. It is the latter which have been submerged to

FIG. 9.11.—The Coasts of Cork and Kerry, Ireland

produce the rias of Bantry Bay, Dingle Bay, etc. On the south coast is Cork Harbour, which is obviously more irregular than any one of the west coast rias. Here the mouths of several rivers have been drowned and a system of rias has been developed. Plymouth Sound, with its branches, is of similar origin.

Closely resembling these ria coasts are sections of the Dalmatian coast of the Adriatic Sea. Here, the totally submerged downfolds and the partially submerged upfolds of the land margins are represented by a series of parallel channels (or canali) and long narrow islets. Inlets resembling the ria systems of Plymouth and Cork are to be found farther from the open sea as in the Boka Kotorska (Bocche di Cattaro) shown in Fig. 9.12. Here ridges of limestone (since the region is part of the Karst) separate arms of water which are linked by transverse narrow straits, where the upfolds have been breached. This is a Pacific coast, whereas rias are usually found on Atlantic coasts.

Yugoslav National Tourist Office
(Photo: Mladen Grčević)

FIG. 9.12.—Boka Kotorska (Bocche di Cattaro), Yugoslavia

The inner part of the inlet is seen, near Kotor. This is some 15 miles from the outlet on the Adriatic Sea coast. Note the limestone ridges of the Karst.

Fjords

The fjord inlets give yet another type of coast which owes much to submergence but in this case there are other factors to consider. Such coasts are found in fairly high latitudes; generally speaking, they are polewards of latitude 50°, N and S, and on the western sides of land areas. These coasts are usually fringed with islands, representing the upper parts of partially submerged ridges, or upland masses. Fjord inlets have many branches which upon close examination show a fairly rectilinear pattern. Fjords penetrate farther inland than do rias; some of the Norwegian examples have their heads as much as eighty miles from the sea.

Although the process of fiord formation has been debated, it is certain that most fiords have common features. Many are valley systems which have been affected both by faulting and glacial erosion before submergence. Faulting determined the pre-glacial, drainage plan, whilst glaciation has developed U-shaped valleys with scalloped floors and tributary hanging valleys. Although the land on the sides of a ria may rise steeply from the water's edge, in a fjord the sides are almost vertical and shore margins are practically negligible (Figs. 9.13 and 4.3) other than at the heads of the main branches of the fjord, where deposition by rivers has produced

Widerøe's Flyveselskap, Oslo

FIG. 9.13.—Lysefjord in Rogaland, Norway

Lysefjord extends some 50 miles inland from near Stavanger. Note the high-lying, U-shaped valley in the foreground.

deltaic areas. Furthermore, with a scalloped floor the depth of water varies from one part of the fjord to another (Fig. 9.14), and in this respect a fjord differs from a ria, which becomes progressively more shallow as it is penetrated from the sea. In fact, with emergence, the fjord would become a lake-studded glacial valley.

FIG. 9.14.—Section of Fjord Inlet

Some Norwegian fjords have side branches, with shallow water compared with the depth in the main inlet. In such cases hanging valleys have been involved in the submergence, and they are quite logically termed 'hanging' fjords.

The westerly position of fjord coasts in high latitudes, referred to above, is probably related to the fact that here onshore westerly winds prevailed and gave abundant precipitation of snow, in the past, to feed the glaciers which helped to produce these fjord inlets.

Other Coasts

The flooding by the sea of land areas with subdued relief may give rise to inlets with many branches. Those on the East Anglian coast, formed by the mouths of the Rivers Orwell and Stour, are good examples. On the east coast of Denmark similar inlets give an irregular coast whose pattern is not unlike that of a fjord coast.

Locally, emergent coasts may have very complex outlines, where the development of offshore bars may enclose arms of the sea. The coast of the United States of America, in the neighbourhood of Cape Hatteras, is of this type (Fig. 9.9). The process of filling-in of such enclosed arms of the sea is clearly a deterrent to the establishment of useful ports.

Wherever such land-locked inlets of the ria, fjord, and other types have deep water penetrating far inland, maritime settlements and ports of major importance are likely to spring up. The value of the inlet of Port Jackson, at Sydney in Australia, lies in the abundant opportunities for wharfage on its many arms. Also, Plymouth, Milford Haven, and Brest are admirably suited as naval harbours. The fjord has, of all these harbours, most advantages, with its deep water and penetration inland (Fig. 9.15), but the position of all fjord coasts in high latitudes associated with cold climates has offset these advantages, since no major port of the world lies on such a coast, with the possible exceptions of those on Puget Sound, and Vancouver.

Local Coastal Features

The process of wave erosion on some sections of a coast is partially balanced by deposition elsewhere as a result of the movement of eroded material by longshore drift. Thus the loss to the land by the destruction of the low cliffs of boulder clay along the coast of Holderness in Yorkshire is offset to a certain extent by the construction of Spurn Head. In Norfolk and Suffolk similar losses and gains are to be noted. Blakeney and Scolt Heads in the north and Orford Ness in the east are gaining on the whole in this region, while the Dunwich area is losing. Actually Orford Ness is shorter at the present day than it was in the past, owing to relatively recent changes in wave directions, so that there is active destruction of part of the long spit.

A spit may grow tangentially from some point on a coast, and eventually seal off a bay into which it has grown. The initiation of such a spit, as usual, is at a point where the coastline changes its

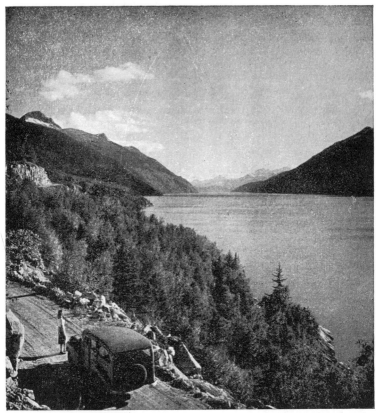

Canadian Pacific Railway Co.

FIG. 9.15.—Dyea Road, near Skagway, Alaska
An arm of a fjord on the Alaskan coast.

direction. Maps of the Baltic Sea coast of Germany and Poland show this process in its various stages. Near Gdynia a spit, or neh-rung, is in an early stage of development, whereas farther east the Frisches Haff and the Kurisches Haff have been nearly sealed off, each by its own nehrung. In Devonshire, just north of Start Point at Slapton, there is an example of a coastal lagoon which has been produced by the complete sealing-up of Slapton Ley, an earlier bay, by a spit. On the French coasts of Aquitaine and Languedoc similar lagoons or étangs may be seen, and most deltas will afford numerous examples (see Fig. 5.21). The lagoon coast may be of value, since in Languedoc the course of the Canal du Midi threads some of these etangs. The Norfolk Broads have been regarded as of similar origin—the result of bar formation by rivers and the sea, in shallow estuarine zones. However, recent investigations show that many of these shallow lakes are man-made hollows, having been dug out for peat. If a spit joins the mainland to an island, there arises a tombolo. Chesil Bank, in Dorset, is an example of such a link bar or spit which joins Portland Isle to the mainland at Abbotsbury, some seven miles to the west of the island.

Finally, a brief reference must be made to some very localized features resulting from the destructive action of the sea waves in conjunction with certain structural patterns. Rocks of varying resistance

Fig. 9.16.—Part of the Coast of Dorset

which outcrop on a coast, must create irregularities through differential erosion, and minor headlands, with their intervening bays, are thus produced, although, as described on p. 138, wave action will reduce such headlands with relative ease. Fault and strike lines usually control the sites of such headlands and bays. Outcrops of rocks lying parallel to the coastline may result in the formation of an inlet known as a cove, as at Lulworth in Dorset, where the coast is bordered by an upfold of limestone with an outcrop of clay, backed by Chalk hills, lying immediately inland. The diagram in Fig. 9.16 will show the geological details. Wave action has breached the outermost zone of limestone, and the sea has penetrated behind the cliffs and opened out, on the clay outcrop, the cove or land-locked bay which extends to the base of the Chalk hills. To the east of Lulworth Cove this process has been carried a stage farther in Worbarrow Bay, which has lost any cove-like pattern, but near Mupe Rocks there is a cove in the early stages of development (Fig. 9.17).

Offshore from cliff coasts there are found stacks. Here joints or faults have given lines of attack from the sea. Undercutting of the cliffs along such lines of weakness produces, at first, coastal arches, but, later, these collapse and leave isolated pillars of rock known as stacks. Durdle Door, on the Dorset coast, just west of Lulworth Cove, is an outstanding example of an arch whilst the stacks off Duncansby Head in Caithness are most impressive—not far away from these is the well-known stack, the Old Man of Hoy, off the Orkney island of that name.

Coral Reefs and Islands

Of somewhat limited extent and significance in the world are the reefs and islands which are built of calcareous material whose source

Aerofilms Ltd.

FIG. 9.17.—Worbarrow Bay, Dorset

This bay lies east of Lulworth Cove. In the foreground is a minor cove, near Mupe Rocks. At the far side of the bay are two escarpments, the inner one of Chalk, and the other of limestone (see Fig. 9.16). Dip slopes face inland. The Chalk scarp shows the rounded nature of Chalk landscape (see also Fig. 8.10).

is almost exclusively organic, since it depends particularly upon the activity of corals, together with various other marine organisms. A coral is an organism known as a polyp; and has a soft, sac-like body which is normally embedded in a calcareous depression. The protective outer layers of calcium carbonate of these depressions are produced by the corals from sea water, which contains this substance in solution as calcium bicarbonate. Since corals usually live closely packed in colonies of thousands, the coralline structures of adjacent organisms become cemented together, often with the help of nullipores which are minute plants that attach themselves to the corals and secrete calcium carbonate as well. As corals die, so fresh corals build upon the structures of their predecessors, and the mass of coral rock is increased.

Corals are restricted to certain parts of the oceans since they require a mean annual temperature of, at least, 68° F (20° C). Apart from local areas of the seas where the influence of warm currents of water permits them to thrive, they are not found far outside the tropics. Since within the tropics the temperature of the sea water is usually higher on the western sides of the oceans than in the eastern parts, there are most corals off the eastern shores of land areas. The abundance of corals in the Pacific waters off Queensland and the East Indies is therefore understandable. For similar reasons large numbers of corals occur in the Caribbean region, although the warmth of the Gulf Stream permits corals in Bermuda, at 32° N. Corals flourish in brackish waters, but the water must be free from the suspended terrigenous material that may be carried far out in the surface waters of the oceans lying off the mouths of large rivers. They grow best where breaking waves and tidal influences give them abundant supplies of fresh oxygen and marine food. Whilst corals can exist near the surface of the sea they must be covered with water during part of the day.

The coralline structures form fringing reefs to islands, barrier reefs that surround islands (with an intervening stretch of water known as a lagoon), and atolls which are like barrier reefs without an inner island. The atoll is essentially a ring-shaped island of coral rock

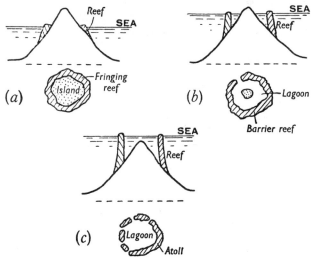

FIG. 9.18.—The Development of Coral Reefs and Atolls

After Darwin

enclosing a lagoon. Lagoons of this type are not the same as the coastal lagoons referred to on p. 150. The origin of these various features has given scope for much investigation.

The earliest theory of their origin, that of Darwin, called for a submerging island which was usually volcanic, since many reefs are associated with the Pacific islands of this type. The gradual development of the three types of reef is shown in Fig. 9.18. In (*a*) the island has a platform of coral or a fringing reef, perhaps half a mile in width, extending out from the shore at low tide, with its outer edge dropping steeply to the sea floor. In (*b*) the island has sunk, and the reef has grown upwards, keeping pace with the subsidence of the sea floor which, it is assumed; was not too rapid. The average rate at which coralline structures can grow upwards is about a foot in a decade. Too rapid a subsidence would cause the death of the corals and the reefs would cease to grow. Actually, corals can live at a depth of about 150 feet, and nullipores still deeper, but it is the rate of upgrowth which is of importance to this argument. The fringing reef of (a) has now become detached from the island, and is therefore known as a barrier reef which completely encircles the island, apart from a few breaks in its continuity. Further subsidence has caused the complete disappearance of the island above sea-level as in (c), but the reef has grown still further upwards and produced an atoll.

There is one significant difference between the enclosed lagoons of the atolls which have been surveyed and the atoll as envisaged by Darwin's theory. Most lagoons, inside atolls, are uniformly deep over their areas instead of being deepest at their outer edges. The larger lagoons have a depth of some 250–300 feet, whilst the smaller ones are only about 150 feet deep which is not too deep for live corals to be found. It is clear that sea waves are responsible for the

FIG. 9.19.—A Typical Pacific Atoll

comminution of dead coralline structures, and some of this waste is carried by waves over the reef and deposited in the lagoon. The quantity of coral mud which would be required to fill up the deep parts of the lagoon in Fig. 9.18c and so produce a level floor around the subsiding island cannot be accounted for by the likely supply of such material by wave action alone.

It would appear, from the extensive surveys that have been made in many Pacific atolls and their lagoons, that the reefs have been built upon a platform, generally at a depth of some 250–300 feet (Fig. 9.19). In order to explain this platform, Daly has put forward the following theory. At the height of the Pleistocene glaciation there was so much water held in the ice sheets that the level of the oceans was 200–300 feet lower than it is at present. When the sea-level was at its lowest, there were created wave-cut platforms at about this level. A low-lying volcanic island at the beginning of the Ice Age would be truncated by wave action as the slow depression of the sea surface occurred. In other cases it is probable that a pre-existing submarine plateau may have been abraded by wave action during the Ice Age. In some instances, the platform, on which the atoll stands, belongs to a guyot (see p. 343). Since the close of the Ice Age the sea has risen sufficiently slowly to enable fresh colonies of corals (most corals were killed off, even in tropical waters, by the cold of the Ice Age) to build up the bulk of the present-day reefs on these platforms. It will be observed that the development of atolls has also depended on submergence in Daly's theory, as in Darwin's, but the prime cause has been a rising sea level, and not a sinking island.

The Great Barrier Reefs which extend for some thousand miles off the east coast of Queensland are unique. There are many reefs included in this zone but they are not continuous—thus, giving passages for navigation. The main outer barrier reefs mark the edge of the continental shelf whilst, towards the land, are inner reefs and many islands, some of the latter having fringing reefs (see Fig. 9.20). The sea over the shelf is equivalent to a lagoon. The edge of the shelf and,

FIG. 9.20.—Great Barrier Reefs of Queensland
(after J. Steers)

therefore, the line of the main outer reefs, is not at a constant distance from the mainland coast. In fact, the distance varies from 15 miles, off Cape Melville, north of Cooktown to 160 miles, off Cape Manifold, near Rockhampton. Where the shelf is widest the adjacent uplands of the mainland extend far inland whilst the shelf is narrow where these uplands are least wide and more or less coastal in location. There is a close relationship between the shelf and these uplands. In fact, the shelf may be regarded as the down-faulted eastern half of an earlier fold mountain system which had been reduced to a peneplain before submergence. The main reefs have been built on submerged ridges which rise up on this drowned peneplain. Most of the reefs have grown upwards with a recent rise of sea level, as discussed above, in relation to atolls. The islands are the exposed summits of partially submerged ridges. The lagoon has a fairly level floor because of recently deposited sediments.

CHAPTER 10

Insolation and Temperature

Introduction

Meteorology is a branch of science which may be justly called applied physics, since most of its measurements are exact, and from these an attempt is made to give an orderly statement of atmospheric conditions. Primarily, meteorology is concerned with the conditions which obtain in the lower layer of the atmosphere, some seven or eight miles in thickness, known as the troposphere, whereas the layer above is known as the stratosphere. Regular measurements of weather conditions are made at meteorological stations which have been established throughout the world, although there are very large areas which are ill-equipped in this respect. Meteorological stations record the temperature of the air, atmospheric pressure and humidity, the force and direction of winds, the height, type, and movement of clouds, the amounts and types of precipitation (rain, hail, sleet, and snow), the extent of visibility, and many other factors such as the duration and intensity of sunshine, the temperature at the ground surface and below it at certain depths. To the geographer the most important measurements are those of temperature, pressure, winds, humidity, and precipitation.

Temperature

The temperature of the air is a measurement of basic importance It represents the balance between the heat received from the sun and that dissipated from the surface of the earth by radiation and, to a less extent, by conduction, convection, and turbulence in the lower layers of the troposphere. As the earth's surface is becoming neither appreciably hotter nor colder than at present, this balance is maintained in part by transfer of heat from hot regions to cooler ones by movements of air and water and these will be discussed in due course in this book. Rays of heat emanate from the sun and pass through space and the atmosphere to the surface of the earth. It is when the rays strike the earth's surface that their energy is converted into heat. This supply of heat energy from the sun is known as insolation, but all the rays that come from the sun towards the earth do not succeed in reaching its surface. As the rays pass through the troposphere they are subject to scattering, absorption, and reflection by dust particles and clouds. The latter have a very potent influence in obstructing these rays, and many are reflected back into the atmosphere from their upper surfaces. Even some of the rays which reach the earth are reflected from its surface, and so their energy is not converted into heat. However, a considerable fraction of the rays does produce heat on the surface of the earth, but the amount of heat developed on small unit areas of this surface depends on several factors.

Insolation and Incidence of Sun's Rays

The most important factor of all is the incidence of the rays on the surface of the earth since there is a great variation in the angle which the rays make with the surface. These variations depend mainly on the latitude and the season of the year. In Fig. 10.1 are shown three

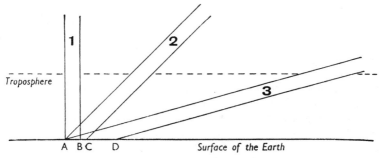

FIG. 10.1.—The Effect of Varying Incidence of the Sun's Rays on Insolation

bands of the sun's rays which are equal in breadth, so that if we assume that there has been equal scattering and absorption in each band with its passage through the troposphere, then the base of each band may be regarded as producing the same amount of heat at the surface of the earth. As each band is inclined to the surface at a different angle, the area covered by each is represented by the lines AB, AC, and AD. Obviously the heat developed from the rays in band (1) is concentrated in a smaller area than either that of band (2) or band (3). The difference is dependent on the angle between the rays and the surface: rays at low angles cover greater areas than rays which are vertical or nearly vertical. Thus vertical rays, as in band (1), concentrate the heat received in each unit area, so that heating is at a maximum, whilst the rays at lower angles give relatively less heat to each unit area, reaching a minimum when the rays are horizontal. In the above statement it is assumed that the heating up has continued for the same period of time in each case. Actually it must not be assumed that the insolation received on each of the three surfaces AB, AC, and AD is the same. Clearly the rays at

157

lower angles have had longer paths through the troposphere, so that the amount of absorption is greater than with vertical rays, and thus the amount of insolation received by each surface will be different.

Let us examine more closely the factors which cause the insolation to vary because of the variation of the angle between the rays from the sun and the surface of the earth. It may be assumed that all the rays of the sun which fall on the surface of the earth at a given instant are parallel to one another. In Fig. 10.2 the earth is shown at the position of its orbit when it is the summer solstice. Its axis is tilted at an angle of $66\frac{1}{2}°$ to the plane of the ecliptic,[1] and the rays of the sun are parallel to this plane. Several rays are shown, striking the earth at various latitudes, with the angles between them and the surface of the earth shown. Clearly the greatest insolation per unit area of

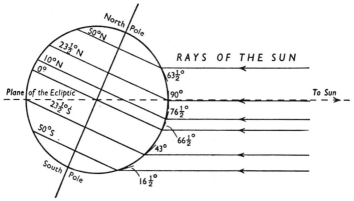

FIG. 10.2.—Incidence of the Sun's Rays at various Latitudes at the Summer Solstice

surface is received at $23\frac{1}{2}°$ N, where the sun is overhead at noonday. At all other latitudes the rays are spread out in varying degrees according to the angle. Thus latitude has a control over insolation.

Seasonal Variation of Insolation

The angles given on the above diagram and on the two which follow are for the noonday sun. Hence the degree of insolation at any particular latitude as indicated by these diagrams is for the noonday period only. This observation is of importance, because allowance should be made for the number of hours of sunshine at different latitudes, and this has a great influence on the insolation received during the daytime at any particular latitude and is not directly related to the angle of incidence of the noonday sun's rays.

[1] This is the plane in which the orbit of the earth around the sun lies (it is the plane in which eclipses take place).

In Fig. 10.3 the incidence of the rays of the sun at the same latitudes as given on the previous diagram is shown for the winter solstice, when the earth is at the opposite position to that of the summer solstice in its orbit around the sun. The angles between the rays of the

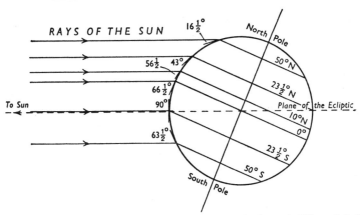

FIG. 10.3.—Incidence of the Sun's Rays at various Latitudes at the Winter Solstice

noonday sun and the surface of the earth are all different from their previous values at corresponding latitudes, with the exception of the Equator. These differences may be shown in the form of a table:

Latitude	Angle between the rays of the sun at noonday and the surface of the earth at the summer solstice	Angle between the rays of the sun at noonday and the surface of the earth at the winter solstice	Difference
90° N	23½°	0°†	23½°
70° N	43½°	0°†	43½°
66½° N	47°	0°*	47°
50° N	63½°	16½°	47°
23½° N	90°	43°	47°
20° N	86½°	46½°	40°
10° N	76½°	56½°	20°
0°	66½°	66½°	0°
20° S	46½°	86½°	40°
23½° S	43°	90°	47°
50° S	16½°	63½°	47°
66½° S	0°*	47°	47°
80° S	0°†	33½°	33½°

* Rays are just horizontal.   † Rays are below the horizon.

In six cases there is a difference of 47° between the angle at one solstice and the angle at the other solstice. This is true of all places between the tropic and polar circle in each hemisphere. At all other times in the year the angles would have values between those shown for a given latitude in the table above. It must be remembered that the solstitial positions are extreme ones, and that in the intervening periods of the year the sun is moving overhead between the tropics, where all places receive overhead sun on two occasions in each year. Thus at the various latitudes between and including $23\frac{1}{2}°$ N and S, shown in the table above, the noonday sun angle varies from 90° to the smaller solstitial value shown. Between the tropics and the polar circle ($66\frac{1}{2}°$) in each hemisphere this difference is 47° at all latitudes. But within the polar circles the difference is less than 47° and decreases polewards. Thus there is a seasonal variation of insolation which is related to both latitude and the revolution of the earth around the sun.

FIG. 10.4.—Varying Lengths of Night and Day at different Latitudes at the Summer Solstice (reverse is true at the Winter Solstice)

Within the tropics the noonday angles of the sun are never very low and their seasonal differences at any latitude are not so great as elsewhere. In middle and high latitudes when the noonday sun is at a low angle there is very great spreading of the rays at the earth's surface so that large areas receive an amount of radiation from the sun comparable to that which, in low latitudes, is concentrated on small areas. Thus, on these grounds alone, we may arrive at the conclusion that insolation, taken over the whole year, is greatest within the tropics.

Exclusive of other factors the larger the noonday angle the greater is the insolation received in the day. Reduced insolation, with rays at low angles, may be offset in very high latitudes in the summer by very long hours of daylight (Fig. 10.4). Whereas at the Equator the lengths of night and day are the same throughout the year, north of

$66\frac{1}{2}°$ N, at the time of the summer solstice, the day lasts for twenty-four hours. Thus there is the apparent paradox that the polar zones receive the highest computed insolation of any part of the earth's surface, but only for a very short period in the year is this true. This theoretical maximum is offset partly by absorption of heat as the rays traverse the atmosphere, but even more insolation is lost by reflection of the rays by clouds and surfaces of ice, snow and sea in these high latitudes. As day and night are of equal length at the Equator throughout the year, and since the noonday angles of the sun's rays are never less than $66\frac{1}{2}°$, insolation in the equatorial zone is always great, but the regular diurnal (daily) development of a cloud

RAYS OF THE SUN

Slope AB has the most effective insolation

FIG. 10.5.—Incidence of the Noonday Rays of the Sun in Mountain Terrain

cover helps to reduce the total insolation as compared with that received by the tropical regions just outside these zones. In the savana and hot desert areas the mean temperatures in the hot season are higher than those of any month at places near the Equator.

Insolation and Aspect of Surface

Apart from the variations which have been mentioned, the resultant heating of any part of the surface of the earth may depend upon two other factors, namely, aspect of steep slopes and the nature of the surface.

A very steep hill or mountain slope in high latitudes may receive rays of the sun at a relatively high angle, so that the effective insolation is much greater than on level valley floors or mountain tops in the vicinity (Fig. 10.5). It is quite apparent that in some Alpine areas the choice of the sites for small villages and their croplands is controlled by the aspect which affords the greatest insolation over the whole year. The slopes which are in the shadow for much of the day are usually shunned by these communities, and there are distinctive names for these shaded and sunny slopes (in the French

161

Alps they are called 'ubac' and 'adret' respectively). Under overhead sun, the reverse would operate in deep mountain valleys in the tropics, and the high angle of the sun's rays would not give the most effective insolation on the sides of the valleys. The intensely cold slopes which are in the shadow during the day in the Andean areas may be quoted as examples.

Heating and Cooling of Land and Water

The nature of the surface on which the sun's rays fall also controls the heating up by day and, for that matter, the cooling down at night. For the moment we may regard the surface of the earth as being either of land or of water and compare these two types of surface. As important climatic distinctions depend upon the differences between these surfaces, it is desirable to examine fairly fully the factors which are involved.

There are three important factors:

1. The absorption of heat depends upon the nature of the surface. Water reflects the rays of the sun more than does land, and therefore for surfaces of equal area and with the same insolation water absorbs considerably less heat than does land in a given period of time, or, in other words, land absorbs more heat than does water. On the other hand, at night, when radiation occurs, land loses heat more readily than does water, because good absorbers are good radiators.

2. The heat capacity of the substance forming the surface on which the rays fall is of importance. Heat capacity is the amount of heat required to raise the temperature of a mass of a particular substance through one degree of temperature. Water has a much greater heat capacity than has land. Therefore, for equal masses and with the same insolation, water needs more heat than land to warm up to the same degree. In other words, land heats more quickly than water; it also cools more rapidly than water.

3. Finally, the rate at which heat is transmitted into the body of water or of land from the surface layers has its effect. As explained in (1), heat is absorbed by the surface layers of land and water at different rates. However, in water there is a great penetration of the heat rays, so that a slight warming of water occurs to fairly great depths. At night heat is brought to the surface by conduction in both land and water, but also by convection in the case of water, since once radiation has cooled its surface layers, these sink and displace slightly deeper and warmer layers which therefore rise to the surface. The conduction produces a loss of heat from both water and land, as once the heat has reached the surface it will be radiated, in the case of land, very rapidly. But in addition to the slower radiation from water surfaces, there is a continual replenishment at the surface of fairly warm water from below by convection.

Thus, on all three counts, water warms up and cools down more slowly than does land, although another factor which helps to maintain the relative coolness of the oceans is evaporation, since this causes heat to be lost from its surface layers—this is a source of heat for the troposphere.

This unequal heating and cooling is a daily phenomenon, but it can also be applied to the long-period contrast between summer and winter. Thus arises the distinction, that is so important in climatological discussions, between oceanic and continental climates, in which the difference between winter and summer temperatures is much less on the margins of the continents, near the oceans, than it is in situations within great land masses, particularly in temperate latitudes (see p. 357).

Yet another factor, which affects only the heating and cooling of land surfaces, is the type of soil. Soil contains air spaces and, since air is a poor conductor of heat, in very porous soils heat is concentrated in the surface layers which warm up readily by day, unless there is a considerable water content in the pore spaces, when the heating is slower and may eventually be carried to fairly great depths. A dry sandy soil will warm up in its surface layers quickly, whereas a close-textured clay soil with less air and a fair amount of water in the pore spaces will warm up slowly. On the other hand, the former soil cools more quickly than the latter. Surfaces of snow and ice may be compared with sand in so far as they lose heat rapidly, but they do not gain heat readily because the reflection of the incoming heat rays from these surfaces is very great.

From the foregoing arguments it would seem that at night the temperature should fall steadily until the renewed onset of insolation with daytime. This rarely occurs, because clouds act as reflecting surfaces for the radiant heat rays, which are therefore returned to the surface of the earth and so help to maintain the heat balance. Also the introduction of warm air into a given area often prevents the normal nocturnal chilling. In Britain importations of tropical air in winter are particularly effective in this respect.

Temperature Records

Air temperatures are measured at meteorological stations by thermometers which are housed in a Stevenson screen.[1] This screen is a wooden box with ventilated or louvred sides which permit the free movement of air through the box and yet prevent any direct or reflected rays of the sun from entering it. The screen is mounted preferably over a grass surface so as to reduce the chance of increased heating such as would occur with the reflection of the sun's rays from bare soil or a roof top. For the measurement of air tem-

[1] Designed by Thomas Stevenson, a lighthouse engineer and father of the author, Robert Louis Stevenson.

peratures in the shade, that is, in the screen, two thermometers of special construction are used to give records of the highest (or maximum) and the lowest (or minimum) temperatures in a given period, irrespective of when the instruments are read. It is usual to read the thermometers at frequent and regular intervals. Some meteorological stations take only one set of readings in every twenty-four hours (normally at 09.00 hours), but it is more usual for several sets of readings to be made during the day and, at some stations, hourly readings of temperature are recorded.

Also the screen should house a self-recording instrument known as a thermograph. This gives a continuous trace on paper of the temperature by means of a pen which moves on an arm coupled to a coil of two metals. Changes in temperature are reflected by the expansion and contraction of this coil, and these movements are transmitted to the pen. The trace is known as a thermogram.

In view of the fairly recent official recognition of the Celsius (or Centigrade) scale of temperature by the Meteorological Office in this country it is perhaps useful to be able to make the conversion from one scale to the other.[1] With few exceptions, no changes have been made from the Fahrenheit to the Celsius scale where temperatures are quoted in this book. For those wishing to make these conversions frequently the linear scales in Fig. 10.6 are provided. On the pages showing climatic regions with statistics for relevant stations a vertical linear scale of comparison has been provided.

[1] The fixed points on the two scales of temperature are freezing point 0° C or 32° F and boiling point 100° C or 212° F. Thus, for the same range of temperature, there are 100 degrees Celsius and 180 (32 − 212) Fahrenheit. For conversion, it is necessary to reduce these relations to:

$$\frac{180\,(F)}{100\,(C)} = \frac{9}{5} \quad \text{and} \quad \frac{100\,(C)}{180\,(F)} = \frac{5}{9}.$$

Thus, 0° C to 10° C is equivalent to $10 \times \frac{9}{5} = 18°$ F. This 18° F is eighteen degrees above 32° F and, therefore, the corresponding temperature to 10° C, on the other scale, is 32 + 18 = 50° F. On the other hand, 59° F is, in fact, a temperature of 27° F (59 − 32 = 27) above freezing point on the Fahrenheit scale. On the Celsius scale, this would be $27 \times \frac{5}{9} = 15°$ C. The formulae expressing these contrary conversions are:

$$x° \text{ C} = \left(\frac{9}{5}x + 32\right)° \text{ F} \quad \text{and} \quad y° \text{ F} = (y - 32)\frac{5}{9}° \text{ C}.$$

Since it happens that the two scales coincide at −40° C and −40° F, this is proved by:

$$-40° \text{ C} = -40 \cdot \frac{9}{5} + 32 = -72 + 32 = -40° \text{ F},$$

whilst

$$-40° \text{ F} = (-40 \text{ F} - 32) \cdot \frac{5}{9} = -72 \cdot \frac{5}{9} = -40° \text{ C}.$$

From the highest and lowest temperatures recorded in a given day the mean daily temperature for that day is obtained as an average of the two values. The difference between these two temperatures is known as the daily range of temperature. For example, if the maximum and minimum temperatures on a certain day are 60° F and

FIG. 10.6.—Conversion of Temperatures on Fahrenheit and Celsius Scales

40° F respectively, then the mean temperature will be 50° F, and the daily range will be 20° F. Over a month readings are taken each day, and the average of the mean daily temperatures for the several days of the month yields a figure known as the mean monthly temperature. For climatological purposes the mean temperatures for each of the twelve months of the year are used for comparisons. However, the figures quoted in climatic statistics are based on long-period observations covering several years. The period that is considered adequate to include all the likely variations which may occur is one of thirty-five years. Thus a mean temperature for a given month is really an average of probably at least thirty-five mean monthly temperatures based on records extending over thirty-five consecutive years. With the more uniform conditions which prevail in the tropics as compared with the temperate areas, a ten-year period, sometimes less, is often sufficient. The difference between the highest and lowest mean monthly temperature in the year gives the mean annual range of temperature.

It is of value to take into account the extremes of temperature, since they may be critical to plant growth. It is possible, from daily temperature records taken over many years, to extract the means of the daily maxima and minima for a period such as a month. The two means which are thus obtained are known as the mean daily maximum and the mean daily minimum temperatures respectively, and their difference is the mean daily range of temperature. By taking the means of the highest and lowest temperature recordings in a particular month in each year over a period of observation, it is possible to obtain the mean monthly maximum and the mean monthly minimum temperatures, and their difference is called the mean monthly range of temperature. The absolute highest and lowest temperatures recorded over a given period are also of some value.

Lapse Rate of Temperature

Elevation produces a general fall in the temperature of the air at any latitude, the decrease being at a rate which may be as much as

165

1° F in 300 feet (it may be considerably less, viz., 1° F in only 225 feet). This rate of decrease is known as the lapse rate of temperature in the troposphere. The following records will illustrate this lapse of temperature:

| Fort William (171 feet) | January mean temperature 38·7° F | 15·3° F | July mean temperature 57·1° F | 15·4° F |
| Ben Nevis (4,406 feet) | January mean temperature 23·4° F | | July mean temperature 41·7° F | |

Note that the difference in elevation between Fort William and Ben Nevis is about 4,200 feet. With a lapse rate of 1° F in 300 feet, there should be temperature difference between the two stations of about 14° F. The differences shown by the above records are reasonably in accord with this computed difference.

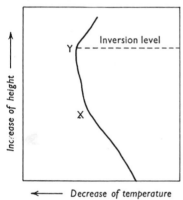

Fig. 10.7.—Lapse Rates of Temperature in the Troposphere

Note that lapse rates rarely remain constant, the graph shows minor variations at all levels.

It is possible for the rate of decrease of the air temperature to slacken at higher levels in the troposphere, as shown at X in Fig. 10.7, and it is not uncommon for an increase of temperature to occur with height, as above Y, in the diagram (the lapse rate is then negative). This increase is known as a temperature inversion and it occurs above an inversion level. The troposphere has for its upward limit a marked inversion level which is known as the tropopause above which, in the stratosphere, temperatures tend to be constant, not changing markedly with further increase in height. The height of the tropopause varies as will be shown in p. 195.

Isothermal Maps

In order that a general comparison of temperatures in different parts of the world may be made, it is usual to make use of isothermal maps. Isotherms are drawn as smooth lines with temperature values obtained from as many places as possible for a given period, such as a month. They are boundary lines, and must be regarded as separating zones with temperatures above and below a certain value. Reduced temperatures are usually employed for isotherm maps, when they are drawn for world distributions as shown in most atlases. Since altitude produces lower temperatures than at sea-level in all latitudes, it is of little value for comparative purposes to draw isotherms from actual mean temperature values, since they will give, in essence, a contour map with inverted values, i.e. low-value isotherms will delimit elevated areas and vice versa. Reduction of temperature is effected by adding to the mean temperature 1° F for every 300 feet that the station of observation is above sea-level. The map which is obtained, showing mean sea-level isotherms, is of some value, although its worth can be over-estimated. However, for broad comparisons of the temperatures in widely separated areas, it is the only map which has been devised for the purpose. It should be clearly understood that these maps have been produced by smoothing the actual temperatures and are, in many ways, theoretical maps, although they do show the effects on temperature of such factors as latitude and continentality, and are of great value in the study of climatology.

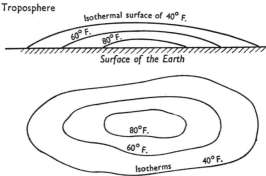

FIG. 10.8.—The Relation of Isothermal Surfaces to Isotherms

It is possible to regard an isotherm as the intersection of an isothermal surface with the surface of the earth. Fig. 10.8 shows the relationship between isotherms and isothermal surfaces.

World Distribution of Temperature

World maps of mean sea-level isotherms for the months of January and July are given in most atlases. Study of such maps will reveal that the zones of greatest heat, with mean monthly temperatures in excess of 80° F, are not only tropical, but extend to more than 40° N in the northern summer and to about 30° S in the southern summer. The two maps show clearly the migration of this hot zone, which is obviously related to the movement of the overhead sun between the tropics. However, the extensive land areas in the northern hemisphere give a much greater hot zone than in the

167

south in the respective summer seasons, thus showing the effects of the great heating of land in summer. This difference between the hemispheres is further emphasized by the three fairly large areas in North America, North Africa, and Asia respectively, which have mean July temperatures of over 90° F. There are two corresponding areas in southern Africa and North-west Australia in January, but they are fairly small.

Polewards from these hot zones in each map there is a general decrease of temperature as would be expected. In the southern hemisphere the isotherms show a considerable uniformity of trend from east to west, which suggests that, in general, temperatures decrease regularly with increasing latitude. However, in the northern world the isotherms are far from regular in their courses across the maps. In winter they have marked poleward bends over the oceans and equatorward bends over the continents, indicating that along a given line of latitude the continents are much colder than the neighbouring oceanic areas. In January, along the Arctic Circle, it may be observed that the interiors of Canada and Siberia have mean temperatures of —20° F and −30° F to −50° F respectively, whilst over the North Atlantic Ocean, between Norway and Iceland, the mean temperatures are between 30° F and 40° F, giving a zone of winter warmth. The cold pole of the northern world is located at or near Verkhoyansk, on the Arctic Circle in Siberia, which in January is colder than the North Pole. The mean temperature in January at Verkhoyansk is given as −58° F, although −85° F has been recorded there.[1] Similar areas of intense winter cold are found in Greenland and in northern Canada. The difference between the most northerly part of an isotherm loop over an ocean and its most southerly position over a continent, in January in the north, may be of the order of more than twenty degrees of latitude, or some 1,500 miles. The July map shows that in the northern hemisphere the contrast between continents and oceans is reversed. Observing the North Atlantic Ocean and the adjacent regions of North America and Eurasia the difference of temperature between land and sea at a given latitude is of the order of 10°–15° F. Both interior North America and Eurasia have summer temperatures of about 70° F in the fifties and sixties of north latitude, whereas over the adjacent oceans the temperature is about 55°-60° F. This contrast between the summer and winter isotherms in the north is related to the difference in the heating and cooling of land and water as discussed on p. 162.

In the southern world the ocean surfaces are predominant, which explains the more uniform trend of the isotherms, although there are slight poleward loops over the continents in January (summer) which are maintained in July (winter), except in the case of the

[1] See footnote on p. 337.

widest southern land mass, Australia, where there is an equator-ward loop. In fact the loops in South America and Africa are produced mainly by the effects of warm and cool currents of water passing along the shores of the continents (see p. 350). The equability of temperature in the southern continents is shown by the fact that the differences between mean summer and winter temperatures are considerably less than in comparable latitudes in the northern lands. A few, small areas in the south show seasonal differences of the order of 30° F to 40° F, whilst there are large areas of land in the north where the difference is over 40° F. In fact, over quite considerable areas of the northern continents, this range may increase to 60° F and even 70° F.

These general differences are shown even more vividly by maps that indicate the mean annual range of temperature over the world. On such maps the very small range of 5° F which is restricted to an equatorial belt is most striking. The effect of a land mass is seen by the great ranges in the northern continents, whilst the moderating influence of oceanic areas is particularly clear in the southern world. Perhaps the most outstanding feature of all is afforded by the extensive north-ward loop the isopleth[1] of 20° F mean annual range of temperature in the North Atlantic Ocean, showing the tempering effect of water.

Maps of temperature anomalies may also be found in some atlases. An anomaly of temperature is the departure of the mean sea-level temperature from the average temperature for the latitude of the place concerned. This latter temperature is a purely theoretical one.[2] Anomalies of temperature may be positive or negative, and they show where parts of the surface of the earth are respectively warmer or cooler at a given time than they would be if the earth had a uniform surface so that there was a regular decrease of temperature in a poleward direction.

Some atlas maps of temperature distributions may show the thermal or heat equator. This line joins the points which, on each line of longitude, have the highest mean temperature for a given period. It is usually shown on January, July and annual temperature maps. The annual heat equator reveals that the zone of highest mean temperature tends to lie mainly in the northern hemisphere and even the January (southern summer) heat equator runs partly to the north of the Equator. Whilst the slightly longer sojourn of the overhead sun in the northern hemisphere may help to explain these facts, the more extensive land masses in the north play an important rôle in producing this effect.

[1] An isopleth is a line joining places with the same quantity. The term covers all such lines as isotherms, etc. (Gr. Isoplethes—equal in quantity or number.)

[2] This temperature is obtained from readings taken at as many places as feasible which are spaced as evenly as possible along a line of latitude.

CHAPTER 11

Pressure and Winds

Air Pressure and its Measurement

The various gases, which make up the atmosphere, have a very considerable weight that exerts a force upon the earth's surface which is known as the air pressure. At ground level, this is equivalent to the effect of a weight of about 15 lb on every square inch of the surface. This pressure is not appreciated by human beings, since our

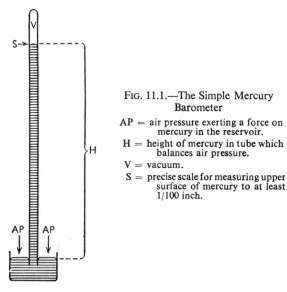

FIG. 11.1.—The Simple Mercury Barometer

AP = air pressure exerting a force on mercury in the reservoir.
H = height of mercury in tube which balances air pressure.
V = vacuum.
S = precise scale for measuring upper surface of mercury to at least 1/100 inch.

bodies are adapted by nature to withstand such weights. Air pressure is measured by a barometer (Gr. baros—weight, heaviness). There are two types of instrument; one makes use of mercury, and the other of a vacuum. In the simple mercury barometer which is illustrated in Fig. 11.1, a vertical glass tube contains mercury and opens into a reservoir of mercury. Normally the air pressure (AP) supports a column of mercury thirty inches in height (H), and for this reason the tube must be about a yard in length. Above the mercury there is a vacuum (V). Since the pressure of the air is continually changing, the varying length of H is a direct measure of these changes. It is thus customary to indicate the air pressure in terms of inches or millimetres of mercury. In most parts of the world the fluctuations of pressure which occur over several hours, and even days, are usually quite small, and it is necessary to use a very precise scale, which has a vernier, in order to register the changes in the height of the mercury column to the nearest hundredth of an inch. In British meteorological stations the Kew type of mercury barometer is standard—it is essentially a very precise instrument of the type as described above. It is more usual in meteorology to record the pressure of the air in millibars. The weight of the air may be expressed as a force of so many dynes. Pressure at sea-level is equivalent to a force that is usually in the neighbourhood of 1 million dynes per square centimetre, or 1 bar.[1] A millibar is therefore equal to a force of 1,000 dynes per square centimetre. When the pressure changes by 1 millibar, it is equivalent to a rise or fall in the mercury column of about $\frac{3}{100}$ inch.

The second type of barometer is known as the aneroid (without liquid), and it consists of a small metal box with corrugated sides, from which most of the air has been evacuated. Such a box will react very readily to changes of air pressure, since its sides will move in or out very slightly as the pressure increases or decreases respectively. Such slight movements that occur in the sides of the box are coupled with a series of levers and other mechanism, so that eventually these movements are recorded by a pointer moving over a scale which reads directly the value of the air pressure. The instrument is calibrated by reference to a standard mercury barometer. Obviously, its dependence on mechanism means that in the course of time the readings become inaccurate, so that frequent checking with a mercury barometer is essential. The compactness of the instrument is of great value, since it is easily carried about; precise instruments of this type, no larger than a pocket watch, may be constructed. It is also readily adapted to give a continuous record of pressure changes by a line traced by a pen moving up and down over paper on a revolving drum. This instrument is known as the barograph and its trace of pressure is a barogram.

Variations of Pressure

In the first few thousand feet above sea-level, pressure decreases at the rate of about 1 millibar in every 10 metres (1 inch in 1,000 feet).

[1] Standard pressure is regarded as that produced by a column of mercury 76 cm in height. In a tube of 1 sq cm cross-section, this is equal to the weight of 76 cc of mercury. The density of mercury is 13·6, so that the weight of 76 cc of mercury is $13·6 \times 76$ grammes. One gramme weight is equivalent to 981 dynes. Therefore, standard pressure is equivalent to a force of $13·6 \times 76 \times 981$, or 1,014,000 dynes per square centimetre, which is slightly more than 1 bar.

171

At about 18,000 feet, the air pressure is reduced to about half of its sea-level value but there is very much more than another 18,000 feet of the atmosphere above this height; in fact, the atmosphere reaches to heights which are better expressed in miles than in feet. This means, of course, that the pressure does not decrease uniformly with height. Without giving a detailed explanation of how pressure readings are reduced to sea-level, it is sufficient to say that a formula has been devised to make this correction. It involves a knowledge of the height and temperature of the barometer and of the local force of gravity, as well as the temperature of the outside air in a screen.

Under normal conditions the pressure of the air fluctuates fairly considerably, but it usually ranges between about 28·5 and 30·5 inches (or 965 and 1,033 millibars). Just as there is a daily range of temperature at places on the surface of the earth, so is there a diurnal rhythm of pressure. This rhythm is well marked on barograms at tropical stations, but in middle and high latitudes considerable fluctuations of pressure are experienced within short periods, often within a few hours, which make it very difficult to detect this rhythm. Nevertheless, it exists, and may be shown by averaging out long-period records for extra-tropical stations. The air pressure increases to a maximum about 10 a.m. and 10 p.m. and decreases to a minimum at about 4 p.m. and 4 a.m. This fluctuation is probably related to diurnal changes of temperature. Seasonal changes of pressure may be observed as well, and these are most certainly related to seasonal temperature changes. For instance, in the interiors of the great northern continents, the winter chill is reflected in the higher values of pressure, whilst the summer heat results in lower pressure than is usual in other areas of the world. The low-pressure zone of the equatorial belt, usually known as the Doldrums, is partly dependent on the uniformly high temperatures which prevail there.

High and Low Pressure

A knowledge of the exact values of the air pressure is not of compelling importance to the geographer. In general, the recognition of high- or low-pressure zones is sufficient, because it is the effects of pressure distributions that matter to us, and the interactions between areas of *relatively* high and *relatively* low pressure are of paramount importance. Again, between two areas of markedly high pressure there must of necessity be air at *relatively* lower pressure, although it may not be low as judged by the value of normal pressure. In studying the wind systems of the world the distribution of these *relatively* high- and low-pressure zones is of greater value than is the precise knowledge of average pressure values which obtain in different areas as shown by the seasonal pressure distributions in atlas maps.

Isobaric Maps

It is possible to draw isobars, which are lines joining places with the same pressure value for a given month or for any period which may be considered desirable. The values of pressure used are reduced to sea-level. Reduced isobars are perhaps of even less value than are reduced isotherms, because pressure changes at ground-level are often dependent upon changes at high levels in the atmosphere which cannot be indicated by sea-level isobars. However, sea-level isobars do present a picture of the average conditions of pressure over the earth's surface, although large areas on atlas maps are covered with isobars which have been drawn from the most scanty information. Again, the student is warned against placing too great a reliance on such maps, but to regard them as useful summaries of world-wide conditions. It is convenient to visualize isobaric surfaces which are comparable with isothermal surfaces as described on p. 167. From both isobars and isobaric surfaces it is possible to conceive of a pressure gradient, which means that there is a fall of pressure at right angles to the isobars and in a direction from high values of pressure to low values. This means also that there should be a movement of air across isobars according to the direction of the decline in pressure and also across isobaric surfaces in a horizontal direction as shown diagrammatically in Fig. 11.2.

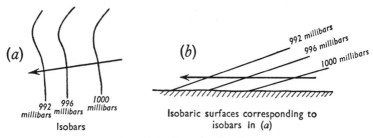

FIG. 11.2.—Pressure Gradient

World Distribution of Pressure

A glance at atlas maps of the world showing mean sea-level isobars for January and July will indicate that there are contrasts between these months and between the two hemispheres. In both maps it will be seen that in the southern hemisphere the mean sea-level isobars show a tendency to run from east to west, and the same trend is noted in the subtropical ovals or cells of high pressure lying over the oceans. Such behaviour is rare in the isobars of the northern hemisphere, although the east–west trend is shown by the oceanic

173

high-pressure cells in the subtropical latitudes of the north. There are five of these oceanic areas with high pressure in the world as seen on maps, and they are permanent, although in winter in each hemisphere they are linked to one another by extensive areas of predominantly high pressure which lie over the intervening continents, and in the north these extend polewards. Between the two sets of subtropical high-pressure cells lies an equatorial belt of permanently low-pressure air (the Doldrums) which shows a strong tendency to extend polewards over the continents according to the hemisphere which is experiencing summer. These seasonal extensions restrict the high-pressure cells, referred to above, to oceanic areas. The northern continents, particularly Eurasia, develop higher pressure in winter and lower pressure in summer than their southern counterparts.

There are two well-defined low-pressure areas in winter over the northern oceans. One is centred over the North Pacific Ocean near the Aleutian Islands at about 55° N, whilst the other appears to be centred at 60° N over the North Atlantic Ocean between Greenland and Iceland. In summer the former has disappeared from the July map of pressure distributions, but there are vestiges of the latter on this map. There are no counterparts to these low-pressure areas in the southern hemisphere; rather does one find a complete circumpolar belt of low pressure in both winter and summer which is marked by the very even trend of the isobars between 40° S and 60° S. The values on the isobars show that the lowest pressure is probably aligned from east to west in a belt near the line of latitude of 60° S. The observations in polar areas are limited. It has been believed, that thermally induced high pressure prevails over the Arctic and Antarctic surfaces of snow and ice, but aloft low pressure is found, above a shallow high pressure layer, of the order of a mile in depth. Investigations, in Antarctica during the International Geophysical Year (1957–8), show that this view must be modified—centres of both high and low pressure are present. Nevertheless, the highest part of Antarctica seems to be covered permanently by a ridge of high pressure.

These distributions in winter and summer reflect the continentality of the northern hemisphere and the predominant control of the ocean surfaces in the southern world. The winter chill of the northern land masses enhances the values of high pressure, so that, relatively, the high pressure of the subtropical cells is subdued. At the same time the more northerly oceanic low-pressure areas are thrown into greater relief by the development of the continental high pressure. The highest pressure (shown by the 1,040 millibar isobar) has its focus in Central Asia, where structural features induce very cold, heavy air to be concentrated in large mountain-girt basins, so that this region is quite exceptional.[1] In summer great heating of the interiors of the northern continents produces low pressure which causes a relative augmentation of the subtropical high-pressure cells and a relative, if not complete elimination of the oceanic low-pressure areas over the North Pacific and North Atlantic Oceans. In Asia the core of lowest pressure, with isobaric values of less than 995 millibars in July, is more southerly than the winter focus of high pressure, being located over the north-west of India. During summer, the low pressure over North America is in much the same area as the winter high-pressure zone.

The extensive ocean surfaces of the southern hemisphere remain fairly uniform throughout the year in regard to temperature, and this is reflected in the relatively simple pressure distributions of the south. The continental areas have but slight effect, and it is only in the summer (January) that there is a development of distinct continental low-pressure areas. These may be regarded as poleward extensions of the intertropical low pressure of the Doldrums belt and they lie between the three separate oceanic cells of high pressure in the sub-tropical regions.

Wind

Wind is air in motion, and a pressure gradient must be established before a wind may blow. If a series of isobars is considered as in Fig. 11.2, then a wind should blow at right angles across them from high pressure to low pressure as shown by the arrow. A wind has both force and direction; the former is indicated by the spacing of the isobars, which may be regarded as showing steep or gentle pressure gradients, in much the same way that closely or widely spaced contours show contrasted gradients on Ordnance Survey maps. The direction of the wind is indicated by a wind vane; its arrow head points *into* the wind and, therefore, indicates the point of the compass *from* which the wind is blowing. Consequently, a wind is named by the point of the compass, indicated by the arrow head of the vane. Winds are classified also by their speeds, in knots, which are recorded by a very complicated instrument, known as a pressure-tube anemometer, which gives a continuous trace or anemogram. The anemometer is an adaptation of the wind vane, in that it records both direction and speed. For most geographical purposes, a knowledge of the direction of the wind is of greater importance than knowing its force.

The wind has a force which may be given in terms of speed or as a pressure (lb per square inch). However, it is customary to use the Beaufort scale of wind force which was drawn up by Admiral Beau-

[1] It should be remembered that the pressure values quoted are reduced ones and that actual values will be less since the areas concerned are quite elevated.

fort for use at sea in the days of sailing vessels. There are thirteen forces on this scale, and they are numbered from 0, 1, 2, . . . 12, ranging from calm (0) to hurricane (12) through various grades of breeze and gale. Originally the scale was developed on a purely qualitative basis according to the effects that the winds had on the sailing of ships, but in modern times it has been placed on a quantitative basis, using measured wind speeds. The velocities which are used range from less than 1 knot for calm to over 65 knots for a hurricane. The scale will be found in full in most standard textbooks of meteorology, and may be referred to by the reader.

Circulation on a Stationary Globe

Assuming for the moment that the earth is stationary, in that it does not rotate on its axis, then there would be a very simple system of air movement in the troposphere. There would arise, in fact, a transfer of heat by air currents from the hot equatorial zone to the cold poles in the way that is suggested by Fig. 11.3. Let us see how this movement may arise by the consideration of isobaric surfaces. In a perfectly uniform atmosphere which is resting on a uniform surface with no temperature inequalities, there would be stationary layers of air which would exert a uniform pressure over the whole surface (Fig. 11.4a). Let us suppose that heating occurs at one point of this surface, as, for instance, at the Equator, then the isobaric surfaces are disturbed above this point (Fig. 11.4b), so that a pressure gradient is established at relatively high levels and a flow of air is initiated towards each pole as shown by the arrows. However, in time a further disturbance must develop by the collection, at the poles, of air that has been transferred from the equatorial regions, and this will result in an increase of air over the poles. The isobaric surfaces would then appear as shown in Fig. 11.4c, with the consequent development of a return flow of air towards the Equator along the surface of the earth. It must be emphasized that such movements are limited in a vertical direction by the tropopause (see p. 195).

Ferrel's Law

This simple system is upset by the fact that the earth is not stationary, but is rotating on its axis, and air moving in any direction in either hemisphere, does not follow a consistent track, but suffers deflection. This effect of the rotation of the earth is summarized in Ferrel's Law, which states that any object that moves freely. (i.e. under natural conditions) over the surface of the earth will be deflected to the *right* of the path in which it is travelling in the northern hemisphere and to the *left* of its path in the southern hemisphere. It is important to understand clearly what is meant by to the right

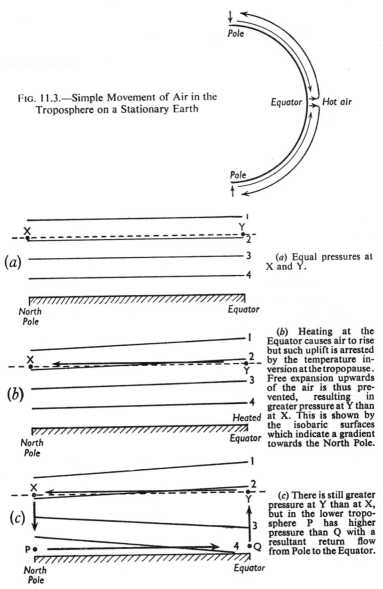

FIG. 11.3.—Simple Movement of Air in the Troposphere on a Stationary Earth

(a) Equal pressures at X and Y.

(b) Heating at the Equator causes air to rise but such uplift is arrested by the temperature inversion at the tropopause. Free expansion upwards of the air is thus prevented, resulting in greater pressure at Y than at X. This is shown by the isobaric surfaces which indicate a gradient towards the North Pole.

(c) There is still greater pressure at Y than at X, but in the lower troposphere P has higher pressure than Q with a resultant return flow from Pole to the Equator.

FIG. 11.4.—Simple Circulation on a Stationary Earth as shown by Isobaric Surfaces and Pressure Gradients (in Northern Hemisphere)

1, 2, 3, and 4 indicate increasing values of pressure on isobaric surfaces – – – marks a uniform height above surface of earth.

(or left) of the path, since confusion may arise in applying this law. Fig. 11.5 shows two objects, A and B, which set off, in the northern hemisphere, to move northwards and southwards respectively. The rotation of the earth causes deflection from these initial tracks as indicated by the broken lines, so that A is eventually moving towards the north-east and B towards the south-west. Both have moved away to the right of the path in which they are travelling, despite the apparent leftward trend of B. It may help the reader to understand this point quite clearly if the full arrow is regarded as a vehicle moving along a road which it leaves, irrespective of obstacles such as hedges, by gradually turning off to the right.

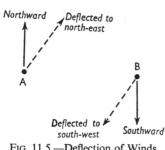

FIG. 11.5.—Deflection of Winds (in Northern Hemisphere)

The explanation of this deflection is far from simple. On a rotating globe all points are moving with the same angular velocity, that is, they move through 360° in a day and travel round in a circle. The higher the latitude of the point the smaller is the circumference of its circular path. Thus a point on the Equator moves round, in an easterly direction, at a speed or with a circumferential velocity of 25,000 miles in twenty-four hours, whilst a point at 60°N or 60° S. moves round a path of only 12,500 miles in the same time. Thus the circumferential velocity is greatest at the Equator, and decreases with increasing latitude to nil at the poles of the earth.

As the earth rotates from west to east, an object which starts to move northwards from the Equator has an initial eastward speed of 25,000 miles per day, but as it proceeds towards the North Pole it acquires a slower eastward speed. The reduction in speed of a mass of air moving in this manner is produced by frictional drag in its lower layers which are in contact with the surface of the earth. When this air has moved from the Equator into a higher latitude, although its eastward speed has been retarded by this frictional drag, it is not reduced to the value of the circumferential velocity of the latitude that it has reached. In other words, it is travelling slightly faster in an eastward direction than a point moving on the circle of latitude which is immediately below it. Thus northward-moving air tends to be deflected eastwards (or to the right). Conversely, south-ward-moving air in the northern hemisphere should gradually gain in circumferential velocity, but frictional drag prevents a complete adjustment, so that it is travelling slightly slower in an eastward direction than is the surface of the earth immediately below it. It thus tends to have a westward deflection (to the right). Obviously the same argument holds for the southern hemisphere, but the deflections are leftward. The above argument does not explain that even when the initial movement of the object is in an eastward or a westward direction, there is still a deflection. However, it can be shown that precisely similar deflections, that is, to the right or the left according to the hemisphere, will occur. It may be noted also that at the Equator there is no deflection at all.

Since these deflections occur, it is necessary to regard the upper arrow in Fig. 11.4c as representing a wind which is not moving to the north, but more eastwards than northwards, whilst the lower arrow shows a wind moving more to the west than southwards. Remembering that a wind is named from the point of the compass from which it is blowing, there would be winds with westerly components at high levels and winds with easterly components at low levels. However, another factor must be considered, namely, the establishment on dynamical grounds of a belt of high-pressure air at 30°–35° of latitude (the Horse Latitudes) in each hemisphere. The control which sets up these belts of high pressure in the subtropics is that of the rotation of the earth on its axis. Each hemisphere is therefore divided by this high-pressure air into two parts, and near the surface air moves both polewards and equatorwards from each of the Horse Latitudes. This means that in high latitudes in each hemisphere air will move polewards and be deflected so as to give a westerly wind, whilst in low latitudes air will move equatorwards and be deflected as an easterly wind. The two parts of each hemisphere which are separated by these subtropical belts of high pressure are very nearly equal in area, which suggests that a balance is thus struck between the area influenced by easterly winds and that which is under the control of the westerly winds. This division does not take account of the polar caps where high-pressure air resides over the surface, and from which air moves out in a westerly direction as a result of the operation of Ferrel's Law.

Pressure Belts and Wind Systems

It is now possible to consider that in the lower layers of an atmosphere which are resting on a rotating globe of uniform surface, there would arise several belts of pressure with their related winds. Fig. 11.6a shows the globe with its five main pressure zones, to which must be added the circumpolar low-pressure belts. The latter must inevitably arise, since in between the polar caps of high pressure and the subtropical belts of high pressure there must be air at lower pressure in general. Fig. 11.6b shows the winds which should develop as a result of the pressure gradients that exist between adjacent pressure belts, without taking into account the effects of Ferrel's

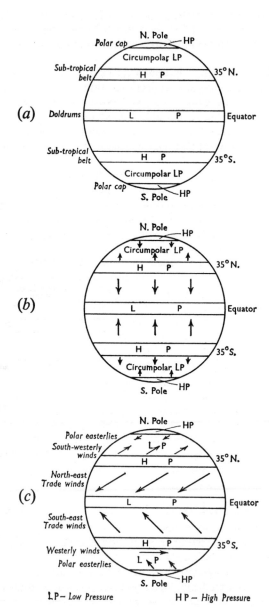

FIG. 11.6.—Wind Systems of the World

Law. The consequent deflections, according to Ferrel's Law, are shown by the arrows in Fig. 11.6c. It will be seen that there are six groups of winds, and the name of each set is shown on the left of the diagram.

The simple circulation envisaged in Fig. 11.4c must now be revised. Instead of a continuous equatorward flow of air at the surface of the earth from each pole, there are three distinct wind belts in each hemisphere. The circulation within the troposphere is probably somewhat as shown in Fig. 11.7 although it must be understood that no final interpretation of this circulation has been given by meteorologists.

There is another law which links wind directions and pressure distributions, known as Buys Ballot's Law. In Fig. 11.6c any wind arrow in the northern hemisphere is in such a position that if one imagines that one is standing with one's back to the wind which it represents, then higher-pressure air lies to the right and lower-pressure to the left. In the southern hemisphere the converse is true.

The ideal wind system or planetary circulation which is shown in Fig. 11.6c is far from being realized in actual world conditions, although it is not impossible to recognize, from a study of wind charts of the world, that all of the six winds do prevail over quite large areas of the earth's surface. Departures from this simple system are fairly common, and to give the picture greater reality, we must consider once again the effects of the large continental and oceanic areas. Just as with its pressure distributions so with its winds does the southern world approach more

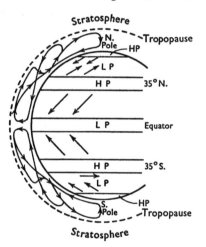

LP – Low Pressure   HP – High Pressure

Fig. 11.7.—Circulation within the Troposphere

Note that the height of the troposphere is not shown to scale.

closely to the simple pattern, because of its preponderant ocean surface, which gives that hemisphere greater uniformity than has the northern world. The diagrams in Fig. 11.8 attempt to show with reasonable accuracy the state of affairs which exists as a result of this uneven distribution of land and water in the two hemispheres. The land masses are represented by an isosceles triangle with its base in the north and its apex opposite to this base projecting into the

181

southern hemisphere. Such a triangle represents the combined American continents or the Old World, that is, Eurasia with Africa, or with Australia and New Zealand.

Several observations must be made on this diagram. Firstly, the pressure distributions are in accord with the world distributions which have been discussed. Secondly, it is necessary to explain briefly the clockwise and anti-clockwise circulations which are indicated by the wind arrows around the several ovals of high and low pressure in different parts of the diagram. If one considers such a cell of high pressure, then pressure gradients will exist in all directions from its centre to its periphery (Fig. 11.9a), whilst in the case of a

FIG. 11.8.—Pressure and Winds as modified by Land and Sea
After Kendrew

low-pressure area there will be gradients in the opposite sense (Fig. 11.9b). Applying Ferrel's Law, the directions of the winds which arise from these gradients will produce what amount to clockwise or anti-clockwise systems, the sense being dependent on two factors, the interior pressure of the particular cell and the hemisphere in which the cell is situated Fig. 11.9c shows the four cases which arise, although there are, strictly speaking, only two distinct types of circulation, cyclonic around low pressure and anticyclonic around high pressure. Thirdly, in the northern part of the triangular land mass the marked effects of continentality on the pressure values in the two seasons and the appearance of the monsoon area on its eastern side must be stressed. It must be observed, in connection with the latter feature, that whereas in most parts of Fig. 11.8 the winds compare quite well with those shown in the diagram of the planetary circulation of Fig. 11.6c, in the monsoon area in the summer season there is a complete divergence from the ideal pattern. Whereas in winter the continental high pressure creates gradients which result in north-east winds blowing over the tropical area of the north, in summer the very opposite holds, and instead of north-east winds there are winds from the south, south-east, and east over this

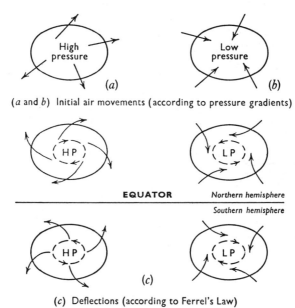

(a and b) Initial air movements (according to pressure gradients)

EQUATOR   Northern hemisphere

Southern hemisphere

(c) Deflections (according to Ferrel's Law)
and resultant circulations (broken lines)

Fig. 11.9.—Circulations in ' Highs ' and ' Lows.'

eastern part of the land mass. This almost complete reversal of the wind directions constitutes the chief characteristic of the monsoonal climate, which is probably the most outstanding of all the effects of continentality. The Indian climate is unique in this respect, but several other areas of the world are affected in a similar way. It will be noticed, for instance, that in the northern winter season the north-east trade winds transgress the equator, and upon entering the southern hemisphere they are deflected to the left, according to Ferrel's Law. This means that some areas, such as northern Australia, have north-west winds, instead of the south-east trade winds, as would normally be expected.

Before leaving the topic of winds and pressure, a final warning must be given to the reader. Vast areas of the global surface are but slightly known, and the picture which has been built up is based on the average conditions. Hence the reader must not be unduly surprised at finding apparent and real contradictions to some of the facts that have been presented in this chapter. For instance, no account has been given as yet of the depressions which are of such regular occurrence in the circumpolar low-pressure belts in each hemisphere. These depressions, as will be shown in Chapter 13, result at times in the establishment of systems of winds which blow, in turn, from almost all points of the compass. Thus the zones which are habitually regarded as being affected by the westerly winds may often have winds other than westerly ones. Even so, winds which have a westerly component (i.e. north-west, west, and south-west winds) are most common. Once again the southern hemisphere is more uniform, and in its circumpolar belt of low pressure westerly directions prevail over all other wind directions. The effect of these prevalent west winds is so pronounced that in the days of sailing-ships the belt of the oceans lying between 40° S and 50° S was called the 'Roaring Forties'. Frequently, the 'Roaring Forties' are made synonymous with the 'westerly winds' in the southern hemisphere, but this is an unfortunate use of the term.

CHAPTER 12

Water Vapour in the Air and Condensation Features

Humidity

Humidity indicates the water vapour content of the air. Normally, air is capable of receiving evaporated water (or water vapour) from a water surface. The extent to which evaporation goes on depends upon the air temperature, winds promoting evaporation, the amount of water vapour already in the air, and on the supply of water for evaporation at the time. At any given temperature, high or low, there is a limit to the amount of water vapour which a given volume of air can absorb. When this limit has been reached, the air is said to be saturated. At high temperatures much water can be held as water vapour in a given volume of air before the saturated state is reached, whereas at low temperatures only a relatively small quantity is required to saturate the same volume of air. It is possible to determine by physical experiment how much water in the form of vapour is in the air at a given time, and also how much water could be held as vapour if the air was saturated, assuming that there was neither an increase nor a decrease of air temperature. The relation between these two quantities is known as the relative humidity of the air.

Suppose that a given volume of air at 60° F contains 40 gm of water as vapour, and, let us suppose, that this air at 60° F could contain (if saturated) 50 gm of water as vapour. Then, the relative humidity of this air is given by the ratio 40/50 gm—40/50 is, in fact, expressed as a percentage—and, in this example, it would be 80 per cent. Obviously, if another 10 gm of water as vapour were allowed to evaporate into this air at 60° F, which already holds 40 gm, it would become saturated. The relative humidity would then be expressed by the ratio 50/50 or 100 per cent. But this air at 60° F, containing 40 gm of water as vapour, may become saturated in another way. Let us suppose that, at 40° F, this same volume of air would be saturated when it held only 30 gm of water as vapour. Then, if this air at 60° F with 40 gm of water as vapour were cooled to 40° F, it would become saturated and it could hold no more than 30 of these 40 gm of water. Therefore, there would be 10 gm of water

185

as vapour to spare, and this would return to the liquid state in the form of small drops of water, as the air cooled to 40° F. The values quoted above are hypothetical ones. The amount of water held by a given volume of air, irrespective of saturation, is known as its absolute humidity.

All air contains some water vapour, although in the hot deserts, where high temperatures prevail and where there is little surface water to charge the air with evaporated water, the extent to which the process of saturation has proceeded is often very slight. The relative humidity of desert air is frequently as low as 5 per cent, but it must be borne in mind that with such high temperatures, as prevail in deserts, it is possible, if evaporation could go on indefinitely from a water surface, for a very large quantity of water to be assimilated in the form of vapour before saturation occurred in a given volume of air. By the very nature of desert zones, with their paucity of rainfall, and therefore their lack of extensive water surfaces, the chances of the air becoming saturated are remote.

Measurement of Humidity

The measurement of relative humidity is made in several ways, but there are only two instruments which need be described.

(a) The Wet and Dry Bulb Thermometer

This instrument consists of two thermometers of the same pattern, but the bulb of one is kept moist by a muslin bag served by distilled water held in a small reservoir; the other thermometer is used normally. Into air which is unsaturated, evaporation of water will take place from the muslin around the wet bulb thermometer and, since water requires heat for the purpose of evaporation, this is extracted from the bulb of the thermometer with a resultant depression of its reading. The difference between the readings of the two thermometers, which are usually housed in a Stevenson screen (thus reducing evaporation by both wind and direct sun heat), is an indication of the relative humidity of the air. A small difference indicates a high value of the relative humidity and vice versa. If the air is saturated there will be no difference between the readings of the two thermometers, as no evaporation can take place from the muslin of the wet bulb thermometer. Tables of figures are provided so that, in conjunction with a knowledge of the air pressure, the relative humidity may be determined from any pair of readings, recorded by the thermometers at a given time. Wet bulb thermometer readings, alone, are of value since when these are regularly above 70° F in the tropics, white people are liable to the physiological dangers of heat stroke.

(b) The Hair Hygrometer

The second instrument for measuring relative humidity makes use of hair that has been made non-elastic by stretching under load. Such hair will increase its length with an increase of the relative humidity of the air and vice versa. This effect can be used to construct a direct-reading instrument, so that the value of the relative humidity is shown by a pointer which moves over a scale. The instrument is liable to develop mechanical inaccuracies after a period of use, and there is need of fairly frequent recalibration against a wet and dry bulb thermometer.

Dry and Saturated Air

Air which is not saturated may be regarded from a meteorological point of view as dry air, and it is reasonable to say that cold or hot air which is dry is more tolerable and less dangerous to human beings than either cold or hot air which is nearly or completely saturated. Dry air is capable of becoming saturated if its temperature is reduced to what is known as the dew point, when its water vapour content is just sufficient to produce saturation at that lower temperature. Further cooling results in the return of some of the vapour to the liquid state. The processes by which such cooling is effected naturally are of importance, since they can lead to the formation of clouds, mist, and fog, as well as to the production of rainfall and other forms of precipitation. If a mass of dry air is forced to rise from the surface of the earth to higher levels in the troposphere (or lower atmosphere) then a series of changes occurs:

(i) The air will move to a level where the pressure of the atmosphere is lower, since there is less weight of air upon it at these higher levels.

(ii) This reduction in pressure causes the rising air to expand.

(iii) Since air is a gas it will cool as a result of such expansion. This cooling is known as an adiabatic change because it is internal to the ascending and expanding air, and not because the air is moving into colder regions of the troposphere.

Adiabatic Lapse Rate

In discussing the temperature of the air, it will be recalled that there is a lapse rate in the troposphere of 1° F for every 300 feet rise. This is known as the environmental lapse rate. Dry air, in the sense that it is not saturated, cools more readily than this as it expands on rising through the troposphere. It has what is known as the dry adiabatic lapse rate of 1° F for a rise of 185 feet and this rate is independent of the original temperature of the air at ground level. This difference in the lapse rates may be shown diagrammatically as in Fig. 12.1. At the level XY, the temperature of the troposphere has

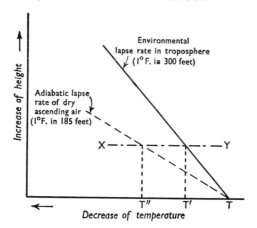

FIG. 12.1.—Stability

In Fig. 12.1 and eight others in this chapter the various graphs are not drawn to the same scale. They are intended to show some possible changes in the behaviour of ascending air under various controls. For the sake of argument, lapse rates are assumed to be constant where the graph is straight. Where the letters T, T′, T″ etc., are used it does not necessarily follow that they represent the same temperatures in different diagrams. Each diagram must be regarded separately in this respect.

fallen from T, at ground level, to T′, whilst the rising air has cooled from T to T″, a lower temperature than T .

Stability

Whereas the adiabatic lapse rate for dry ascending air may be assumed constant at all times, the environmental lapse rate in the troposphere may vary. It may be greater or less than the rate of 1° F in 300 feet, or, in other words, a fall of temperature of 1° F will occur with a rise of less than 300 feet or more than 300 feet, respectively. Let us examine air which is rising through a troposphere that has a lapse rate of 1° F in 300 feet. Returning to Fig. 12.1, let us assume that some air has risen through the troposphere from ground level to the level of XY. Now, at all stages in its ascent it can be seen that the temperature of the rising air is lower than that of the surrounding troposphere. As soon as the air leaves the ground, where it has the same temperature as the base of the troposphere, this difference of temperature appears. Now, the rising air not only becomes cooler, but also it becomes denser than the surrounding air of the troposphere as it rises, and this rising air would tend to sink, so that it returns to ground level. In fact, unless some external force is at work, the air cannot rise because of this difference in temperature and density. Under these conditions there is a state of stability as far as rising air is concerned.

Instability

Now let us see what happens if the environmental lapse rate in the troposphere exceeds the constant adiabatic lapse rate of dry air (i.e. the lapse rate in the troposphere is 1° F in *less* than 185 feet), admittedly a somewhat unusual state of affairs. Fig. 12.2 shows such a condition, and once again we will examine the respective temperatures in the troposphere and rising air at ground level and at the level XY. The temperature in the troposphere has fallen from T to T″, whilst the ascending air has cooled by expansion only from T to T′. In this case at all stages in its ascent the rising air is warmer and, of course, less dense than the surrounding air in the troposphere. Consequently its ascent will continue, since the denser surrounding air tends to force it up to greater heights. This rising unsaturated air is said to be unstable and, under the circumstances described, it would appear that it could rise indefinitely owing to its instability in the troposphere.

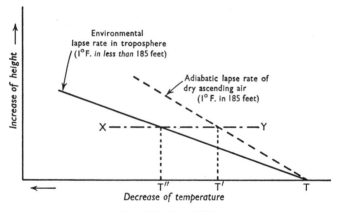

FIG. 12.2.—Instability

Convection

One common cause for the ascent of air is an initial rise in its temperature at ground level through local heating, which thereby induces convection. Some of the dry air is then forced upwards by the surrounding air, which is slightly cooler and denser, pressing on it (Fig. 12.3). Let us now follow the course of air which has been set moving upwards by convection through a troposphere which has an environmental lapse rate of 1° F in 300 feet. Fig. 12.4 demonstrates its history. Clearly up to the level PQ the rising air would be warmer than the surrounding troposphere, whilst above this level it would be cooler. Consequently the air would rise to the level PQ, but if it went higher it would sink back to this level. In

189

other words, conditions are unstable below PQ, but above they are stable as regards the rising air. Thus it would seem that under conditions of instability rising air will ascend until it cools by expansion to the temperature of the surrounding troposphere when its ascent is arrested. Convection currents may help to form clouds (Fig. 12.5).

Fig. 12.3.—Convection

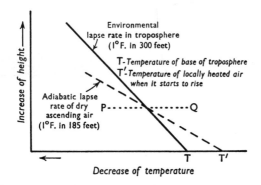

Fig. 12.4.—Unstable Air rising to a Level where it becomes Stable

Changes in Ascending Air

However, it is possible for ascending air to rise above this level, PQ in Fig. 12.4, if its rate of cooling by expansion is retarded. Before reaching this level the rising air may have cooled sufficiently for the condensation of water vapour to take place within it. The water so formed collects in droplets around particles of dust and other substances which are available, and a cloud is formed. Two other changes occur which are of importance. Firstly, when the water vapour condenses to water heat is liberated in a comparable amount to that which was required to evaporate the same amount of water. This liberated heat is helpful, since it reinforces the upward movement of the air in much the same way that convection set it off from the ground. Secondly, the heat so released reduces the rate of cooling of the air with its further ascent as compared with the adiabatic lapse rate for dry (unsaturated) air. The saturated or wet adiabatic lapse rate, after condensation occurs, is not constant, but is usually less

190

Official United States Navy photo

FIG. 12.5.—Cumulus Cloud

This cloud has been produced by convection currents caused by a fire in a cane sugar plantation at Pearl Harbour, Hawaiian Islands.

than the environmental lapse rate. The result of this change is shown in Fig. 12.6. Air rises to C, where condensation takes place, and continues to rise indefinitely above this point. Obviously unstable conditions allow it to rise to C, and its decreased lapse rate above that point makes the conditions relatively more unstable, because there is an increasing difference of both temperature and density between the rising air and the surrounding troposphere, so that the air does not halt at the level of PQ as in the former example (see Fig. 12.4).

FIG. 12.6.—Increasing Instability

191

It would appear that the rising air is so unstable above C in Fig. 12.6 that it would go on ascending, since the surrounding troposphere becomes progressively colder than it. Such is not the case, because higher up the water droplets in the rising air freeze, and again the adiabatic lapse rate changes, when it approximates to that of dry air. Fig. 12.7 shows the effect of this last change on the cooling of the ascending air. From C to F the air cools at the reduced rate for saturated or wet air. At F freezing occurs and further cooling is shown by the slope FS,[1] and at S this air may be assumed to be as cool as the surrounding troposphere. It would be under stable conditions if it rose above S, so that it is actually halted at this point. In passing it should be noted that the freezing of water in the rising air does not necessarily occur when its temperature has fallen to 32° F, since water may remain in the liquid state at temperatures well below normal freezing-point.

FIG. 12.7.—Instability reduced by Freezing Conditions

Before leaving this account of air which rises because of instability, some further possibilities must be investigated. In all the examples which have been illustrated the environmental lapse rate has remained constant, but that is unusual. It frequently changes, and at higher levels in the troposphere the environmental lapse rate almost invariably decreases. In Fig. 12.8 air is shown rising through a troposphere whose environmental lapse rate decreases above Z, and the air would be halted at X and not rise higher, as it would if the lapse rate in the troposphere had remained unaltered. Sometimes the environmental lapse rate changes so that there is actually an increase of temperature above a certain level, known as a temperature inversion. The effect of an inversion is shown by Fig. 12.9, where it will

[1] Actually, a release of heat occurs with the freezing of the water droplets and temporarily, the adiabatic lapse rate would decrease above F. The slope would become practically vertical for a very short distance on the graph.

be seen that stable conditions are imposed upon the rising air at a lower level than in the previous case discussed. In this particular example unstable air rises to C where condensation occurs, and it proceeds with a reduced adiabatic lapse rate (for saturated air) but does not reach heights where freezing occurs because of the halt which is forced upon it at K, above which stable conditions prevail.

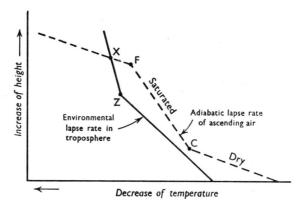

FIG. 12.8.—Ascent of Unstable Air halted by a Decrease in the Lapse Rate in the Troposphere at a High Level

The various examples which have been discussed are merely a few of the many possible histories of ascending air. In addition to the variations of the environmental lapse rate in the troposphere, which affect the limits to which air may rise, there are two other factors to bear in mind. Firstly, the greater the disparity between the tem-

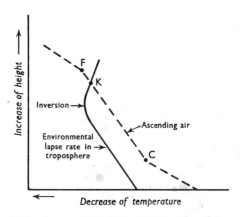

FIG. 12.9.—Ascent of Unstable Air halted by an Inversion

perature of the heated air, which is about to rise, and the temperature of the surrounding air at the base of the troposphere, the greater is the possible instability. This difference is shown in Fig. 12.10, where the environmental lapse rate remains unaltered, and whilst warm air at

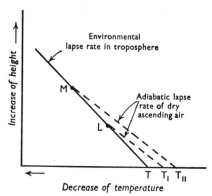

FIG. 12.10.—Varying Instability, dependent on the Original Temperature of the Rising Air

T, will rise to L, the warmer air at T„ will rise higher to M before it becomes stable. Secondly, the higher the humidity of the air that is about to ascend, the lower will be the condensation level beyond which it proceeds at the reduced adiabatic lapse rate for saturated air, and this means that it is relatively more unstable than if it had a lower humidity at the start. This difference is also shown diagrammatically in Fig. 12.11, in which it is assumed that the environmental lapse rate of the troposphere and the initial temperature of the rising air

are constant. These various factors, the environmental lapse rate in the troposphere, the initial temperature of the rising air, and its humidity, are all variable, and since they interact with one another it is obvious that the possibilities are limitless.

XY - *Same height in each part of diagram*
C - *Condensation level*

FIG. 12.11.—Varying Instability, dependent on the Humidity of the Rising Air

(In these diagrams ' dry air ' means that it is unsaturated).

Tropopause

It has been mentioned that the environmental lapse rate usually decreases at high levels in the troposphere. Above a certain level, which is not constant, the temperature becomes steady and may, in fact, increase to some extent. This change occurs at an inversion level called the tropopause—the effective limit of ascending air, assuming that unstable conditions have permitted air to rise so high. The tropopause separates the upper troposphere from the lower stratosphere. Its level is higher over low latitudes than over high latitudes of the earth's surface and it varies in height with the season of the year, especially in mid-latitudes. On the average, it lies about ten miles above the Equator and less than seven miles above the poles. At such heights, the temperatures are very low but a low tropopause is relatively warm with temperatures in the range of $-40°$ to $-75°$ F whereas at a high tropopause temperatures may be as low as $-100°$ F. The temperature of the troposphere has fallen to freezing point usually at a height of not more than two miles. In the troposphere cloud formation is possible because of unstable conditions which permit upward movement of air, whilst in the stratosphere, clouds are absent, thus making this layer of the atmosphere suitable for aeroplane flights. The stratosphere is also free from fluctuating pressure distribution which cause air pockets in the troposphere.

Condensation

The condensation of water from vapour in air which has cooled to saturation point is not effected with quite the simplicity which has been suggested. Air may become super-saturated, in that not all the excess water vapour condenses to water as the air cools below the dew point. This is common with air which is very clean. In general, air contains minute particles of impurities which act as nuclei and these initiate condensation in the form of minute droplets of water. These condensation nuclei are often very small fragments of substances, such as ammonium sulphate and sulphuric acid—the products of combustion, particularly, in industrial areas. Larger nuclei of salt are derived from the evaporation of sea spray. Some authorities regard the latter as the most important of all these nuclei since they are probably present in all rain drops. They are found mostly in the air over the oceans and windward coasts but they also occur inland. Particles in industrial smoke are particularly hygroscopic (that is, they will absorb water from vapour very readily) and may induce condensation in air that is far from being saturated.

Condensation is manifest in the atmosphere as fog and clouds; by the precipitation of rain, snow, hail, and sleet; as well as by the formation of dew and hoar frost at ground level. It is thus obvious that ice may be formed in the air by condensation. We may note that water may be cooled far below freezing point, and yet remain liquid as super-cooled water. In fact, small quantities of pure water will not freeze until super-cooled to temperatures of the order of −40° C (−40° F). However, other nuclei in the air help the water to freeze at higher temperatures than this. Particles of clay minerals and various insoluble substances will induce super-cooled water to freeze at temperatures between −10° C (14° F) and −15° C (5° F). It will be seen later (p. 200) how the existence of super-cooled water and ice together in clouds is of importance in the formation of large rain drops.

Clouds

Clouds are divisible into two main groups which are related to the stability and instability of the troposphere:

1. Layered (or stratiform) clouds show a fairly horizontal stratification and little vertical extension (Fig. 12.12). The most common form of layered cloud is known as stratus. Fog is closely related to this form of cloud, and if fog is forced to rise from the surface of the earth it will develop into low stratus cloud. A stable troposphere is essential for the development of layered clouds. The stratification and the slight depth of layered clouds result from rising air halting at, or just above, condensation level because of the stability of the troposphere at that height. Not infrequently a line of layered clouds marks the level of a temperature inversion. If dry air rises to such an inversion level without condensation of water, it is usual to see a continuous line of smoke haze in place of stratus cloud.

2. Heap (or cumuliform) clouds are developed when there is considerable uplift of air by convectional currents assisted by instability which causes these clouds to have a much greater vertical extension than the layered forms. There is a distinction amongst heap clouds which is dependent upon whether the ascent of the air is limited or unlimited. In the first case the vertical development of the cloud is limited by the rising air entering a stable layer of the troposphere, usually at an inversion level. On the other hand, heap clouds may form in a troposphere in which instability persists to great heights, and then the clouds may show an upward extension so that their tops are as high as the tropopause. One of the most common heap clouds is known as cumulus (Fig. 12.5.). Heap clouds, with their marked vertical extension, are not individually stratified, but groups of these clouds may show a certain amount of layering (Fig 12.12.).

In addition there are very high cirrus clouds which resemble feathers or appear as mere wisps of cloud composed entirely of ice crystals. Like many clouds they show both stratiform and cumuliform features (Figs. 12.12 and 12.14).

FIG. 12.12.—Layered and Heap Clouds

Most of these clouds are layered but the lower ones also show cumuliform features.

Clouds may also be grouped according to their level in the troposphere, into high, medium, and low clouds. The cloud diagram (Fig. 12.13) shows the appearance of the most common clouds and their average levels above the earth's surface. The inner part of the diagram may be regarded as a triangle having cirrus, stratus, and cumulus clouds at its apices, and intermediate types along its three sides. The very high clouds may be stratiform (cirro-stratus), in the form of a thin, whitish sheet, and others may be cumuliform (cirro-cumulus), composed of many small rounded cloud masses which are arranged in lines, thus resembling the sand ripples on a seashore. Stratocumulus cloud resembles both stratus and cumulus (Figs. 15.1 and 18.6). Like cirro-cumulus cloud, it consists of detached masses of cumuliform cloud which are often in parallel bands, although the individual masses often appear to overlap one another. Lying between the very high cirrus group and the low clouds are the alto-cumulus and the alto-stratus types, which are similar to, but thicker than, cirrocumulus and cirro-stratus clouds respectively. Two other clouds appear on the diagram and both may have very great vertical development, in that their bases are low and yet their tops may be as lofty as some of the high clouds. These clouds are called nimbo-stratus and cumulo-nimbus. The former has a fairly low stratified base, with a shapeless and massive top, whilst the latter appears from

197

Fig. 12.13.—Cloud Diagram

After J. Osborn Fuller

Ci — Cirrus Cs — Cirro-stratus Cc — Cirro-cumulus Cu — Cumulus
As — Alto-straus Ac — Alto-cumulus St — Stratus Sc — Strato-cumulus
Ns — Nimbo-stratus Cb — Cumulo-nimbus

Paul Popper Ltd.

Fig. 12.14.—Cirrus Clouds

These cirrus clouds are above part of Antarctica. The glacier on the right is entering the Barne Inlet and the foreground shows part of the Ross Ice Shelf. In the distance are seen strato-cumulus clouds.

below rather like a nimbo-stratus cloud, but it towers up to very great heights with cumuliform characteristics and often with a peculiar flat top, elongated at one end like an anvil, which marks an inversion. Both of these clouds are productive of heavy rainfall, and the cumulo-nimbus cloud is associated with thunderstorms (Fig. 14.4).

In some cases, it would seem that strato-cumulus, alto-cumulus, and cirro-cumulus clouds may form by the disintegration of earlier-formed stratiform clouds. Convection or shear waves may break the clouds into a series of cloudlets. Cirrus clouds are very thin, because convective conditions have reached the highest limits of the troposphere where the slight condensation which is possible is in the form of ice particles rather than water drops. Ice crystals are responsible for the haloes produced by the light of the sun or moon shining through various types of thin high cloud.

Stratus cloud may develop into nimbo-stratus by a considerable vertical extension, and this results in quite heavy rainfall from the upper layers of the cloud, although the rain appears to come from the base of a layered cloud. In cumulo-nimbus cloud the cumulus type has developed on similar lines, but to even greater heights,

199

where its top, at a height of some 20,000 feet, has temperatures of the order of $-20°$ C, or less. It is quite common for great upthrusts of cumuliform cloud to rise out of a cloud mass. Such upthrusts indicate the presence of a local column of air which is unstable. These upthrusts are much better seen from aeroplanes than from ground level. Although rain may fall from most clouds it is only from those of great vertical development, such as nimbo-stratus and cumulo-nimbus, that heavy rain can be expected.

Precipitation

The water or ice formed in clouds by condensation may descend mainly as rain, snow or hail. This precipitation may not reach the ground, since it may evaporate in unsaturated air lying below the cloud, or be sustained aloft by strong up-currents in the air or the cloud. Initial condensation of water in clouds is in the form of minute droplets but for a rain drop of average size (about 1 mm in radius) to form, something like a million cloud droplets must join together in some way or another.

When only water droplets are condensing it is more or less impossible for many large drops to develop. If the concentration of the condensation nuclei is low then, by condensation alone, some rain drops may form but these are unlikely to produce significant rainfall.

The presence of super-cooled water droplets and ice particles in clouds which are below freezing point (such will happen normally where the cloud is about two miles high) has been regarded for many years as essential for the development of large-scale rainfall. Super-cooled water can evaporate in such clouds and then condense on the ice particles as ice and not as water. This process leads to a very considerable growth in the ice crystals, so that they fall through the air and melt at lower levels, forming large drops of water. As these pass still lower, they tend to pick up more water by collision with cloud droplets—thus, within certain limits, they continue to grow.

Rain drops may form in clouds that are above freezing point by collision between droplets. Some droplets are relatively large and can sweep up smaller droplets to form rain drops, but only light rain or drizzle will develop in this way.

Collisions between ice crystals produce snow flakes by a process known as aggregation. Between temperatures of $0°$ C and $-4°$ C, quite large flakes may form and change to rain on falling to lower levels. When snow flakes collide with super-cooled water droplets accretion occurs and the water droplets freeze on the flakes as rime (rime is white, opaque ice). Hail may also form, particularly, if there is a large liquid content in the cloud.

Snow and hail start to melt when they fall below the freezing level in the air. Hail can persist to the ground even when this freezing level is as high as $2\frac{1}{2}$ miles, but usually snow has melted by the time it has fallen a kilometre below the freezing level. Snow will persist if the air is very cold or dry near ground level. Continuous falls of snow are sometimes caused by the chilling of the lower air by the earlier-melting snow, which removes heat from the air, so that the later-falling snow succeeds in reaching the ground. Sleet is a transitional stage between water and snow, or, it may be partially melted snow.

It is of interest to note that, in Australia, rain has been produced by the introduction of crystals of solid carbon dioxide into the upper parts of clouds from which no rain has fallen. In England, similar experiments proved unsuccessful in an attempt to end a prolonged drought in 1947. Scientists have yet to find out the necessary conditions required to precipitate rain from clouds by artificial means.

The nature of precipitation from stratiform clouds is markedly different from that associated with cumuliform clouds. Fairly gentle, but persistent, rain or drizzle lasting many hours is typical of the former clouds, whereas relatively short-lived showers (rarely lasting more than an hour) with heavy rain are more usual from cumuliform clouds.

The measurement of precipitation and its distribution in the world are discussed in Chapter 14.

Mist and Fog

Various cooling processes other than adiabatic ones may lead to the condensation of water in the lower levels of the troposphere with the formation of mist or fog. There is no essential difference between mist and fog other than the greater reduction of visibility which occurs with the latter. At meteorological stations fog is recorded when the visibility is less than one kilometre. Evaporation may take place from a water surface, or a shallow surface layer of very humid air which is warm, into a superior layer of cooler air in the lower part of which, after saturation occurs, there will be condensation if water continues to evaporate from below. In this process a very thin mist may form such as gives 'steaming' over a lake surface that is overlain by cold morning or night air. The vertical extent of such mists is slight and they rarely persist for long.

Condensation frequently occurs when fairly humid air lies over, or passes over, a surface which is very cold. Such surfaces are usually cooled through the radiation of heat, which is taking place at all times from the surface of the land, and also, from particles of solid material in the troposphere. During most days insolation more than makes good this loss of heat, but at night, when insolation is absent, much heat is lost from the surface of the land, particularly when the night is cloudless. It is with radiation chilling that the temperature of the air in contact with these surfaces is reduced very readily to the dew point. The water droplets that form may collect on the ground as dew, or, if the temperature is low enough, a cover of hoar frost will be formed. Rime, which is very much coarser in texture than hoar frost, is produced by super-cooled water freezing on a cold surface. In the lowest layer of the troposphere which lies above a chilled surface condensation takes place on solid particles, and radiation fog or mist is formed, at first just above ground level. Such fog or mist may extend upwards if there are slight winds which can produce a certain amount of turbulence that creates a vertical spread of the chilled air. This results in an increase of condensation and a thickening of the fog layer. Obviously dead calm will not give this necessary turbulence, but if the winds are moderately strong, with speeds of more than 8 or 10 m.p.h., their turbulent effect is too great, and the chilled air is dispersed too widely and too rapidly for the temperature of the higher layers to be lowered to their dew point. The density of the fog may be increased by the loss of heat from the particles upon which condensation occurs, since they, too, are capable of radiating heat.

Although such radiation fogs may develop at any season in Britain, they are most common in autumn and winter. In the former season, which is characterized by fairly calm and clear weather of anticyclonic origin (see p. 215), there is an intensification of radiation at night which produces relatively greater chilling, whilst in winter the longer and colder nights are conducive to well-developed fogs. The persistence of a fog is dependent upon the difficulties of its dispersion. The most effective agent for this dispersion is a strong wind, but insolation in the daytime is helpful in creating convection currents which in turn produce vigorous turbulence. In winter, with deeper fogs and less insolation, the period required for dispersion may be prolonged until the warming of the lower layers of the fog is sufficiently advanced. Again, in winter, low temperature means that cold air, which is more readily saturated than warm air, will require heating before it can accommodate the evaporated water from a fog.

Fogs in densely populated areas, particularly those which are industrial, are often more pronounced than those that form in rural areas. This is largely explained by the presence of abundant hygroscopic particles in the air of towns that readily cause condensation of water drops from air which is far from being saturated. Observations show that the upper level of many fogs is coincident with a temperature inversion. Such an inversion may be detected on a clear day by a fairly horizontal layer of smoke. An inversion is also responsible for a high fog, which may consist very largely of a layer of densely clustered particles, with or without condensation features. At street level, in a large town, with such a fog visibility may be perfect, although the sky above is completely obscured, so that it appears like night. Much of the sun's heat that is required at ground level for fog dispersion is either reflected from the upper surface of the fog layer or absorbed by the particles in the fog, in which case the temperature of the air at the inversion level is increased, thus strengthening the inversion and helping to prolong the fog.

Some fogs are produced by advection, when warm, humid air moves more or less horizontally over a cold surface. Such fogs are common in our winter, when a prolonged spell of radiational chilling and severe frost is followed by mild weather, with winds of oceanic origin. They are rarely persistent over land areas, since the warm air stream will soon cause an increase of temperature in the colder land surface, with a resultant evaporation of the fog. Sea fogs are advective, and are usually developed in the neighbourhood of cold sea currents, as along the coasts of Peru and California, although they are very common in offshore tropical air masses which have dew points exceeding the sea temperatures. In polar regions pack-ice surfaces produce in much the same way a shallow layer of mist or fog which is called 'sea smoke'.

The fogs off Newfoundland are of particular interest since they form despite the presence of strong winds which normally prevent the formation of fog. In this region the mixing of warm and almost saturated air, blowing from the south, with cold humid air from the north results in very heavy condensation of water vapour as fog. These fogs are certainly related to the temperature contrast in the air over the warm Gulf Stream drift and the cold Labrador current.

CHAPTER 13

Air Masses, Depressions, and Associated Systems

Air Masses

Weather conditions in many parts of the world are dependent upon the interaction of air masses. An air mass is a very large part of the lower troposphere which covers a very extensive area of an ocean or continent known as the source region, and which has certain meteorological characteristics. Important changes may occur in these characteristics as a result of the movement of the air mass from its source region. The usual sources of air masses are the main centres of dispersal of air, and these are essentially the chief zones of high-pressure air. It has been shown that the location of the fairly permanent high-pressure areas is over the oceans in subtropical latitudes and in the polar regions, to which must be added those which develop in winter over the continents of North America and Eurasia (Fig. 13.3). Air masses may be classed as polar or tropical, according to the temperature at the source, and as maritime or continental, according to the humidity at the source. Polar air masses will be colder than tropical ones, whilst maritime masses will be more humid than continental ones. There may be distinguished four primary types of air mass, namely, polar maritime, polar continental, tropical maritime, and tropical continental. There are only two large source regions of tropical continental air, namely, the Saharan area and central Australia. Other sources are south-western U.S.A. and Mexico, Northern India and small areas in South Africa and South America, all of which are typical of summer only.

When air masses move from their sources, the effects are varied, and the precise history of the changes which occur is not known in the majority of cases with anything like accuracy. In general, a tropical air mass which moves polewards will tend to be cooled by the surfaces over which it passes, and conversely a polar air mass, moving equatorwards, will be warmed. It is, however, only the lower layer of an air mass which is so affected, the upper part remains relatively unaltered in regard to its temperature. These changes, which occur in the vertical distribution of the temperature within air masses as they move from their sources, tend to produce a fairly high degree of stability at the base of a tropical air mass and of instability in a polar air mass. Fig. 13.1 shows how the lapse rates within these two types of air mass change with their movement. The full lines represent the lapse rate at

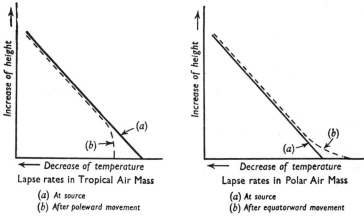

FIG. 13.1.—Lapse Rates in Tropical and Polar Air Masses

the source, and the broken lines show the changed lapse rate after movement of the air mass in question. Reference to Fig. 13.2 will show the relative instability of the polar air mass, since ascending air would halt at X in the tropical mass, but would rise to Y in the polar

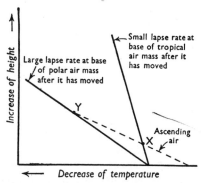

FIG. 13.2.—Instability at Base of Air Masses
Note scale is greater than that of Fig. 13.1.

mass. Air masses which move from ocean surfaces on to continental areas, or vice versa, will also be transformed by the changes in their humidity. For instance, when a tropical maritime air mass moves from an ocean to a fairly cool land surface it will tend to become very stable in its lower layers, whilst a polar continental air mass, moving out over an ocean, will become unstable. On the contrary, a tropical maritime air mass moving on to a very hot continental surface will become very unstable with the production of copious rainfall as experienced on many tropical coasts with prevalent onshore winds.

It is over the oceans that the interaction between air masses is most likely to occur, and so there are shown in Fig. 13.3 three lines at which moving air masses converge. These lines are known as the polar fronts of the north and south, and the intertropical front. These

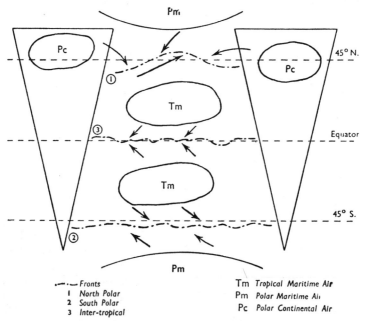

—·— Fronts
1 North Polar
2 South Polar
3 Inter-tropical

Tm Tropical Maritime Air
Pm Polar Maritime Air
Pc Polar Continental Air

FIG. 13.3.—Distribution of the Chief Air Mass Sources and the Interaction of Air Masses at Fronts (generalized)

various fronts are often discontinuous on a world map, but they usually run, more or less, in an east-west direction, although, locally, they may trend otherwise. When two air masses, one of tropical and the other of polar origin, meet at one of the polar fronts there is usually a considerable difference in their respective temperatures and humidities. This contrast results in the release of kinetic energy which, in combination with the effect of the earth's rotation, leads to the formation of a depression (or cyclonic disturbance). Into equatorial regions air masses move from north and south, and converge at the intertropical front, but as the opposed air masses are alike in regard to both temperature and humidity, because of the similarity of their sources (over warm ocean surfaces), the subsequent development of depressions is practically impossible.

Formation of Depressions in the Northern Hemisphere[1]

The effects, which result from the interaction of two air masses of polar and tropical origin respectively, are considerable. Whilst fronts which separate converging air masses are represented by lines on maps, such as in Fig. 13.3, it is important to realise that, in fact, the air masses are lying above and below a gently-sloping frontal zone which extends from the earth's surface towards the tropopause.

(a) At surface of earth   (b) Section of Troposphere (not to scale)

FIG. 13.4.—A Front showing Frontal Zone

Fig. 13.4 may help to clarify this. XY in Fig. 13.4a shows a part of the northern polar front, as on a map. In Fig. 13.4b, a section across this front along AB shows that the frontal zone has a depth of the order of a mile and a slope of about 1 in 100. Thus, it would meet the tropopause at a distance of some 500–600 miles on the cold side of the front. With such a gentle slope the front is some 60–100 miles in width at the earth's surface. The arrows, in Fig. 13.4b, show tropical air rising along the upper side of the frontal zone whilst cold, dense polar air lies below. The frontal zone must be regarded as occupied by warm and cold air which are mixing with one another. As has been mentioned elsewhere (p. 195), temperatures at the tropopause are usually less than $-40°$ F and, at this height, the air which has risen is tropical only in the sense of its origin. The term 'front' refers both to the front at the earth's surface and to the frontal zone in most accounts of these two features. The simple front XY, in Fig. 13.4a, is rarely maintained and becomes modified by the development of a bulge (Fig. 13.5) which alters the relative direction of the air flows on either side of the front at the earth's surface. This bulge or frontal wave upsets locally the balance between the two air masses

[1] Whilst the following five sections of this chapter describe depressions in the northern hemisphere, the facts given are fundamentally true for depressions in the southern hemisphere.

at the surface. It is probably initiated by several causes such as a local increase in the contrast between the temperatures of each air mass whilst, in some instances, relief features on land are responsible. The frontal wave can be looked upon as a forward thrust of warm air at X, and this is followed by a similar thrust of cold air at Y (Fig. 13.5). These two thrusts produce a wave, resulting, it is thought, from shear at the frontal surface, and this travels along the front at the surface level of the earth, and in most cases in an easterly direction, irrespective of the hemisphere in which it occurs. With this movement the part of the front at X is known as the warm front, since at the surface of the earth warm air will appear to advance at the expense of cold air, and the other part at Y is known as a cold front, for here cold air is advancing and replacing warm air at ground level. The moving wave constitutes a depression.

FIG. 13.5.—The Development of a Frontal Wave (Plan)

The earliest accounts of depressions showed the relationship between wind and pressure distributions, together with the associated weather. Very simply a depression was a system of low-pressure air which was indicated by isobars that formed an oval pattern (Fig. 13.6), and with wind directions as shown. It will be noticed that Fig. 13.5 shows a comparable circulation of air although less well developed. Clearly the injection of warmer air at the surface inside the bulge at the front will induce low-pressure air, since it will consist of relatively light air. The later history of the depression depends on the moving wave, which may migrate along the front as a minor disturbance, with little or no change from its initial state, or it may develop very considerably. If the wave has a wave-length of very much less than about 600 miles, it is not likely to develop, but migrates along the front until it is destroyed by frictional effects. When the wave-length is about 600 miles the wave is likely to evolve into a vigorous depression. The wave of Fig. 13.5 becomes

FIG. 13.6.—Pattern of Isobars in a Depression (Northern Hemisphere)

much deeper, as in Fig. 13.7a, with further complexity of air-flow directions. The tropical air at the surface of the earth occupies a zone known as the warm sector, which is bounded by the warm and cold fronts. Sections through Fig. 13.7a will clarify the directions of the air movements in relation to the two fronts (Fig. 13.7b and c). In both sections it will be seen that the warm air is being lifted above colder air.

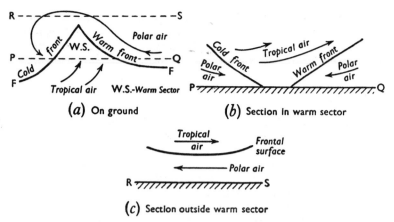

(a) On ground (b) Section in warm sector

(c) Section outside warm sector

Fig. 13.7.—Further Development of the Frontal Wave

Occlusions

A further stage in the development of the depression concerns the relative positions of the fronts to one another. As the disturbance progresses eastwards, each front will move in that direction, but the cold front will often overtake the warm front (Fig. 13.8*a–c*). The result is that the air of the warm sector is being lifted more and more from the ground. This process is called an occlusion, and it culminates with the elimination of the warm front at the ground where warm air has been completely replaced by colder air. Occlusions are of two types, warm front and cold front. In the former the warm air is lifted up the surface of the warm front, and in the latter it moves up the cold front (Fig. 13.8*d* and *e*—these sections refer to XY in *c*).

The low pressure which forms at the centre of a depression in its earliest stages is focused at the junction of the two fronts (Fig. 13.8). With the evolution of the depression and the extension of the occlusion, the focus of low pressure usually remains at the end of the occluded front, whilst the junction of the active fronts shifts from the centre of low pressure; at the same time the low pressure deepens and becomes more extensive (Fig. 13.8*c*). It will be noticed (Fig. 13.7) that the lower layers of air in the depression are mainly of polar origin, and the tropical air at the surface decreases with the shrinking warm sector in the later stage of the history of the depression. However, there is a contrast between parts of the polar air since some has been transformed by a longer passage across an ocean surface, and this is partly responsible for the continued energy of the depression. Once this contrast in polar air disappears the depression virtually ceases to exist. As most depressions are of oceanic origin they usually though not necessarily, die out near to coastal areas or over land

209

masses where the contrast between air masses is reduced to a minimum. The weather conditions associated with the fronts of a vigorous depression are significant to the geographer. Two considerations must be borne in mind when discussing these fronts: (*a*) the polar air

(*a*) Depression with fully developed warm sector

(*b*) Cold front overtaking warm front to produce an occluded front

(*c*) Occluded front is much extended and warm sector has almost disappeared

(*d*) Warm front occlusion

(*e*) Cold front occlusion

P — Polar Air

Warm Front

T — Tropical Air

Cold Front

L Low Pressure

Isobars

Occluded Front

FIG. 13.8.—Frontal History of a Depression

is becoming unstable whilst the tropical air increases its stability, and (*b*) tropical air is being lifted above polar air in the depression.

Weather at a Warm Front

The warm front shows a succession of condensation features, either as clouds or in the form of precipitation (Fig. 13.9). In reading this diagram one must realize that X is a point on the surface of the earth well ahead of the warm front (WF) and that in the course of time conditions as shown at Y in the warm sector will have progressed to X. At the time indicated by the section, tropical air lies high above X, perhaps near the top of the troposphere, where it has been lifted by the wedge of cold air. The stable nature of the tropical air in the warm sector is reflected by the stratiform clouds. Ascent of tropical air has resulted in filamented cirrus clouds high up, and well forward, above X. These clouds are replaced by a succession of stratiform clouds which cover the whole sky and become lower as the front at the ground approaches the observer. Surface winds are likely to be easterly or south-easterly and are accompanied by fairly low temperatures. Detached stratus and cumulus clouds move westwards in this polar air. Precipitation is seen to fall from most of

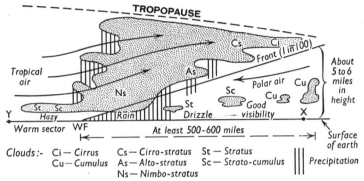

Clouds:—
Ci — Cirrus   Cs — Cirro-stratus   St — Stratus
Cu — Cumulus   As — Alto-stratus   Sc — Strato-cumulus
                Ns — Nimbo-stratus

||| Precipitation

Based on a figure in 'A Course in Elementary Meteorology', with the sanction of the Controller of H.M. Stationery Office

FIG. 13.9.—Section through a Warm Front

these clouds but the ice crystals, that fall from the forward cirrus clouds, rarely reach the ground as they turn to vapour in the cold polar air. Near the front rain appears to fall from nimbo-stratus clouds but these obscure alto-stratus clouds above. Much of the rain starts to fall as snow, particularly from the higher clouds.

With the passage of the warm front and the arrival of the warm sector at X rain ceases, apart from drizzle, temperature rises, and stable stratiform clouds prevail. Pressure falls quite markedly, and the wind changes from easterly to westerly or south-westerly. Advection fog is common in winter as the warm front passes over the point of observation, bringing damp air in contact with cold ground. The warm sector is characterized by stable air which is reflected in the poor visibility, caused by haze produced by dust particles which hang in the air below an inversion level. However, light rain or drizzle may accompany the passage of the warm sector.

Weather at a Cold Front

There is also a succession of clouds and precipitation associated with the passage of a cold front. Reference to Fig. 13.10 will show that the polar air advances from behind the cold front CF and that the frontal zone has a steeper slope than is the case with a warm front. Rising tropical air often moves opposite to the flow of polar air below. Ascent of the stable tropical air produces a mass of stratiform clouds similar in type to those at a warm front except that, with the relatively steep inclination of the front, the lateral extent of the clouds and the belt of precipitation are much reduced. With the passage of the cold front, winds change from south-west to north-west, accompanied by a fall in temperature and a rise in pressure.

Clouds:-
Ci — Cirrus   St — Stratus   Cu — Cumulus
Cs — Cirro-stratus   Sc — Strato-cumulus   Cb — Cumulo-nimbus ||| Precipitation
Ac — Alto-cumulus   As — Alto-stratus   Ns — Nimbo-stratus

Based on a figure in 'A Course in Elementary Meteorology', with the sanction of the Controller of H.M. Stationery Office

FIG. 13.10.—Section through a Cold Front

Once the cold front has passed there is usually a rapid improvement in visibility, associated with the unstable polar air. Detached cumulus and cumulo-nimbus clouds appear, often these produce heavy showers of rain.

Observations show that both warm and cold fronts can vary considerably. It is by no means uncommon for clouds to be limited to the lower levels of the troposphere when only fairly thick stratiform clouds are found in the tropical air. Usually it is a temperature inversion which prevents high clouds from developing. In fact, tropical air from above subsides and is largely cloud-free. Under these circumstances, it is generally found that the tropical air above a cold front moves in the same direction as the polar air below and not as shown in Fig. 13.10. At fronts, with subsiding tropical air, the succession of weather takes longer to pass an observer than is the case with the more active fronts described above. At best, light rain will fall but much of the precipitation is in the form of drizzle. In conclusion, it may be noted that every front has its own variety of weather so that it is well nigh impossible to speak of a typical warm or cold front. Furthermore, it is rare for both fronts in a given depression to show equal activity. Hence in part, the vagaries of British weather are explained.

Observation of the Passage of a Depression

In Britain the weather changes indicated at the two types of front are fairly common. It is possible to observe these changes, although the picture which has been drawn may not be seen in full until very many observations have been made. Unfortunately, it is not easy to see the whole sequence in one period, for the passage of a depression takes several hours, and in many cases some of these hours will be nocturnal. The speed of eastward movement of most depressions cannot be determined accurately, but it is unlikely to exceed 30 m.p.h. As shown in Fig. 13.9, the high forward cirrus clouds may be five miles above ground level at X, and at least 400–500 miles ahead of WF, the warm front. Thus the gradual overclouding and the arrival of the warm front is likely to take more than twelve hours from the time of the first appearance of high cloud. The warm sector may take several more hours in which to pass, although this period will be reduced if the observer lies in the track of the junction of the warm and cold fronts or relatively near to this track. Then, after the cold front has passed the point of observation there will be several hours before the final stage of the disturbance arrives. Changes of wind direction from south-east or east in the early stages of the depression to south-west in the warm sector and to west or north-west behind the cold front, accompanied by varying temperatures, may be noted quite easily. It is possible to observe the lower clouds moving westwards in the polar air and to see higher clouds passing eastwards in the tropical air or vice versa according to the type of front. The passage of a warm front may be detected by the physiological reactions of the body; the change from cool or moderately warm easterly air streams to mild or even quite warm south-westerly air with high humidity creates a sense of mugginess, which may occur at any time in the day or night. Almost invariably, a period of muggy weather in the warm sector is followed by the chilliness of the polar air advancing behind the cold front of a passing depression. Students may practise sky reading and other observations by daytime in relation to the foregoing account.

If the track of the centre of the depression lies to the south of the observer, then only polar air will be encountered at ground level. The front between polar and tropical air is entirely elevated, but there may be some contrast between the forward and the rear masses of polar air, so that with the eastward progression of the depression there will be temperature changes and a decline of pressure near the centre. Precipitation is from similar clouds to those at a warm front although they are well aloft. If, on the other hand, the centre of the

213

depression passes well to the north of the observer then, in all probability, there will be an extended period of warm sector weather.

Another possible weather sequence is that of the occluded, or partially occluded, depression. The rain belt is more extensive, and this is particularly true of a partially occluded depression where the rain belts of the warm and cold fronts have merged into one large zone of precipitation.

Depressions in each Hemisphere

The establishment of a depression as has been shown, is dependent upon the meeting of two air masses of different quality. In the northern hemisphere, where the unequal distribution of land and sea leads to the rather special development of both continental and marine features, there is a number of recognizable fronts at which depressions may occur. In the southern hemisphere the distribution of land and sea is such that the predominance of sea areas results in a more simple pattern of fronts. Only the southern fringes of the continents in the south are affected by depressions, and the rain, which so frequently associated with the westerly winds of the Roaring Forties (between 40° and 50° S), is largely frontal in origin. One distinction should be made between depressions in the two hemispheres. The distinction is in the movement of the winds about the centre of the depressions; in the north it is anticlockwise, whereas in the south it is clockwise (see Fig. 11.9, p. 183).

In the past, some frontal waves have been described as secondary depressions and others, with marked discontinuities of the isobars, have been referred to as V-shaped depressions (or troughs of low pressure). Both these features are no longer officially recognized in Britain. However reference to troughs of low pressure is still made.

Families of Depressions

It is quite common for a cold front wave to develop on the polar front which trails behind an occluding depression. There may be a sequence of such events giving a family of four or five depressions, each being separated by thrusts of polar air which penetrate into successively lower latitudes on each occasion. Each surge of polar air produces a tongue of high pressure, with cool, if not cold, weather and, generally, clear skies. The family ends with an eruption of polar air into very low latitudes, and before another group of depressions can form there must be a complete reformation of the polar front with an advance of tropical air into high latitudes.

Anticyclones

Anticyclones (or highs) are systems of high pressure which appear on weather maps with widely-spaced isobars (Fig. 13.11)—thus, they have weak pressure gradients and light winds. Their circulation is the reverse of that of a depression—clockwise in the northern hemisphere and anticlockwise in the southern world. Anticyclones are relatively passive systems, without clear-cut characteristics, and are, therefore, in marked contrast to the active depressions which they often separate. The most significant characteristic of anticyclones is that, in the middle and lower troposphere, the air subsides and thus diverges at the earth's surface.

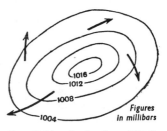

Fig. 13.11.—Anticyclone (Northern Hemisphere)

Anticyclones may be divided into two main groups, cold and warm. The former type is characterized by cold, dense air in the lower troposphere, with relatively warm air above a level of about 10,000 feet. Cold anticyclones are relatively shallow features and are related particularly to the surface chill of the polar regions. In winter, the Arctic high may extend well south over the northern lands, giving clear skies and very low temperatures. Antarctica is similarly covered by a fairly shallow cold anticyclone but the considerable height of the Antarctic ice surface means that the high continent occupies much of the space which would otherwise be taken up by the anticyclone. At times, depressions may penetrate into the Antarctic coastlands (p. 337). Short-lived cold anticyclones often form as ridges of polar air between depressions in our latitudes and a more lasting ridge of this type may develop in the rear of a family of depressions. In most cold anticyclones there is a marked inversion of temperature not far above the ground and it is here that some cloud may form, giving small amounts of rain and drizzle.

Warm anticyclones have relatively warm air near the earth's surface but above is relatively cold dense air which is responsible for producing the characteristic high pressure. Warm anticyclones are essentially areas of descending air. The descent of the air is determined, primarily, by the general circulation in the troposphere—thus warm anticyclones of a more or less permanent nature are found over the oceans in sub-tropical latitudes. The North Atlantic anticyclone of this type is usually centred over the Azores. Then, Britain receives variable weather from depressions which develop on the northern side of this high. On the other hand, if the Azores anticyclone spreads north and eastwards to cover parts of Western Europe, Britain may have very settled and calm weather, with clear skies and radiation fog which, in winter, may be quite persistent and accompanied by frosts. In summer, under these conditions, dry warm

215

weather develops over land, but fog is not uncommon both near and over the sea.

Anticyclones may develop temporarily over some areas as extensions of polar and sub-tropical highs.. Such extensions tend to form north–south ridges in the westerly wind belt of the northern world and they divert or block depressions from their courses. Such blocking anticyclones are common both to the east and west of Britain. For instance, a ridge of high pressure air may link the Azores and Greenland so that very cold air flows, on its eastern side, southward over Britain. A high over Scandinavia, in winter, may give Britain a spell of very cold weather with easterly winds. A depression moving on the south side of such a high may bring heavy snowfalls to southern Britain, with drifting in the east winds. In summer, very warm spells of weather may occur when tropical continental air of Saharan origin covers Scandinavia—these warm spells may persist for several days but they usually end with thundery weather.

Cols

Two tongues of high pressure, one usually of polar origin and the other of subtropical origin, may separate two zones of low pressure, or in some instances two adjacent depressions of a family. The isobaric pattern (Fig. 13.12) resembles that of the topographic col on contour maps, hence the name. Rather varied weather is characteristic of a col, and winds

FIG. 13.12.—A Col

may blow from various directions. With the meeting of air from different sources, fronts may form in the col.

Tropical Cyclones

So far the depressions which have been described have occurred in middle latitudes. Depressions do arise in the tropics but, in general, they move westwards. The deflecting force which is set up by the rotation of the earth is nil at the Equator so that the formation of depressions there is well-nigh impossible. Tropical depressions develop on either side of the Equator, usually between 10° and 20° of latitude, north and south and rarely, if ever, between 5° N and 5° S.

The most recent investigations show that these depressions form first as weak troughs of low pressure in the zone which is usually occupied by the trade winds. Some of these troughs, moving from the east, develop into very active storms known as tropical cyclones.[1] These intense depressions form over ocean surfaces with high temperatures of the order of, at least, 80° F (or 27° C)—if the water is slightly cooler than this, tropical cyclones are unlikely to develop. Strong instability of the warm, humid air, over such sea surfaces, induces its ascent, with the production of very intense rainfall. The condensation releases much energy which maintains the intense storm and, the warmer the sea, the greater is the energy released in this way. Unlike temperate depressions these tropical cyclones have no system of fronts and they appear on maps with almost circular and very closely-spaced isobars. The pressure in the central part, or eye, commonly falls to 920–900 millibars (the lowest recorded pressure in such a storm was 877 millibars). Tropical cyclones often have a breadth of, at least, 200 miles (Fig. 13.13) and near the ocean

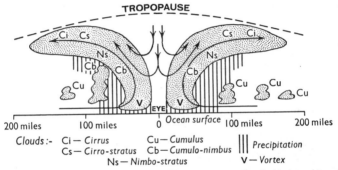

Clouds:-   Ci — *Cirrus*   Cu — *Cumulus* ||| *Precipitation*
        Cs — *Cirro-stratus*   Cb — *Cumulo-nimbus*
           Ns — *Nimbo-stratus*   V — *Vortex*

Based on a figure in 'A Course in Elementary Meteorology,' with the sanction of the Controller of H.M. Stationery Office

FIG. 13.13.—Structure of a Tropical Cyclone

surface a spiral of air, or vortex, moves inwards with the strongest winds. This spiral is between 10 and 20 miles from the centre and forms a ring around the central area (or eye) which is of the order of 5–10 miles in radius. The vortex is characterized by massive convective clouds formed by the rising air of the inward-moving spiral. Cumulus and cumulo-nimbus clouds, accompanied by thunderstorms, pile up and winds may exceed 100 m.p.h., with even stronger gusts up to 180 m.p.h. Rainfall is very heavy—as much as 10 or 20 inches can fall as the storm passes (these depressions move quite slowly so that their passage over any point may take at least 10–12 hours). The most intense rainfall is experienced just outside the ring of strongest winds in the inner part of the vortex. It will be seen from Fig. 13.13 that as the clouds build up towards the tropopause, at about

[1] These are now described by the British Meteorological Office as tropical depressions.

30,000 feet, the spiral moves outwards with the development of nimbo-stratus, cumulo-stratus and cirrus clouds aloft. For a tropical cyclone to persist it seems that divergence of air aloft must be in excess of the convergence of air near the ocean surface—thus convected air is removed.

The eye of the tropical cyclone is occupied by calm, subsiding air with light winds and a few broken clouds. This subsiding air is very warm on reaching the ocean surface and, almost certainly, helps to maintain the low pressure at the centre. The development of the eye is apparently critical for the formation of these intense circulations. The energy of the system is mainly derived from the release of latent heat in the updraught around the eye. The period of calm in the eye, which lasts an hour or so, is followed by the violence of the other side of the vortex as the storm moves on. Here, the wind direction is the reverse of that prevailing in the earlier vortex period. Gradually, air pressure rises as the storm recedes.

The approach of such a storm is marked by the massive pile of convective cloud which is seen as far as 150 miles away by day, and, at night, is detected from a distance of 250 miles by the vivid display of lightning. These tropical cyclones are very destructive and, if they approach closely to the shore of a land mass, they tend to heap up the sea and, thus, inundate coastal towns.

As has been said, tropical cyclones move westwards over oceanic surfaces but something like half the total number of these storms show a recurvature, swinging round the western fringes of one of the sub-tropical high-pressure cells at about 20–30°, north or south, and, thus, away from the Equator. Very often they enter the westerly wind belt on the poleward side of the high-pressure area. The curve followed by the storm is approximately a hyperbola. It is on recurvature that a tropical cyclone may come into close proximity to land areas—if they pass onshore, thus leaving the oceanic source of humid air, their intensity is reduced very rapidly and, assisted by frictional effects of an irregular land surface, they soon become disintegrated. It would seem that recurvature occurs when a tropical cyclone encounters polar air which may lie off eastern shorelands—in particular, on occasions when the polar front is very considerably displaced towards the Equator. Then the tropical cyclone proceeds as a very intense polar front depression, moving more or less eastwards. Occasionally, the remnant of a very active tropical cyclone may bring very destructive winds to Britain. The passage of tropical cyclones from the tropics into temperate latitudes is regarded by some authorities as a factor in helping to maintain the general circulation of the atmosphere, whereby heat is transferred to the relatively cool high latitudes.

In the northern hemisphere, tropical cyclones are most frequent in August and early September whilst, south of the Equator, the very active period is about February and March. Whilst it would appear that their frequency, then, is related to the very warm ocean surfaces it is much more probable that the critical factor is determined by the behaviour of the trade winds at these times. The trade winds tend to withdraw from the shores of lands on the western sides of the oceans late in the hot season, particularly in the Caribbean area and the seas near the Philippine Islands. Normally, above the surface trade winds there lies a very well marked temperature inversion. When the trade winds withdraw from the above mentioned sea areas this inversion becomes very weak so that the great vertical development of cloud, typical of a tropical cyclone, is permissible.

Areas which are most regularly visited by tropical cyclones are the Caribbean zone (hurricanes),[1] the Indian Ocean (cyclones) and, in particular, the south coast of China (typhoons).[2] In the southern hemisphere they are relatively infrequent but the east coasts of most continents are visited by these storms, as is shown by their distribution in Fig. 18.2. The freedom from these depressions which is enjoyed by Brazil seems to be related to the fact that the trade winds do not withdraw from the western side of the South Atlantic Ocean.

Special Winds Associated with Depressions

These winds fall into three groups:

1. Winds associated with the passage of the fronts of depressions.
2. Cold winds, such as the bora and the mistral.
3. Warm winds of the föhn type.

Of the first group it may be said that the winds are typical of all depressions where tropical air streams of the warm sector alternate with polar air streams. In some areas, particularly in the warm temperate latitudes, they have local names. In the Mediterranean Sea basin warm southerly winds blow from the Sahara and are known as the leveche[3] in Spain, sirocco[4] in Italy, and khamsin[5] in Egypt. The cold bora and mistral from the north are discussed below. In California a warm desiccating wind called the Santa Ana[6] is drawn north by depressions in somewhat higher latitudes, whilst cold northers flow southwards over Texas and the Gulf States in the rear of depressions. The cold blizzard of Canada and the buran of Siberia are of similar

---

[1] Hurricanes—god of the storm (in various languages—anglicized to hurricane from the Spanish word 'huracan').

[2] Typhoon—big wind (tai-fung in Chinese).

[3] Leveche—wind from the south.

[4] Sirocco—from the Arabic 'Sharq', meaning the east.

[5] Khamsin—meaning 'fifty', since the wind was said to blow for fifty days.

[6] Santa Ana—the name of the valley down which the wind blows.

origin. In Argentina, eastward-moving depressions may bring the warm zonda in front and the cold pampero in the rear, whilst in South-east Australia there are warm brickfielders and cold southerly bursters associated with troughs of low pressure (see Fig. 18.5).

Mistral and Bora

These are winds of restricted extent, the mistral blowing in Provence and Languedoc, the bora on the north Adriatic shores in Yugoslavia.[1] Although related to the rear of winter depressions moving eastwards through the Mediterranean Sea basin, they are also dependent on cold areas with high pressure lying over the Central Plateau or the Maritime Alps of France and over the Dinaric Alps respectively. Cold air descending from the mountains is warmed adiabatically, and yet arrives on the Mediterranean coast of each area as a very cold local wind.

It is possible that these are katabatic winds. Such winds are caused by nocturnal radiation which chills the mountain air and thus increases its density so that it flows downhill. Katabatic winds are responsible on winter nights for pools of cold frosty air which collect over valley floors with a temperature inversion above. In daytime anabatic winds are induced by the heating of the lower slopes in mountain valleys, when the air in contact with these surfaces is warmed sufficiently for it to flow uphill, being displaced by cold air from above.

Föhn Winds

The föhn wind belongs properly to the northern slopes of the Swiss and Austrian Alps. Similar winds are found elsewhere, such as the chinook on the eastern slopes of the Rocky Mountains between Alberta and Colorado, the nor'wester from the Southern Alps of New Zealand, and the Berg wind in the Cape region of South Africa.

Föhn winds blow down mountain slopes into adjoining lowlands and valleys and bring very warm and dry air. Local increases of temperature are remarkable (particularly in winter) and of the order of 40° F in twenty-four hours, although an increase of 30° F in an hour has been recorded. The onset of the wind is shown on thermograms by fluctuating temperature, but after three or four hours a steady high temperature is recorded which persists for several hours at least. Fig. 13.14 shows the difference in temperature values at corresponding levels on either side of the mountain area.

The wind has been explained in this way. A depression to leeward of the mountains draws air up the windward slopes and at C condensation occurs with the release of heat. Further ascent is accompanied by adiabatic cooling at the more gentle lapse rate for saturated

[1] Mistral = masterly. Bora = north wind.

air. The mass of cloud which accumulates at the crest of the range is known as the föhn wall (or chinook arch). The air descends on the leeward slopes as dry air, and throughout most of the descent it is warmed adiabatically at the dry lapse rate which is relatively rapid. The process is illustrated graphically in Fig. 13.15, which shows the lapse rates in the air at different stages in the passage of the air over

FIG. 13.14.—The Föhn Wind

the mountains and demonstrates the higher temperature at the end.

Today this explanation is not regarded as completely satisfactory, because the temperature contrasts are greater than can be expected if the process described above operates alone. Furthermore, condensation, with the formation of clouds, does not always take place, so

FIG. 13.15.—Lapse Rates at Different Stages of the Föhn Wind

T_1 = Temperature at base of mountain on windward side.
C = Condensation level.
M = Mountain summit.
T_2 = Temperature at base of leeward slope.
  Note.—No cloud is brought down from M, so that air descends the whole way with dry adiabatic lapse rate.

that the air remains 'dry' throughout the process. Recent studies of the chinook suggest that the föhn effect is primarily caused by turbulence in the air over the leeward slopes. Fig. 13.16 indicates that an air stream on crossing mountains causes great eddies on the lower leeward slopes, which in turn create a forced descent of air. Some of the air which is thus forced to descend is of tropical origin, and will be relatively warm and becomes warmer by adiabatic compression. Thus

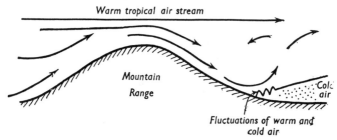

FIG. 13.16.—Modern Explanation of the Chinook Wind

After Willett

its temperature is raised to the high values which are in accord with those registered at the mountain foot. As the warm air replaces cold air there is a series of surges of cold and warm air which is reflected in the alternation of temperature that has been mentioned as typical of the onset of the föhn wind. At the same time the lower layers of the tropical air suffer the transformations shown in Figs. 13.14 and 13.15, so that the earlier explanation is not completely invalidated.

Upper Air Observations and Jet Streams

In recent years, with the help of such instruments as the radiosonde and radar probes, in addition to observations by routine aircraft flights, much has been learnt of the meteorological conditions in the upper troposphere and lower stratosphere. The radio-sonde is essentially a balloon which carries instruments for recording temperature, pressure, and humidity at various heights. Readings are sent back in the form of radio signals which have to be decoded. Radar echoes, from a device attached to the balloon, permit the speeds of the winds in the upper air to be deduced.

The plotting of charts, showing pressure distributions and winds at high levels, has established the fact that wind speeds increase as the tropopause is approached and, furthermore, the winds are much more constant in direction than at the earth's surface. In fact, there are, almost exclusively, westerly winds in the upper troposphere above much of each hemisphere, except over a relatively narrow equatorial zone where easterly winds prevail.

A second feature of interest is the recognition, within this broad westerly air stream, of two narrow belts—perhaps, 200 miles wide and about 3 miles deep—lying not far below the tropopause in which winds may attain speeds of 100–200 knots. These currents, which on occasions can be traced for thousands of miles within the upper troposphere, are known as jet streams. Often the upper air charts of the northern hemisphere show a sub-tropical jet stream which en-

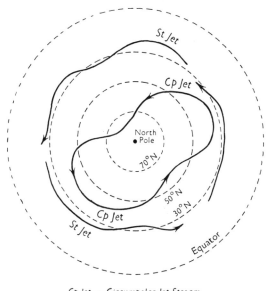

Cp Jet — *Circumpolar Jet Stream*
St Jet — *Sub-tropical Jet Stream*

Fig. 13.17.—Jet Streams in the Northern Hemisphere

circles the earth above the Horse Latitudes and a circum-polar jet stream that is usually in the form of a sinuous belt with large bends (or 'waves') that have a wavelength of many degrees of longitude and an amplitude of the order of many degrees of latitude (Fig. 13.17).

Knowledge of these fast moving jet streams is of importance since aircraft can make very speedy eastward flights with their help. Conversely, flying against such winds seriously increases fuel consumption on westward flights. Persistently strong winds which have been observed on high mountains in fairly low latitudes (such as Mt. Everest) are probably related to the sub-tropical jet streams. Long bands of high cirriform clouds, moving rapidly in the direction of their length (Fig. 12.12), often indicate a neighbouring jet stream.

These fast-moving winds develop as a result of thermal contrasts between cold and warm air masses, such as lie on either side of the

223

upper part of the polar front, just below the tropopause. It seems that turbulence permits of an exchange of energy between the two air masses across the jet stream both northwards and southwards (since the general flow of air in the jet stream is from west to east). Probably there is, also, an exchange of energy in a vertical direction so that air in the lower stratosphere is involved.

It would seem that the tropopause is apparently disrupted near the

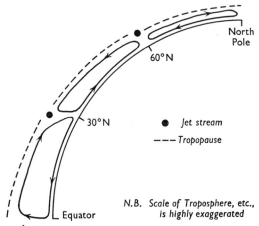

FIG. 13.18.—Jet Streams and the General Circulation

jet streams. Thus, in Fig.13.18, one observes that the tropopause is highest over the tropics and descends in two steps towards the pole. Possibly, the jet streams play a part in maintaining the general circulation of the air in the troposphere by producing an exchange of energy between the several cells as shown in Figs. 11.7 and 13.18 but much has yet to be learnt before a complete understanding of this process is gained. Whilst less is known of the upper air in the southern hemisphere it is fairly certain that two jet streams are found there, corresponding to those of the northern hemisphere.

Jet streams may be related to other air movements at the earth's surface. As a depression develops in temperate latitudes, as shown in Fig. 13.8a–c, the jet stream aloft seems to become distorted. Instead of having a more or less straight west–east axis it takes on a sinuous course as the depression below becomes occluded.

CHAPTER 14

Precipitation and Distribution of Rainfall

Measurement of Precipitation

Rainfall is measured by means of a rain gauge. The essential features of this instrument are shown in Fig. 14.1. It is a copper cylinder in two parts; the upper section has a deep rim around a funnel which leads into the lower part. The rain falls over the area of the

FIG. 14.1.—The Rain Gauge

FIG. 14.2.—The Measuring Cylinder for The Rain Gauge

top of the cylinder and passes through the funnel into a jar. The area of the cross-section of this jar is clearly less than the collecting area. The rain water, thus collected, is poured into a measuring glass which is graduated so as to read directly the depth of rain that has fallen over an area equal to the top of the cylinder. Rain is recorded in inches or fractions of an inch, since on some days the amount is very slight. The measuring glass has a cross-section which tapers very much at the base (Fig. 14.2), and thus, very small amounts of rain may be recorded. The smallest amount that is registered is 1/100 inch, and any quantity which is less than 0·005 inch is recorded as a trace of rainfall. The gauge is placed with its upper rim a foot above the ground. The amount of rain collected may be increased by splashing into the funnel, if it is too close to the ground. Wind eddies tend to carry rain drops beyond the rim of the funnel, and this tendency is increased with the height of the rim, thus decreasing the amount of rain collected. When snow is precipitated, the measurement is difficult, since it must be melted before the equivalent depth of water can be measured. When the snow is deep or when it has drifted an accurate estimate is very difficult to make. One foot of freshly fallen snow may be taken as approximately equivalent to one inch of rain.

FIG. 14.3.—Average of 35 years Rainfall in Dry Regions

Each dot represents total for one year.

As with temperature and pressure distributions on world maps, rainfall may be shown by lines similar to isotherms and isobars. These lines are known as isohyets, and are drawn from mean totals of the recorded rainfall over a given period. No reduction for height above sea-level is necessary. Since rainfall may fluctuate from year to year, the mean values must be regarded with care. This is particularly true in areas with scanty rainfall in warm or hot regions. It will be seen from Fig. 14.3 that the mean annual rainfall of a station with a very dry climate is 1·1 inches. This value is given by the average of 35 totals, most of which are less than 1·1 inches. It is a few 'wet' years that produce a mean value which is not typical as far as most years are concerned. This example is applicable to monthly means as well as annual values, and it also illustrates what is true of many stations in arid or semi-arid areas and of some areas which have quite abundant annual rainfall. Thus records reveal, that, in the past century, eleven places on the east coasts of the United States of America and Australia have shown departures from the long-term (1881–1960) average rainfall. During the last four decades of the nineteenth century, all of these stations showed increases in annual rainfall—some as much as 15–25 per cent of the long-term average. However, between 1901–40, decreases have been noted—of the order of 10–15 per cent in many cases. Annual rainfall at all these stations has shown an increase over the long-term average, during the period 1941–60.

Types of Rainfall

It has been shown that rainfall is dependent on a series of events which are usually initiated by air rising from ground level into the troposphere (see p. 187). There are three types of rainfall, each of which is distinguished by the chief cause of such uplift. They are:

1. Convectional rainfall.
2. Frontal rainfall.
3. Relief or orographic rainfall.

Convectional currents have been illustrated in Fig. 12.3, and all that need be added here is that either convection is great enough to overcome the stability of the troposphere and air is forced to ascend to great heights, or as is more usual, local heating produces the initial impetus which sets air in motion, when its continued uplift is determined by instability. Convectional rainfall is thus typical of hot seasons or of hot periods in a day, for example, a summer afternoon. The rain is usually very heavy, in the form of short showers, sometimes accompanied by thunderstorms. It is typical of equatorial and tropical areas at all seasons, and of continental interiors in middle and high latitudes in the summer season.

The second type of rainfall has been discussed fully in the previous chapter, where the characteristics of the various types of fronts in a depression were described. In this case there is uplift of warm and light air by a wedge of colder and heavier air which, if carried far enough upwards, will give the condensation features that precede rainfall.

Relief rainfall is caused by the forced ascent of air by features of high relief of the land which lie in the path of winds. Wherever onshore winds from oceans are humid and warm in relation to the land barrier on to which they are blowing, the rainfall of this type will be particularly heavy. Relief rainfall starts to increase some distance from the windward slopes of the mountain edge—it is probable that upper air currents are forced up over air which is stowed against the mountain. Whilst there is a tendency for precipitation to increase with height, it can be observed that on the windward slopes of very high mountains there is a level of maximum precipitation above which rainfall decreases. Whilst relief may produce heavy rainfall, its effect is more often than not an added factor to some primary cause of rainfall, such as frontal uplift or the heating of the ground surface, with the development of convection within the upland area. Much orographic rainfall is associated with the air of tropical origin in the warm sectors of depressions.

Thunderstorms

Thunderstorms depend for their generation on cumulo-nimbus clouds which have developed to heights of at least $3\frac{1}{2}$ miles. At such heights there are large concentrations of both water and ice particles in the clouds. The lightning is the giant spark which is

Fig. 14.4.—Cumulo-nimbus Cloud
The cloud shows rain falling from its base.

produced by a discharge of static electricity, whilst the noise of the thunder is produced by the rapid expansion of air, as it is heated suddenly and intensely by the flash.

Figure 14.5 shows that within a thundercloud there are positive charges at the top and negative charges in the lower part, although there may be a small positive charge near the cloud base. On the surface of the earth, below the cloud, there is mainly a negative charge but positive charges are induced in certain areas of the surface by the negative charge in the cloud base above. As the charges grow a very strong electric potential gradient develops, between the zones with opposite charges, so that eventually a discharge takes place as lightning between the cloud and the ground, as well as between adjacent parts of the cloud. The problem of how the electric charges accumulate has given rise to much research and recently discovered facts have considerably modified earlier theories.

Simpson's theory which was widely accepted in the past argued that rain drops could be disrupted so that the larger, positively charged fragments fell towards the base of the cloud whilst the lighter, negatively charged fragments were carried as spray, by up-currents, to the top of the cloud. This distribution of charges is the very opposite of that shown in Fig. 14.5.

The charge distribution, as now known, may be accounted for as follows. When super-cooled water freezes it forms rime which is negatively charged whilst minute splinters of ice, with a positive charge, are ejected from the drop as it freezes. The fine splinters are carried aloft with their positive charge leaving negatively charged fragments of rime near the base of the cloud. This riming process is

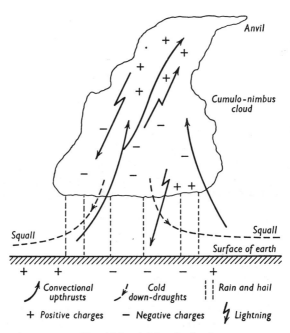

FIG. 14.5.—A Thundercloud

fast enough to account for discharges which have both the intensity and frequency of the flashes of lightning, typical of most thunderstorms. It is possible that the area of positive charge near the cloud base may be explained, in part, by the spray process described by Simpson.

Conditions which favour thunderstorms are those of instability reaching to high levels of the troposphere, combined with a generous supply of water vapour, so that convectional updraughts can form massive high clouds, with temperatures of the order of −20° C to −40° C, which are low enough to produce riming on a sufficiently large scale. Intense ground heating, particularly on summer afternoons, is the most common cause in Great Britain. Turbulence near coasts and, somewhat less commonly, frontal ascent in slow-moving depressions, may also initiate thunderstorms.

A cumulo-nimbus cloud (Fig. 14.4) often shows a flat top, extending as an anvil head where upcurrents cease at an inversion level (often at the tropopause) and where upper winds cause the cloud top to spread out. As these clouds precipitate, downdraughts of relatively cold air are formed which spread out· far below the cloud base at ground level and often give squally conditions, well away from the thunderstorm cloud. Very large hail stones may fall out of thunder clouds; their size is probably related to the violence of the ascending air currents within the clouds.

In equatorial latitudes, thunderstorms are very common, chiefly because of the high moisture content of the air and the considerable instability, at very high levels, in these zones of air mass convergence. Bogor (Buitenzorg), in Java, is noted as the most thundery place in the world.

Distribution and Seasonal Incidence of Rainfall in the World

Having discussed the distribution of temperature, pressure and winds, and air masses in the world in previous chapters, it is possible to show their interrelations which result in the distribution of rainfall over the earth's surface. High temperatures prevailing during most of the year or in a hot season will produce convectional rainfall, whilst pressure distributions, in causing winds to move onshore or to meet high relief, are responsible for rain. Furthermore, pressure distributions control the convergence of air masses which may produce frontal rainfall.

It is necessary to know where there is abundant or deficient rainfall, but it is perhaps more important to know the seasonal incidence of the rain. Rainfall may occur in all months of the year, in certain months only, or no rain may fall in any month of the year. This seasonal incidence of rainfall is known as the rainfall régime.

In discussing the world distribution of rainfall, including its seasonal incidence, consideration must be paid to two factors other than those mentioned above. Firstly, the migration of the overhead sun between the tropics during the year is reflected in a similar but less extensive swing of the pressure and wind belts (as shown in Fig. 14.6) both northwards and southwards. Secondly, there is the effect of continentality caused by large land masses. Whilst such an effect is found mainly in the northern continents, it is of some significance in tropical areas generally, but, more particularly, where monsoonal controls are operative in low latitudes.

The apparent movement of the overhead sun between the tropics has an amplitude of 47° of latitude, whereas the main pressure and wind belts move north and south of their mean positions with a range of not more than fifteen degrees of latitude over the oceans, but over land areas there is a somewhat greater shift of these belts. Referring to Fig. 11.6 it will be seen that there must arise from these migrations three zones in each hemisphere where, during the year, there is a change in the predominant influence. Thus, immediately north and south of the equatorial zone there are regions which are alternately under trade-wind influences and the Doldrums belt. About latitudes 30° and 40° there are zones which have trade-wind influences at one time, and westerly winds with their associated depressions at others, as a result of the movement of the subtropical high-pressure belts. In high latitudes are areas which tend to have polar influences in winter and westerly winds in summer, although the interaction of polar and tropical air masses produces depressions which upset and obscure the simple pattern.

Fig. 14.6 shows the essential effect of such movements by giving the relative positions of the two subtropical high-pressure cells over the oceans, and the Doldrums low-pressure belt, together with their associated winds at the equinoxes and at the two solstices (i.e. when the sun is overhead at the Equator and at either tropic, respectively). Two 'ideal' continents are shown, each between 60° N and 60° S, and separated by an ocean, so that, amongst other features illustrated, there is the contrast between the eastern and western margins of the land masses, with onshore winds on one margin matched by off-shore winds on the other. Inevitably, the diagrams present a generalized pattern which must be modified for a complete account of world rainfall. Nevertheless, they serve as a basis for some of the climatological studies which follow in later chapters. Several areas are indicated on each continent by letters which appear on all three parts of Fig. 14.6, and reference will be made to these in turn. The shaded areas mark regions of adequate, if not abundant, rainfall.

Let us consider first the areas A and B. These are the equatorial zones with permanent low pressure in the Doldrums belt, and are characterized by fairly constant convectional rainfall. At the equinoxes these zones should have an equal extension north and south of the Equator, but at the winter solstice both A and B have shifted to the south, so that areas C and D are now covered by the convection rain-belt whereas at the equinoxes they were relatively dry. At the summer solstice the reverse has happened and now regions E and F have rain, although previously at the equinoxes and the winter solstice they were relatively dry (during these relatively dry periods some rain will be received from trade-wind sources). Thus, as a result of this seasonal migration of the low-pressure belt, there is a zone of well-distributed rainfall near the Equator which merges northwards and southwards into zones that receive convectional rains in the period of the year when the sun is overhead in the particular hemisphere, or in the summer season. There is a gradual decrease in the annual total of rainfall as one moves polewards through these zones.

It will be seen that the trade winds migrate and cover areas of vary-

FIG. 14.6.—Seasonal Movements of Pressure, Wind, and Rainfall Belts

ing size in each hemisphere with the shift of the oceanic cells of high pressure, but the most significant fact is the difference between the eastern and western margins of the two continents in low latitudes, the former margins receiving rain, whilst the latter are dry. At G and H onshore trade winds will give rain, particularly where the relief is high. It should be noted by comparison of all three parts of Fig. 14.6 that these rain-belts on the east coasts have poleward limits which vary with the season. At I and J offshore trade winds prevail at all seasons and these are drought zones, and they are linked respectively to L and N which are also dry at all times of the year. L and N correspond to K and M, since all four regions are poleward of the areas affected by the migration of the tropical convectional rain-belt. Also these regions are inland and therefore remote from any rain brought by the trade winds, and are hot deserts.

Farther north and south the major influence is that of the westerly wind circulation, with its associated depressions. The contrast between the two continental margins is again very obvious, but in this case the western margins receive rain. With the migration of the pressure and wind belts the areas P and S are sufficiently high in latitude to receive rain at all seasons, but Q and R are less fortunate in that they lose the rain-bearing winds and depressions from the west at the summer and winter solstices respectively, or, in other words, they are dry in summer but have rain in the winter season.

Regions X and Y appear to be like areas I and J, completely dry at all seasons, but this is not true, as will be seen below. No account has been taken of the influence of continentality which is so important in each of the great northern land masses. It was noted (p. 168) that the mean isotherms in January and July over North America and Eurasia were very irregular as compared with those in other parts of the world maps. The chief features to be recalled at this point are:

1. The southward bend of the isotherms over these continents in winter which indicates that the east and west margins are much warmer than the interiors in corresponding latitudes. This is particularly true of the west margins, where the isotherms have very nearly a north-south trend.

2. In summer the reverse is largely true, and the interiors are very much warmer than the margins in similar latitudes.

This contrast is reflected in the world pressure maps, where it is seen that over the northern continental interiors high-pressure air which is dominant in winter is replaced by low pressure in summer. The result of these contrasts may be shown diagrammatically as in Fg. 14.7 which is derived from Fig. 11.8.

From this next diagram it will be seen that the northern continents in middle and high latitudes may be divided into three main areas:

1. The western margins which receive rain from the westerly winds

233

and depressions at all seasons, but with greater certainty in winter towards the north, when the buffer of the continental high-pressure region causes most depressions to be deflected polewards.

2. Eastwards of these margins there is an interior zone which is effectively isolated from rain-bearing winds in winter by high pressure, but is open to westerly influences in summer. With the additional convectional rainfall produced by great heat, summer is unquestionably the rainy season of the year.

FIG. 14.7.—The Effect of Continentality in Northern Land Masses

3. The eastern margins are often quite exceptional in that they are under monsoonal controls. Here, as shown by the two diagrams, there is an almost complete reversal of the wind directions between the seasons. Clearly, summer is the period of onshore winds and abundant rainfall. It will be noticed that the summer winds are completely controlled by the low-pressure area of the interior, so that they are deflected very much from the normal directions in these latitudes. In winter, outblowing winds from the continental high-pressure area replace the inblowing winds of summer and, in general, there is little rain at this season, but depressions bring some winter rainfall. Thus it will be seen that region X is not dry as indicated in Fig. 14.6. In corresponding latitudes in the southern hemisphere the lands are too narrow to develop this continentality, and region S in Fig. 14.6 represents Southern Chile, New Zealand, or Tasmania, whereas region Y resembles very closely the Patagonian part of Argentina with low rainfall. The monsoonal régime is probably typical of but one region of the world, namely, the south and east margins of Asia, with the East Indies and Northern Australia, which are represented by G and H in Fig. 14.6, but from what has just been said these tropical areas with their predominant summer rainfall merge northwards with the eastern margins in higher northern latitudes where in Asia, at least, there are monsoonal controls.

The great width of each northern continent makes it very unlikely that rain-bearing winds and depressions can bring much rain to the remote parts of the interiors in summer. Thus there are practically rainless areas within the interiors which may be regarded as poleward extensions of the desert regions of low latitudes (areas K and L in Fig. 14.6). This is particularly the case in Eurasia, but less true of North America. The resultant distribution of rainfall, with its seasonal incidence, on an idealized northern continent is given in Fig. 14.8, and within certain limits this may be reversed for a southern continent.

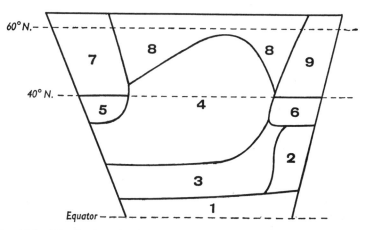

Fig. 14.8.—Distribution of Rainfall and its Seasonal Incidence on an Idealized Northern Continent

1. Rain at all seasons (convectional).
2. Rain at all seasons (convectional and from the trade winds, also monsoonal).
3. Rain in summer season (convectional—one or two periods).
4. Scanty rainfall or none.
5. Rain in winter only (westerly winds and depressions).
6. Rain mainly in summer (monsoonal winds and depressions).
7. Rain at all seasons (westerly winds and depressions).
8. Rain mainly in summer, decreasing in amount to the east (mainly convectional with some from depressions).
9. Rain mainly in summer, in places monsoonal (some in winter from depressions).

CHAPTER 15

Vegetation

Controls of Vegetation

The vegetation of a particular region may be regarded as the community of plants, which includes trees and grasses, that covers the area and gives it a distinct character. From the geographer's standpoint the types of vegetation depend on the appearance of the plant cover, e.g. forest and woodland, grassland and desert. There are no hard-and-fast limits to each of the types, rather do they merge imperceptibly with one another through a series of intermediate types of vegetation. The gradual change from one distinct type to another is largely the result of the primary control of rainfall, and more particularly its distribution throughout the year. However, some differentiation of vegetation is dependent upon the temperature, such as the distinction between tropical rain forests and northern coniferous forests, and locally the soil may be a factor which must be considered.

Before examining in detail the various types of vegetation, it is necessary to consider the requirements of most plants during their growth. When it is growing, a plant must have a supply of water which carries dissolved substances from the soil through the roots and stem to its leaves. To each leaf, these substances are brought from the ground by a solution flow, produced by the combined effects of transpiration (through the leaves), osmosis (passing through the cell walls) and capillarity (moving through fine hair-like passages). These substances combine with others in the leaves, which have been formed by photosynthesis, and produce complex plant foods which are carried back to the cells within the root and stem or trunk, where they are either stored or used to promote further growth. This complex process depends very much upon the constant movement of solutions within the plant. Through the stomata, which are minute pores in the leaves, water vapour is transpired into the air. Broad-leaved trees lose much water in this way during the day and, since transpiration depends upon the same factors as evaporation, this loss is increased by winds and by a dry atmosphere.

Obviously, a growing plant must have an adequate supply of moisture to maintain this solution flow from roots to the leaves. However, the flow is probably arrested, or at least slowed down, by cold, and it is accepted that, in general, plant growth is inhibited when mean monthly temperatures remain below 43° F (the zero of plant growth is sometimes taken as 42° F). Nevertheless, plants and their seeds may exist, without growth, at much lower temperatures, and some are capable of living with temperatures well below freezing-point. It is reasonable to assume that, in the majority of cases, temperatures must be some 10° F above freezing-point for anything like active growth to occur.

With the onset of cold, it is likely that the solution flow will slacken, despite the fact that water may be available in the soil, because evaporation tends to decrease and, thus, transpiration slows down. However, low temperatures also slow down photosynthesis and other vital processes in the plant. This means that the plant ceases to produce food which leads to a fall of the leaves and a rest in growth. Not until fresh leaves have been developed can the solution flow come into operation again and growth start afresh.

When plants remain evergreen during such cold seasons, the leaves have small surface areas (as in the case of the needle leaves of the coniferous trees) or they have thickened cuticles (as in the case of the holly) to reduce the rate of transpiration. It is sometimes necessary for trees to shed their leaves because of drought instead of cold, but again the probable purpose of the leaf fall is to prevent damage to the plant through transpiration at such critical periods when the soil moisture is not replenished by rainfall. Few areas of the world enjoy optimum conditions for plant growth, with high temperatures and abundant rainfall throughout the year, and many plants are therefore adapted to the climate of the region in which they grow.

The relation between climate and vegetation is of the utmost significance. Given suitable growing temperatures, the most important factor in plant growth is the incidence of rainfall. In areas other than those with abundant and well-distributed rainfall, the incidence and the length of a dry season is of great importance in determining the vegetation. Normally, plant growth is most vigorous at the time of the greatest heat. Amongst tropical and warm temperate areas, where mean monthly temperatures are always above 43° F, those with dry seasons are fortunate in having rain at the time of the greatest heat (except for deserts and Mediterranean areas). In cool temperate and cold regions the primary factor in plant growth is the length of the season with mean monthly temperatures above 43° F, but even so, the incidence of rainfall plays a very important rôle as in warmer regions.

The trees of the tropical rain forest are hygrophilous in that they require abundant rainfall at all seasons. In deserts the plants must be adapted in various ways to resist drought and are termed xerophilous. Some plants are tropophilous, being adapted to seasonal changes of

237

rainfall and temperature, such as the deciduous trees of our latitudes which are in leaf in the moist summer and rest in their growth during the cold winter, after the leaf fall. A season of drought will also give rise to tropophilous plants. With the intervention of a dry season, forest is replaced by woodland and scrub which are tropophilous in character. Grassland flourishes where the rainfall is concentrated in the warm season of the year and is insufficient to support forest or woodland—although there is by no means a complete absence of trees. Grassland may be regarded as tropophilous vegetation since in its rest period there is usually a drought, when it may be said to exhibit xerophilous characteristics. Thus, with increasing length of the dry season, forest passes through woodland and scrub to grassland and desert. Scrub (or shrub) consists of woody plants with several stems springing from the roots, in contrast to trees, which have one stem or trunk (Fig. 15.1).

Paul Popper Ltd.

Fig. 15.1.—Thorn Scrub in Kenya

This is short grass savana with thickets of acacia shrubs.
Note the strato-cumulus clouds.

Xerophilous plants are adapted to living deserts, where high temperatures, strong winds, and low relative humidity induce considerable transpiration although the available water is scarce. It is frequently assumed that desert plants transpire very little but it is now known that, with an adequate water supply, the converse is true.

238

Whilst the stomata are reduced in size these are, in fact, relatively more numerous than in many other plants. In some cases the stomata are sunken to reduce transpiration. These plants conserve water in their cells during drought when transpiration is checked by the closing of the stomata. Various other devices, to be referred to later, help these plants to resist drought. Perhaps, above all, whilst some plants remain in a wilted state in the dry seasons they can recover, without permanent damage being done to their protoplasm, with the onset of another wet season.

On the other hand, the flora (or types of plants) within a forest or grassland area depends, not so much on the rainfall, as on the prevailing temperatures. Thus, the particular trees within a tropical rain forest are different from those in a coniferous forest and the grasses within the tropical grasslands are unlike those in the grasslands of high latitudes. In the cool and cold regions, where there are marked seasonal contrasts in temperature and also significant fluctuations in the amount of moisture available to plants during the year, there are relatively few species of trees in the forests and these tend to have specialised mechanisms in order to survive. On the other hand, in the humid tropical forests, with optimum conditions for growth at all times, there are many species of tree but, in fact, these differ from one another only but slightly.

It will be seen that the vegetation of a region is primarily dependent upon its climatic régime, and it may be said that in the cooler regions temperature is more critical in its control than rainfall, whereas in low latitudes rainfall produces the major differentiation of vegetation. However, other factors such as soil may produce local variations, as, for instance, where forest appears on water-retentive clays in grasslands or where grasses flourish on very pervious soils in forest areas. In the remainder of the chapter the close relationship between climate and vegetation will be established.

Forest and Woodland

In forests and woodlands the predominant vegetation consists of woody plants, and of these, trees are the most highly developed. Forest may be defined as an assemblage of trees in such close growth that their crowns touch one another. Woodland is characterized by the considerable development of shrubs which tend to isolate the taller trees. Scrub is the term applied to vegetation where trees are few in number and occur in scattered clumps, accompanied by many of the lower woody plants as well as by grasses. Only within the tropical rain forests and in the forests on the eastern margins of warm temperate regions do trees enjoy the optimum conditions for growth at all times of the year. In all other forests and woodlands there is some restricting factor which imposes a seasonal rest in the growth of the trees.

Trees are distinguished in various ways, and some confusion may arise in the application of certain terms. Probably the most important contrast lies between deciduous trees, with an autumnal leaf fall, and evergreen trees which lose their leaves continuously but never all at one time. Another distinction depends upon the shape of the leaves of the tree, some having broad leaves and others needle leaves. It is incorrect to assume that broad leaves are solely characteristic of deciduous trees, as many broad-leaved trees are evergreen. On the other hand, most coniferous trees bear needle leaves. In general, broad-leaved trees, whether deciduous or evergreen, yield hardwoods, whilst softwoods are mainly derived from coniferous trees which are commonly evergreen. Incidentally, the larch is a needle leaf tree with deciduous behaviour. In eastern U.S.S.R., where larch is dominant, it is probable that such behaviour is governed by the very low winter temperatures. Whilst coniferous forests are evergreen, it should be realised that in the tropics and warm temperate regions, with such prevailing high temperatures, there is no distinct season of leaf fall so that there are several types of broad-leaved evergreen forests in these latitudes.

Forests may be grouped geographically as follows:

1. Tropical Forests

(a) *Tropical Rain Forests*. These are found in regions with abundant rain at all seasons, in equatorial lowlands, and on tropical east coasts, in particular. In the Amazon basin they are known as the selvas. They are broad-leaved evergreen forests, since temperatures permit of growth at all seasons. With no rest period leaves are shed at the same time as fresh ones are developing. The forests have relatively little undergrowth, except near the margins, since the canopy of the tree crowns restricts sunlight on the floor of the forests. The trees are, however, encumbered with climbing plants such as lianas. The forests are extraordinarily rich in species of tree, and include hardwood trees, such as mahogany, rosewood, and greenheart. Mangrove forest, which flourishes in the salt waters immediately offshore from coastal rain forests and in the waters of tidal rivers, may be regarded as a sub-type. The wood of the mangrove is hard and resistant to salt water. Owing to its accessibility, it has been considerably exploited. Tropical rain forest is shown in Fig. 17.2 and 17.3.

(b) *Dry Forests*. These forests belong to the tropical continental interiors where a dry season is characteristic. The forest is semi-deciduous or, more correctly, facultatively deciduous, in that some but not all of the leaves are shed, and the degree of the leaf fall in any year is dependent upon the severity of the dry season. Only in very dry

Fig. 15.2.—Dry Forest in Rhodesia
This is an example of dry forest with acacias. Note undergrowth of thorny scrub.

years do these forests appear leafless. This less dense forest has some undergrowth, since sunlight can penetrate fairly readily, but usually this remains evergreen. Common trees are acacias. In South-East Asia and in India comparable forests are known as monsoon forests, with teak and sal trees which are similarly adapted by a leaf fall to existence through a dry season. Dry forest is shown in Fig. 15.2.

(*c*) *Scrub and Thorn Forests.* These appear in tropical regions with longer dry seasons than obtain in dry forest zones. The trees are almost completely deciduous, and include acacias, euphorbias, and baobabs; the latter develop a water store in their excessively swollen trunks to endure the drought. In north-east Brazil thorn forest is known as caatinga. The Gran Chaco is also, in part, scrub woodland of this type—in it, the quebracho is a common tree. Scrub is shown in Fig. 15.1.

Dry forest and scrub are accompanied by grasses, and it is usual to find them occupying much of the areas that are often referred to as savana. Savana, strictly speaking means a treeless plain.

2. Warm Temperate Forests

(*a*) *Mediterranean Broad-leaved Evergreen Forests and Scrub.* These are of considerable interest, since they are adapted to a summer

241

drought. The mean monthly temperatures permit active growth during the rainy winter, but the trees remain evergreen in summer, instead of becoming xerophilous in character during the drought, by a leaf fall. The trees have various devices to resist the drought and these include spiny leaves, with waxy and hairy surfaces, thickened cuticles, incurved leaves with stomata turned away from the direct sunshine and, in many cases, very long tap roots to draw upon deep supplies of water. Very thick and deeply fissured barks also help to reduce evaporation from the trees.

In general, the trees are widely spaced, and show but moderate vertical development, and they are usually accompanied by woody shrubs. This scrub is known by various names, such as maquis in Europe and chaparral in California. Amongst the trees are cork oaks, sweet chestnuts, and olives, togehter with conifers such as cedars and cypresses. Few areas have true forest although in Swanland, in Western Australia, the eucalypt[1] forest, with jarrah and karri trees, (Fig. 184.) is remarkable. Maquis is shown in Fig. 18.3.

(b) *Broad-leaved Evergreen Forests*. These are found in the eastern marginal areas of continents, the chief areas being in southern China, the Gulf-Atlantic States of the United States of America, and in South-eastern Australia. There is well-distributed rainfall throughout the year, and the winter months have mean temperatures above 43° F, so that the forests are evergreen and almost as luxuriant as the tropical rain forests. The trees include the evergreen oak, mulberry, maple, walnut, and various eucalypts; in some areas lianas are common. Coniferous forests are found on poorer, sandy soils amongst these broad-leaved forests—such as in the coastal plains of the Gulf-Atlantic States of America, where there are several varieties of pine (Fig. 18.7).

3. Cool Temperate and Cold Forests

Amongst these are the deciduous hardwood forests and the coniferous forests, but there are extensive areas of mixed forests with deciduous and coniferous trees. The trees of these forests are compelled to rest in growth for a period of several months by a cold season, which increases in length in a polewards direction.

(a) *Deciduous Hardwood Forests*. These are found mainly south of the coniferous forests, in cool temperate regions, and on the margins of the two great northern land masses. The period of cold, when the forests are leafless is usually less than six months. The trees shed their leaves to reduce transpiration to a minimum in winter. Incidentally, the reduction in transpiration also removes the danger of water freezing within some of the cells of the tree and disrupting

[1] Eucalypt means well covered, in that the seed cases are protected with a cap.

FIG. 15.3.—Virgin Deciduous Forest in Germany
Beech in the foreground and oaks behind.

them. Deciduous trees require time, in spring, for the development of fresh leaves before full growth is possible. The leaves are broad and the trees can transpire freely during the growing season, as the summers are quite moist. Some of these forests have much undergrowth. The oceanic western margins are not so suitable for deciduous trees as farther inland, since strong winds on the coasts promote too rapid transpiration and salt spray is inimical to the growth of trees. These forests persist eastwards in Europe, but decreasing summer rainfall causes them to fail in western Russia. In both North America and Asia similar forests are found on the eastern margins. These forests include trees such as the oak, beech, and ash, as well as the maple, chestnut, and elm (Fig. 15.3).

(b) *Coniferous Forests.* These are found mainly in two great continental belts across North America and Eurasia, in latitudes which reach northwards to the tree limit. This limit is determined by low temperatures, so that there is too short a period for tree growth (apart from dwarf trees in the tundra). In general, the coniferous trees have a growing period, of not more than six months. This period is too short for deciduous trees, which require time for leaf growth, but the needle leaves of the conifers remain during the winter, and in the following warm season, with the onset of temperatures above 43° F, the trees are immediately able to start growing. The needle leaves are small, thus reducing transpiration, but they are abundant enough to promote effective photosynthesis. The sap of the trees is pitchy in nature and, with the thick bark, this helps to

Dorien Leigh Ltd.

FIG. 15.4.—Redwoods in California, United States of America
Note the fairly sparse undergrowth of small trees.

reduce evaporation. The summer rainfall of the interiors is sufficient for conifers but not for most deciduous trees, although a few of these persist into the far north. The chief types of tree are pine, fir, spruce, hemlock, and various larches. On the western mountains of North America in middle latitudes occur forests with very large conifers, including Douglas fir and, in California and Oregon, two trees, the redwood and the big tree, both belonging to the Sequoia family (Fig. 15.4). The latter trees are probably the tallest in the world, only being rivalled by the jarrah and karri of Australia.

In coniferous forests there is little undergrowth as compared with the deciduous hardwood forests which have many shrubs between the trees. The evergreen nature of the conifers and the low sun angles in high latitudes during most months help to restrict the sunlight from reaching the ground so that undergrowth is discouraged. It should be noted that the deciduous hardwood forests usually merge on their poleward margins with mixed forests of deciduous and coniferous trees.

Other conifers, such as cedars and cypresses, are not uncommon in the Mediterranean areas and in isolated highlands of the tropics, such as in Abyssinia and East Africa. They are also found in the islands of South-East Asia, where pines flourish in uplands—often these are adjacent to lowlands which have a marked dry season in the year.

It is of interest to note that conifers extend over a wide range of latitude—in fact, they flourish in both humid and semi-arid areas of tropical and temperate regions. Probably the lack of competition from broad-leaved trees, combined with the ability of the trees to exist in regions with long, cold seasons, explains the great extent of coniferous forests in the northern continents.

Grassland

Grasslands cover very extensive areas of the world (at least 20 per cent of the total area of land is thus described). Grassland is distinguished from forest by the relative absence of trees, and from the deserts by the more or less continuous cover of grasses. However there are transitional zones between grassland and forest, as well as between grassland and desert.

Grasses are fairly simple plants and have a wide distribution in the world, under varying climates—for instance, they are found in the tundra, in deserts, and in tropical rain forests, where bamboos compete successfully with trees. Grasses are resistant to many adverse conditions, including fire, since this only destroys the withered top of the plant, whose larger part lies below ground level. Another factor which assists in the distribution and persistence of grasses is the mobility of their seeds, since they are so easily borne by winds. Grasses are shallow-rooted plants and, during the growing season, they must receive frequent showers rather than more or less

245

U.S. Information Service

FIG. 15.5.—Steppe Grassland in Montana, United States of America

Steppe grasses are seen in the foreground. In the distance (left) the trees are very probably growing naturally alongside water courses.

continuous rainfall, to replenish the moisture which is lost by evaporation from the surface layers of the soil. The matting of the grass roots is helpful in retaining this moisture near the surface.

Grasses have a rest period in their growth, during which it may be said that the prevailing climatic conditions are of no importance whatsoever; they simply wither and die down at the surface until the return of more humid conditions, when they flourish again. Drought in the growing season is detrimental to most grasses—an exception is Mitchell grass, in Australia, which is very drought-resistant. The most suitable areas for the development of natural grasslands are the continental interiors, since here there is rarely drought in summer, which is naturally the vegetative period for grass.

Grasslands show a gradation in their luxuriance which is roughly proportional to the amount of rainfall received in the growing season. With decreasing rainfall, grasslands thin out, becoming steppe which is more or less the very dry grassland of the semi-desert margins. 'Steppe' is used to describe both tropical and temperate grasslands which have scanty rainfall. Grasslands may be divided into three groups:

1. Temperate grasslands—(*a*) near the arid margins are the steppes and (*b*) in more humid areas but merging with the steppes are the prairies.

Fig. 15.6.—Prairie Grassland, Sierras de Cordoba, Argentine

2. Savana or tropical grassland.
3. Meadow grassland.

1. *Temperate Grasslands*

These are found in the continental interiors, in both warm and cool temperate latitudes, with spring and summer rainfall. A distinction is made between the wetter prairies, where tall grasses are dominant, and the drier steppes which have short grasses in the main, although in both types there are tall and short grasses. Steppe has a nearly continuous mat of grasses, rising at maturity to heights of six inches to a foot, but tall grasses may overshadow these in wetter years. In North America, the common varieties are grama grass and buffalo grass. With increasing aridity, the short grasses form bunches, separated by bare soil, as semi-desert areas are approached (Fig. 15.5). The roots of these short grasses can draw on surface moisture but they do not reach an underlying water table.

Prairie grasses, on the other hand, rise at maturity to over three feet and may reach ten feet; their long roots tap water at depths of two feet or more. Bearded grass (Andropogon) and the fescues are varieties which are typical of the prairies in most continents (Fig. 15.6).

With the grasses, in both prairies and steppes, are larger herbaceous plants—in the former, these are more conspicuous and show greater variety than in the latter. Trees are rare but in the otherwise treeless prairies, poplars and willows are not uncommon alongside river courses and, occasionally, isolated trees, such as oaks and elms, may be present (Fig. 15.5).

2. Savana or Tropical Grassland

Tropical grasslands differ very considerably from temperate ones. Trees are quite common and the grass tends to grow in isolated tufts rather than as a continuous cover. These grasslands are typical of the tropical continental interiors, where rain is concentrated in four or five months of the hot season. With abundant rainfall at this time, grasses reach a height of twelve feet or more (Fig. 17.6). The grasses are coarse, parched and brown in the drought but, with the onset of the rainy season, the grasslands rapidly assume the typical green colour. The trees may be so numerous that they obscure distant views. In fact, savana, which strictly speaking, means a treeless plain of grass, is a term often applied to areas which are more suitably described as grass woodlands (Fig. 17.11). Tropical grasslands pass equatorwards, with increasing rainfall, into dry or scrub forest, and polewards, with a longer season of drought, into steppe and semi-desert (Fig. 17.17). Further details of savana are given on p. 279.

3. Meadow Grasslands

These are common in the temperate marginal lands which have neither a season of drought nor severe winter cold. In particular, they have developed, with the clearance of forests, in cool temperate areas. The distinction between natural and cultivated grasslands is far from easy to make, both in Europe and Asia, where much forest has been cleared over the centuries. In fact, few of the characteristics of the original natural vegetation remain.

These grasslands occur also as alpine meadows, above the timber line in practically all the high mountains of the world. The common grasses in such meadows are sedges, accompanied by herbaceous plants, such as saxifrages. These meadows often rely for their moisture on melted snow.

Desert Vegetation

Under desert conditions, aridity restricts the vegetation to such an extent that a complete plant cover is absent. Whilst in some desert areas plant growth is well-nigh impossible because of extreme aridity, most deserts have a representative flora of their own. The areas of waterless desert are very limited, and much of the regions shown as desert on maps is better defined as semi-desert from the point of view of the vegetation. One characteristic of this vegetation is the isolation of the individual plants, each being separated from its neighbours by considerable distances (Figs. 15.7, 17.17 and 18.8).

The vegetation is truly xerophilous, and all plants in the deserts and semi-deserts must seize upon every opportunity to further their existence whilst being adapted to resist or endure the effects of prolonged drought which may last for years rather than for months. The

Black Star

Fig. 15.7.—Desert with very Sparse Grass, Negev, Israel.
The tree is an acacia perched on a water table

seeds of some desert plants are capable of remaining inert for years until the chance incidence of rainfall gives them the opportunity of a brief life. Grasses are not uncommon, but they have specific adaptations for the purpose of drought resistance, such as thickened outer layers, inrolling leaves, and the development of many hairs.

There is a tendency for the plants of the marginal zones, just outside the deserts and semi-deserts, to persist within the areas. For instance, the drought-resistant trees of the acacia family range from the tropical grass woodlands into the semi-deserts. In Australia both the mulga and the brigalow are acacia thickets which lie within the semi-desert regions. The cactus is usually regarded as typical of deserts. It is, by origin, an American plant, but has been

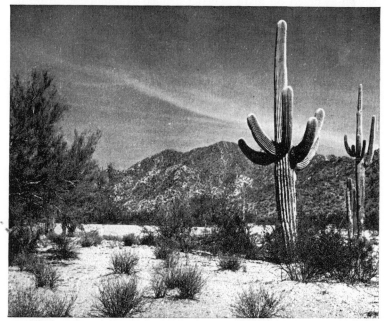

Black Star

FIG. 15.8.—Desert, Arizona, United States of America

The Saguaro cactus and other plants give a fairly rich desert vegetation. On the hills in the background is fairly typical chaparral

successfully introduced into other continents and into regions with more rainfall than is usual in deserts. With its leathery surface, covered with wax and resin, and with its prickles, which are actually its leaves, it reduces transpiration to a minimum, and as a succulent it has distended cells which store much water.

Many plants, including the cactus, have most extensive root systems which may extend for many yards underground, and thus, although the parts of the plants which are visible above the ground are quite restricted, each plant, taken as a whole, cannot be regarded as stunted. By means of their long roots it is possible for many of these plants to collect very large quantities of water to be stored in various ways. Sand has often very great reserves of water at depth despite its very dry surface layers; some of this water is derived from areas of greater rainfall, and has travelled underground to the desert regions.

Probably the most difficult task of desert plants is to ensure that their seeds are scattered and germinated. Some seed pods are preserved in a round cage, made of dried branches, which uncurls only upon contact with moisture. This small cage, or ball, is blown across the desert, perhaps for years, until an opportunity for germination presents itself. Some plants produce succulent, water-laden fruits, the seeds of which may be dispersed when the fruit is eaten by animals.

The desert vegetation of the world may be divided into two main groups, belonging to:

1. The hot deserts and semi-deserts which lie in the arid trade-wind belts of the tropics and sub-tropics.

2. The cool or temperate deserts which are located in the inter-montane basins in the western parts of North America and in Inner Asia. The mountains surrounding these basins isolate them effectively from rain-bearing winds.

The hot deserts and semi-deserts may be subdivided further into those with rain at one season of the year and those which have at least two seasons of rain in each year. The first sub-group has no great variety of plants, and does not include succulents which are found in the wetter deserts, although even the latter have relatively few types of plant (Fig. 15.8). The plants of these regions may be divided into four categories:

(a) Drought-evading plants, which are annuals whose seeds and bulbs await the onset of fresh rainfall. They include desert plantains and desert fescue, as well as poppies, irises, and lilies.

(b) Drought-resistant plants, such as acacias and the mesquite bush of North America, which have long roots that are able to reach a deep water table and therefore flourish in an apparently arid zone.

(c) Succulents which have a water store within their tissues and shallow roots that spread extensively in a lateral direction in order to provide as large a collecting area as possible when rain falls. They are seen to swell with an income of fresh moisture. They have a very slow growth, but they are often long-lived; even after uprooting a cactus may live for several years, drawing almost imperceptibly on its water store. The cactus and the euphorbia are the commonest of the succulents.

(d) Drought-enduring plants, such as the creosote bush of the North American deserts, which have no deep roots, no water storage, and do not evade the drought as do the annuals. Some appear to possess a unique ability to recover rapidly after wilting, with a slight increase in the relative humidity of the air such as occurs after sun-down, or with the onset of rain. This remarkable behaviour is due to a significant and unusual character of the protoplasm of the plant. If this character could be transferred to cereals, it is possible that man might extend the areas of cereal cultivation into quite arid regions.

Some succulents are tolerant of salt, where poor drainage pro-duces saline or alkaline soils (see p. 261). Such belong to a group of plants known as halophytes. Some of these, such as the salt bush, exude crystals of salt, which form a surface layer on the plant. In coastal areas, on the west of the tropical deserts, some plants use these hygroscopic salt crystals to absorb moisture from the sea mists and fogs.

Tundra

Finally, a few remarks must be made about tundra, which lies in the far north of the world. Tundra has often been described as a form of desert, in that the vegetation suffers from a physiological drought because low temperatures prevent the plants from drawing on moisture which is in the solid form of ice. However, modern investigations cast doubt upon the reality of a physiological drought, and it is suggested that the plants of the tundra are adapted to the peculiar climatic conditions of the regions. Some of these plants not only have a tolerance of frost but appear to depend on it, for successful germination. The vegetation consists of grassy plants, such as sedges, but mosses and lichens are very common (Fig. 20.9). Most plants, including dwarf trees, are xerophilous in appearance although not in character.

A summary of vegetation will be found in the following chapter together with a comparable summary of certain soils. As plants and soils are closely related it has been thought fit to place these summaries together (see pp. 262–264).

Further details of vegetation will be given in Part V (Chapters 17–20) and the distribution in the world of the major types of vegetation are shown on five maps therein. It should be mentioned that man has destroyed or modified, very considerably,—by cultivation, with clearance by fires, and by overgrazing—the original vegetation of quite large areas, in many parts of the world.

CHAPTER 16

Soils and Soil Erosion

Soil

The superficial layers of the earth's surface usually consist of soil which is a mantle covering the solid rock below. Soil represents the product of prolonged weathering, and the depth of the soil is fairly closely related to the time during which this process has gone on. Initially, the soil consists of fine mineral particles which are developed from the rock surface by weathering as described on pp. 4 and 5. Once a layer of such fragments has been produced, it is possible for plant life to establish itself on the surface of the soil, and within the pore spaces of the soil bacteria find a suitable environment in which to live. On the death of plants their tissues decay, and this process is materially assisted by bacterial action, which creates various compounds so that a supply of organic substances is added to the minerals of the soil and thus it is enriched. Many of these products, as well as some of the mineral substances, are dissolved by soil solutions. Rain water is a poor solvent, until it has combined with acids and bases derived from rock disintegration and organic decay. These solutions, in passing down through the soil, help to produce very significant changes at lower levels in the soil. The deepening of the soil is clearly dependent on an abundant supply of water, although this alone is not sufficient to develop a good soil, but it is in regions of copious rainfall that the most extensive soil layers are likely to develop. The very deep tropical soils of over 40 feet thickness owe much to the abundant rainfall combined with the high temperatures of these regions.

Mineral Particles of the Soil

The mineral particles which are found in the soil are produced mechanically by the action of heat, frost, and wind. Some of these particles may be further changed by circulating rain-water which introduces the chemical processes of oxidation, reduction, hydration, and carbonation. It was shown in Chapter 1 that the essential end-products of such weathering of granite were clay and sand particles, with carbonates in solution. The size (diameter) of the fine particles in a well-developed soil ranges from 2 mm down to less than 0·002

253

mm. The coarsest are known as gravel and sand (there are several grades of the latter, ranging from very coarse to very fine sand), those with diameters between 0·5 and 0·002 mm are known as silt, and the finest with a diameter of less than 0·002 mm are clay. It should be noted that, in pedology (soil study), these names are used to define the size of particles and, not necessarily, their mineralogical nature.

It will be seen that the nature of a soil must be related to the geological character of the underlying rock or the transported rock fragments which may cover the bed rock. Whilst the rock underneath plays its part, it is far from correct to assume that the final or mature soil is determined mainly by geological factors. Other constituents and various processes, to be described, help to produce much the same soil over large areas irrespective of the various rocks below, although the latter may play a predominant rôle in soil formation in some localities.

Organic Particles of the Soil

The upper layers of the soil are a source of organic compounds since, on the death of plants, profound changes are wrought in this vegetable material, chiefly through the agency of bacteria and fungi, as well as such animals as millipedes. Mixing of various products of decay is done by worms and burrowing animals. These changes are mainly directed to the breaking down of the plant refuse into somewhat simpler substances, and then the development of new and often quite complex substances. The remains of dead animals will also undergo similar changes. Resulting from these various changes is an organic product known as humus, a complex colloidal or jelly-like material which is brown in colour. The presence of humus in the soil permits yet further changes to occur. A plant cannot utilize substances unless they are in solution, and humus has the power of assisting in the formation of such solutions that are so vital to the plant. Furthermore, humus encourages bacteria to flourish, since it is food for these microscopic plants. This property of humus must obviously lead to an increase in the number of bacteria which are likely to reside in the soil, and so there is a further increase in organic material.

Bacterial Action in the Soil

Bacteria of certain kinds find a lodgment on the roots of plants such as clover, beans, and legumes. Certain characteristic nodules on the rootlets of these plants are indicative of bacterial colonies. The prime function of these particular bacteria is the fixation of nitrogen from the air which permeates the soil spaces. Nitrogen is an important element in plant nourishment, but plants can only use it in solutions of nitrates and ammonium compounds, the latter being converted to nitrates and nitrites. The fixation of nitrogen is encouraged by the presence of phosphorus.

Bacteria are reduced in numbers in the soil if the air supply is poor, consequently humus is less readily developed. A soil which is poor in oxygen, due in all probability to water-logging, is known as anæro-bic, and, with a drastic reduction of bacteria, plant refuse in such a soil is hardly changed at all, but remains as a layer of material which has a markedly acid reaction. The very important compounds, derived from soil particles and by fixation of nitrogen, which give the essential solutions on which a plant is to feed are substances containing potassium, nitrogen, and phosphorus, with some calcium and sodium, in conjunction with oxygen. It is known that for successful plant growth additional compounds containing what are known as trace elements, such as iodine, manganese, copper and boron, should be present in the soil but the precise function of these elements is obscure.

Characteristics of a Good Soil

Since the soil is the medium in which plants grow, it is of value to assess the qualities which make a good soil. These may be summarized as follows:

1. In order that plants may produce food, solutions of various compounds are required, and this of necessity calls for an adequate supply of soil moisture.

2. For the provision of humus and other organic products air, with its oxygen for the support of bacterial life and with its nitrogen to provide, by bacterial activity, nitrogenous compounds, must permeate the soil.

3. Soil must therefore have an abundance of spaces to permit the free circulation of both moisture and air. This circulation is most effective when the soil possesses a suitable texture, which is largely determined by the size of the mineral particles, for these may be regarded as nuclei around which various compounds collect in solution. Very fine clay particles form what are known as clay colloids.

4. Furthermore, the soil may have a flocculated structure which is produced by the grouping of individual particles into large irregular masses or floccules. The colloids, referred to above, are of great value in producing this crumb structure—they also attract moisture and retain it, thus safeguarding the supply of soil solution and nutrients for plants during a period of drought. Soils vary in the kind of structure which may be seen in them. Apart from crumb structure there may be prismatic, platy and columnar structures.

Acidity and Alkalinity of Soils

Carbon-dioxide is dissolved in soil water, some of it being extracted from the air and some is formed by bacterial action. The dissolved gas forms carbonic acid (H_2CO_3). This slightly acid solution may become more markedly acid in cases where organic acids are formed also by humus in the soil. On the other hand, there are usually compounds of calcium and sodium in the soil which have an alkaline reaction. Soils may be classified according to their pH value. This pH value expresses the concentration of hydrogen ions in the soil solution. With a neutral solution the value is 7 when the concentration is, very nearly, 10^{-7} grams of hydrogen ions per litre of solution. This figure 10^{-7} may be regarded as a fraction, $\frac{1}{10^7}$. An increase in this concentration of hydrogen ions indicates acidity. For instance, with a pH value of 6 the fraction is $\frac{1}{10^6}$, which is ten times greater than $\frac{1}{10^7}$. On the other hand, a pH value of 8 means a smaller concentration of hydrogen ions. Acidity in the soil is therefore expressed by values of pH which are below 7 but usually not less than 4·5. When the hydrogen ion concentration decreases so that the pH value exceeds 7, the soil is alkaline. In general, soils range from 4·5 to 9 as regards pH values.)

Soil Profiles and Leaching

It is customary to describe a soil by reference to its profile—that is, a vertical section through the soil to the underlying bed-rock or parent. In most cases, such a section will show more or less horizontal layers of varying thicknesses which are usually distinguished from one another by their different colours and structures. Each distinct layer is called a horizon of the soil, and the horizons usually form two groups, the A group at the top and the B group below (Fig. 16.1). The underlying rock is often referred to as the C horizon. In general, water in the soil moves downwards, and the solutions of organic compounds and mineral salts are frequently transferred from the A horizons to the B horizons. In regions of abundant and heavy rainfall, this is a process of great significance, and results in the leaching of the upper horizons. This means that there is eluviation (washing out) of humus and minerals or a depletion of much plant food in these upper horizons. Clearly the lower horizons, in particular the B horizons, are enriched by the illuviation (washing in) of these solutions and minerals. Often a soil profile shows a B horizon darker in colour than the A horizon, the lightness of which is due to this depletion. Usually the top of the A horizon is fairly dark because there is much humus near the surface and, not all of this is leached by the rain.

Podzolization and Laterization

The effect of leaching is known as podzolization in cool humid regions, although it can be observed in the tropics, particularly at relatively high altitudes. Decay of vegetable matter is slow in high latitudes, resulting in highly acid soil solutions with pH values as low as 3·5. In the tropics, the effects of leaching is markedly different and the process is known as laterization. Here decay of vegetable

CALCIFICATION— resulting from upward movement of soil water containing dissolved salts which are deposited in the A horizons

In dry and semi-arid climates | In wet climates

HUMUS LAYER

Lime accumulation

A HORIZONS — Eluviation

B HORIZONS

Illuviation

C HORIZONS (parent rock)

LEACHING— resulting from downward movement of soil water and dark-coloured particles which accumulate in the B horizons

FIG. 16.1.—A Soil Profile
No scale is given as relative thicknesses of horizons vary with profiles.

material is very rapid, partly because of the great abundance of bacteria, but mainly because most organic and chemical processes are accelerated by great heat. The soil solutions which produce tropical leaching have pH values between 5 and 7—in other words, the solutions are mildly acid to mildly alkaline in this respect.

In cool regions, the acid solutions remove most soluble materials from the upper A horizon and enrich the B horizons of the soil. All that is left in the surface layers, below a dark humus layer, is silica and unaltered mineral matter which give an ash-grey horizon, with a loose texture, which is typical of the podzols of the Russian coniferous forests from which the name (podzol) is derived. Illuviation, in the B horizon, introduces a high content of clay colloids which are tinted red, brown and yellow by iron oxides the latter having been removed almost entirely from the upper horizon which is left bleached (Fig. 16.2a). These colloids, combined with the fact that the soil solutions are less acid at depth, produce a well-flocculated B horizon.

In the tropics, the result of laterization is markedly different. The soil solutions are much less acid and remove silica downwards (the

257

A

B

(a)

A

B

(b)

Illustrations prepared by D. McKinley, from photographs by Dr. A. Muir and Dr. D. A. Osmond

FIG. 16.2.—Soil Profiles

(a) Profile of a leached soil. The A horizon is bleached below a surface layer which is rich in humus. The B horizons show darker hues with enrichment by iron oxides (see text). The soil is a pedalfer and is known as a podzol (see p. 333).

(b) Profile of a soil which has undergone calcification. The humus-rich A horizon under a grass cover passes down into the light-coloured B horizons which are accompanied by white masses of calcium compounds (see text). The soil is a pedocal and is known as a chernozem (see p. 335).

The boundaries between horizons in soils are rarely clear-cut. Each profile is about 4 feet in depth—the parent rock is not shown in either profile.

very opposite of podzolization) as well as other soluble substances and these are literally washed right out of a well-drained soil, eventually passing into streams. The various iron oxides are left throughout the profile, giving it a dominant red colour, where oxidation is effective, but, also, there are parts with a yellow colour, where hydration of the iron oxides has occurred. There tends to be little contrast between the horizons of the profile, in respect of colour or texture. In addition, insoluble aluminium oxide collects as bauxite in the form of irregular whitish masses which are usually stained red, with iron impurities. Bauxite may be regarded as a mineral rather than a soil and it yields the main ore of aluminium.

Soils which have been developed by podzolization, or laterization,[1] are referred to as pedalfers, i.e. soils with an aluminium (Al) and an iron (Fe) content.

[1] Laterite has aroused much controversy as to its origin. It is now widely accepted that this reddish clay is formed as a hardpan in tropical soils, where drainage is impeded, and where a dry season (such as in monsoonal south-east Asia) promotes evaporation, thus producing an upward movement in the soil of solutions which deposit this iron-rich layer. Since laterite is apparently not formed in well-drained soils, it cannot be regarded as a normal product in soil development. Therefore, it has been suggested by some soil scientists that the term laterization be replaced by ferrallization. Whilst this seems eminently reasonable, it is not proposed to adopt this change of terminology in the present text.

Calcification

It is possible for water in the soil to move upwards. This occurs in deserts or regions with a low rainfall. The upward lift of the water is effected by capillarity. Water which has sunk by gravity may be drawn up through the pore spaces of the dry upper horizons. This process is comparable to the absorption of water by a good cloth as used in drying crockery. The water on the damp crockery is not wiped off so much as drawn into the fine pore spaces of the cloth. Such water, in the lower layers of the soil, is often heavily charged with dissolved carbonates and other salts, and upon reaching higher levels, evaporation produces an accumulation of solid calcium carbonate and other salts, in the A horizon. This process is known as calcification (see Fig. 16.1) but, in addition to the upward movement of calcium salts, there may be some leaching from the surface layers so that calcium salts are deposited in the B horizon.

In semi-arid regions, such as the continental grasslands of temperate latitudes, the soil profile has much organic material near the surface—there is less bacterial action than in more humid areas but there is an abundant supply of potential humus, since so much of the grass plants lies below ground level. The affinity of grasses for calcium helps to retain organic colloids near the surface, thus producing a flocculated soil (Fig. 16.2b).

Soils which accumulate calcium are known as pedocals, i.e. soils with a calcium (Cal) content. With this high content of calcium carbonate, pedocals may show pH values, at the surface, of well above 7.

The drier the region, the higher is the zone of accumulation and, in some desert areas, the surface may become encrusted with salts, such as chlorides and sulphates of sodium, calcium and magnesium. This process is known as salinization and is usually associated with poor drainage which is typical of many areas of inland drainage (see Fig. 7.8). However, evaporation plays an important rôle.

Classification of Soils

It is possible to classify soils in several ways. It is not necessary that a farmer should distinguish a pedalfer from a pedocal or that he should know the soil processes which have produced them. The farmer is much more concerned with the texture and chemical reaction of his soils; in fact, it may be argued that an adequate knowledge of either is sufficient for practical purposes. On the other hand, more detailed and world-wide classifications must have reference to soil profiles and soil processes.

The interest of the farmer in the texture of his soils has led to a textural classification. On p. 254 reference was made to the dimensions of the mineral particles in soils, and three types of particles were noted, namely, sand, silt, and clay. The texture of a soil will depend primarily on the proportions of the various particles which are included within it. It is possible to define a variety of soils as shown by the diagram (Fig. 16.3). The corners of this diagram represent soils with 100 per cent clay, silt, and sand particles, respectively. Nearly equal proportions of sand and silt, together with a little clay, produce a loam soil which passes on the one hand to sandy loam and on the other to silty loam, with less silt and sand respectively. Similarly, sand and sandy loam develop into sandy clay loam and sandy clay, and finally clay, when more than 50 per cent of the particles are of clay texture. Silt, with increasing clay particles, passes to silty clay loam, then to silty clay, and finally to clay and so on.

FIG. 16.3.—Soil-texture Diagram

The texture of the soil is important, for soils with fine particles have larger particle surface areas than soils with very coarse particles, and this affects directly the economy of the plants in regard to the available food, since a larger surface area means a greater food supply in the form of aqueous solutions. Flocculation is very desirable, because it ensures a structure which keeps the soil effectively aerated. Calcium carbonate, humus, and other organic products are of value in producing flocculation. Some clays are impermeable, unless they have been artificially flocculated by the addition of lime or organic fertilizers.

The classification of soils by their chemical reaction depends upon the determination of the pH values of the particular soils. Much work has been done in correlating the success of various crops with the pH values of the soils in which they flourish, and undoubtedly such relationships are invaluable to the farmer. With most crops it is found that slightly acid soils with pH values of 6·0–6·5 are best. Too acid a soil produces unfavourable conditions; in particular, bacterial action is restricted. On the other hand, alkaline soils do not permit plants to avail themselves of certain trace elements.

Liming of the soil may be necessary to reduce soil acidity to some extent. It is quite erroneous to regard liming as effective only when it creates strong alkalinity, because such a state is as undesirable as considerable acidity. Liming should normally produce a pH value between 6·0 and 6·5.

When discussing the world distribution of soils, it is customary to refer to the major soils as zonal, in that very often they cover great tracts of continental surfaces, and their characteristics are largely dependent upon climatic controls. The parent rock has little influence on the type of zonal soil which is found in a given region. Thus, a soil derived from a granite parent in the tropics is unlikely to resemble a soil, also with a granite parent, which is developed under cool or cold climates. When it is remembered that the end-products of the disintegration of rocks are essentially particles of sand, clay, and carbonates (see pp. 5–6) and that any rock will yield some, if not all, types of mineral particles for soil production this may seem rather extraordinary. However, it is the predominance of some particular process, such as leaching or calcification, which is primarily responsible for the type of zonal soil which is produced, and it is therefore the climatic control that is of paramount importance. Under wet climates pedalfers are common as a result of podzolization or laterization, whereas in arid or semi-arid regions pedocals will be typical.

The main zonal soils are distributed broadly in the world as shown in Fig. 16.5. Since it has been shown that climate controls soil development as well as the major vegetation belts, it is not surprising that the zonal soils show a fairly close correspondence with the distribution of the major vegetation belts as shown in Fig. 16.4.

In addition, there are intrazonal soils which may cover extensive areas within the regions of the various zonal soils—this fact should be borne in mind when atlas maps showing soil distributions are consulted. Intrazonal soils depend usually upon some special factor —such as the nature of the parent rock, drainage and slope. Many intrazonal soils are caused by impeded drainage which interferes with normal soil development. There are three groups to be mentioned:

1. Soils in which salinization has occurred, are typical of dry regions with poor drainage—such as in inland drainage basins. Soils which contain a very high proportion of salts are known as solonchaks. The salt forms a soft friable zone at the surface, otherwise there is a fairly normal profile below. With moderate leaching,

a solonchak may be converted into a solonetz, which is a relatively alkaline soil on account of included sodium hydroxide. As the salts are flushed away by rains, or irrigation, there is eluviation from the A horizon to the B horizon, with the formation of a prismatic structure and a distinct reddish-brown to black coloration which is the result of the dissemination of organic residues by the powerful

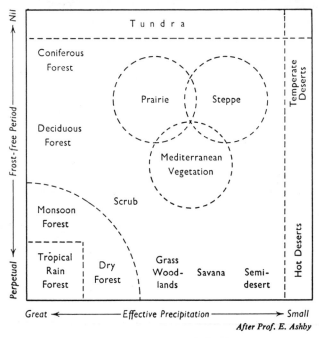

FIG. 16.4.—A Summary of Vegetation

hydroxides. The A horizon loses its good structure so that it may be seriously eroded by winds. However, it has been discovered that this horizon may be flocculated by the addition of gypsum—a calcium salt which has the ability to stabilize the colloids near the surface. The solonetz may, in turn, be effectively leached to produce a soloth which shows some degree of podzolization—the very alkaline soil solutions, with pH values of 8·5–9·4, produce changes which resemble those effected by highly acid solutions; thus the A horizon is bleached. The results of salinization are seen in Fig. 7.8.

2. Soils in which gleying or gleization has occurred, are found with water-logging near rivers, in bogs and in the swamps of forests. They are frequently dark at the surface, owing to a high organic content, but, below, the water-logging excludes oxygen so that chemical reduction takes place changing the iron oxides to ferrous

compounds—the latter produce blueish or greenish grey clays which are very sticky.

3. Rendzinas are soils with a limestone or Chalk parent. Usually these soils are very shallow and vary in colour from dark grey to yellow and reddish-brown when they develop on a hard, impermeable limestone. They are then known as terra rossa soils, as seen in the Mediterranean region of Europe and elsewhere. When the parent

(F) — Pedalfer   (C) — Pedocal

FIG. 16.5.—A Summary of Zonal Soils

rock is a soft limestone the soils are quite dark (almost black), as in the Black Belt of Alabama which is famous for its cotton crops. Terra rossa is a term which is used rather indiscriminately for soils with a reddish hue. In south-east Brazil, for instance, the soil of the coffee belt is known as terra roxa but it is developed on a parent of diabase (an igneous rock, often called dolerite).

Finally, there are azonal soils which are of very slight importance. They may be considered as barely changed rock. Much ground moraine, screes at scarp feet and at the base of mountain slopes, water-logged river alluvium of recent formation, and dry sand of dunelands are of this type. They may be regarded as skeletal soils since

263

they often possess the necessary mineral content for the formation of good soil, but lack the organic fraction which is so necessary. Loess is technically a rock, not a soil—however, development of a loessic soil, on account of its richness in minerals and soluble salts, is possible. High mountain zones are somewhat exceptional in regard to their soils (as they are from a climatic point of view). Many soils of such regions are skeletal in form. Steepness of slopes creates downward movement of soil material and helps to increase erosion. Extremes of temperature and exposure to winds and rain are also factors which result in marked local variations in the soil of mountain areas.

Variations, of course, occur in all soils and this gives rise to a classification into soil series, types and phases. Individual soils within an area may show practically identical features so that they form a series, each soil being distinguished by its texture as a soil type of the series. Minor variations within a soil type are called soil phases.

The outstanding soils of the world are discussed in relation to the climatic regions in which they occur (see pp. 295, 313, and 333).

A Summary of Vegetation and Zonal Soils

It has been shown that climate determines both vegetation and zonal soils. Thus, there is a relationship between the vegetation cover and the zonal soils in extensive areas which have the same type of climate, as will be discussed in the following chapters. However, at this stage it seems appropriate to indicate the broad relationship between the major types of vegetation and the zonal soils in the world in the form of a summary of these, with accompanying diagrams.

The diagram (Fig. 16.4) takes account of two significant controls on plant growth:

1. The length of the frost-free period in the year.
2. The effective precipitation, which may be regarded as the moisture available to the soil and plants, after allowance has been made for loss, to both, through evaporation and run-off.

The diagram attempts to show the relationship for the northern hemisphere between the major vegetation groups and these two controls. The bottom left-hand corner represents the tropical rain forests, where frost-free conditions are obviously at a maximum, and also the effective precipitation remains great. Along the left-hand side of the diagram the effective precipitation remains great but, with less favourable temperature controls, towards the top, there is a sequence of forests which gradually pass to tundra. Along the bottom is the tropical sequence, with less and less effective precipitation but with high temperatures at all seasons. Here, tropical rain forests pass through grass woodlands, thence to savana, and finally to hot desert. The latter passes through the temperate deserts to tundra on the right. The inner zone is occupied with overlapping areas representing prairie, steppe and Mediterranean vegetation, the latter being rather difficult to place precisely within this scheme.

Fig. 16.5 shows the approximate distribution of zonal soils in the northern hemisphere. There is quite obviously a considerable similarity in the layout of this diagram and the one showing vegetation in the world. To the left, with abundant rainfall, are the soils known as pedalfers which have been well-leached, whilst, to the right, are pedocals, in semi-arid and arid areas. Many zonal soils are thus capable of being related to a major vegetation belt, although one must be careful not to make too precise a comparison, particularly in the central part of Fig. 16.5. As has been mentioned above, Mediterranean areas prove difficult to place in such a scheme.

Soil Erosion

Soil erosion is an evil which has affected many areas of the world in this century, and whilst it is largely man-made, it can be legitimately included in a study of physical geography. Under a cover of natural vegetation the chances of destructive soil erosion are practically nil. Apart from desert areas, removal of large quantities of surface rock waste in a relatively short time is almost negligible. There has been, over thousands of years, a vast removal of rock waste and earlier developed soils as rivers have done their work, but it must be remembered that this process has been extraordinarily slow. Yet, in a matter of a few decades, man has destroyed the work of nature which has taken so very long.

Once man has removed by cropping or over-grazing the natural mat of vegetation, particularly in grasslands where the lack of trees enables wind erosion to be so effective, then soil erosion has been an almost certain consequence. Thus dust bowls are literally man-made deserts where deflation has proceeded very rapidly. However, much soil erosion has been caused by rain storms and this has been most common in semi-arid regions. The continental grasslands in temperate and, to a large extent, in tropical latitudes have suffered most of all where they have been cropped or where the grass has been thinned by heavy grazing. The soil erosion in these regions is certainly aggravated in part by the incidence of the rainfall in short but very heavy showers, which create a considerable run-off once the surface layers of the soil have become temporarily water-logged.

Apart from wind erosion there are two main types of soil erosion which can be regarded as truly destructive. Firstly, there is sheet erosion, in which a uniform layer or depth of the soil is removed by rain washing down a slope. This is much aggravated if cultivation has led to ploughing up and down the slopes, because the individual furrows become shallow gullies down which the soil moves with the water. At the foot of such slopes there may accumulate soil deposits which are stratified as a result of successive rains. This is a very widespread form of soil erosion, and it is not easily detected in its earliest stages because the surface of the land shows no radical alteration in appearance. The degree of sheet erosion depends upon several factors, such as the angle of the slope, the texture of the soil, and local climatic conditions, together with the methods of tillage which have been employed.

The second type of erosion is known as gully erosion, and whilst wrong methods of cultivation may lead to it, more usually it is local relief which sets up this type of erosion by the establishment of a small-scale drainage system that is in turn used by each additional rush of water after a heavy storm of rain. The effect of gully erosion is to create 'bad land' surfaces, and each gully extends in a headward direction with later erosion, so that a dendritic pattern is produced. Such gullying may be seen very frequently on spoil heaps in industrial regions of this country. The waste of rock and soil is carried from the land down these gullies, and collects as a fan of soil and stones which may unfortunately overwhelm and destroy the value of other adjacent crop lands that have not so far been eroded.

Soil Conservation

Various methods have been adopted to check soil erosion where it has commenced, and these are mainly devices to prevent the downward movement of the soil on slopes. It is almost impossible, with cropping of the land, to avoid having the bare soil exposed during certain periods of the year, but one preventive method is known as strip cropping, in which the areas of the soil exposed at any time are restricted. They are separated by strips carrying a vegetative cover of grasses or some leguminous crop. The down wash of the soil is also prevented by contour ploughing and terracing. In the first method the furrows are ploughed by following the contours of the land, which means that the furrows are rarely straight but in sweeping curves. Each ridge between the furrows is therefore level and lies across the down slope. The second method is terracing, which is devised to fulfil one of two purposes. Either the terraces trap the water so that it is gradually absorbed by the soil, or they deflect water, which would otherwise wash down-slope, into drainage channels that carry it away. In the former case each terrace is level and has soil piled up to retain and absorb the water, and in effect this is the same as contour ploughing. In the latter case the terrace has a low ridge of soil on the down-slope side, and the terrace slopes laterally across the down slope into a drainage channel. Another method of preventing soil erosion in crop land is to use a lister with a basin-forming attachment. The lister is primarily for setting seed. Its front part produces a broad furrow, but it is further improved by the addition of the basin-forming attachment. This creates a series of basins in each furrow by throwing soil athwart the line of the furrow. These soil dams hold the rain in small basins or pools which gradually drain into the ground. Where wind is a predominant agent of erosion, the planting of wind-breaks is a measure to restrict erosion. Flood control of large rivers is closely linked with these various efforts to prevent or arrest erosion.

Part V   Climatology

CHAPTER 17

Introduction – Hot Climates

Climatic Classification

Attempts at a classification of climate may be said to date from the time of the Greeks, who had a qualitative scheme involving thermal belts, but it was not until the late nineteenth century and even later, in this century, that quantitative classifications of climate were formulated. Supan in 1879 attempted to correlate the boundaries of the Greek thermal belts with isotherms which had appeared on a map, for the first time, in 1848. Later, in 1884, Köppen, whose name is inevitably linked with climatic classifications, modified these belts of Supan.

However, Köppen was concerned, primarily as a botanist, in an attempt to establish fairly rigid limits to the major vegetation zones of the world, using temperature and rainfall values. This led him to publish his classifications of 1900 and 1918. In the former some of the climatic types which he recognized were actually named after plants, e.g. baobab, liana, and birch. In trying to fit the salient vegetation types within his limits of temperature and rainfall, Köppen may be said to have been too rigid. Consequently we must accept the evidence of later workers, such as Russell and Thornthwaite in America, who have shown that clear-cut climatic boundaries are very rare, and that just as one distinct vegetation zone merges into another through a transitional zone, so climatic types must be allowed such transitions. It is quite possible that, within a period of a quarter of a century, the controls which are deemed to separate two distinct climatic types may change, and it is therefore reasonable to assume a shift of the accepted boundaries in such a period. However, there is no doubt that the major vegetation zones as well as the major soil regions reflect very closely the control of climate.

In this book, limits of temperature and régimes of rainfall are used to determine the climatic regions which are closely related to the natural vegetation regions and, very largely, to the regions of zonal soils. It has been considered of value to discuss both vegetation and soils separately in previous chapters, but in the following section of this book further discussions of both topics are given in appropriate places.

The mean monthly temperatures and the mean monthly rainfall totals may be used to show graphically the essentials of the climate of a given place. Throughout the following chapters such graphs are employed to illustrate the text, and it may be mentioned that all the graphs are on the same scale as shown in Fig. 17.1, and that all carry the same ancillary information, namely, the mean annual range of temperature (above the continuous line) and the total annual rainfall in inches (above the columns showing the rainfall for each month) as well as the height, in feet, above sea level (in brackets) after the name of the place. Temperatures are shown on the Fahrenheit scale but conversion to the Celsius scale may be made by the reader, using the linear scales provided. The graphs are placed beside the several maps which attempt to show the regional distribution of the climatic types and sub-types that

Buenos Aires (82)

Fig. 17.1.—Climatic Graph

are reviewed. Where places are referred to in the text, it will be found that, in most cases, there is the climatic graph for that particular station in the same chapter.

Also, the maps show the related natural vegetation. It has been observed above that transitional zones do exist, and that it is well-nigh impossible to develop a scheme of climatic boundaries which perfectly fits all vegetation zones. The purpose of the various maps is to show as far as possible the vegetation which lies within the limits of temperature and rainfall that have been adopted.

The classification which is adopted is as follows:

1. Hot climates—with mean annual temperatures of, at least, 70° F.

2. Warm temperate climates—with the coldest month having a mean temperature of not less than 43° F.

3. Cool temperate climates—with one to five months having mean temperatures below 43° F.

4. Cold climates—lying polewards from the regions with cool temperate climates and divided into cold temperate, tundra, and polar climates by various temperature controls, as will be seen in due course.

Several subdivisions of each of the above types, excepting the tundra and polar climates (since no sensible distinctions can be made), are determined by the régime of rainfall and, in some cases, by the occurrence of monsoonal controls.

Hot Climates

(a) Introduction

The areas with hot climates are enclosed by the mean annual isotherm of 70° F (see Fig. 17.4). Most of this zone is tropical, but parts are extra-tropical and extend to approximately 30° N and S. The areas are thus within the trade-wind belts of each hemisphere, and include the Doldrums belt with the intertropical front. Three major types of climate with their subdivisions may be distinguished as follows:

1. *Equatorial.* With rain at all seasons, and sometimes exhibiting a double maximum of rainfall.
2. *Tropical.* (i) Continental, with rain in the hot season only.
   (ii) Marine, with rain at all seasons, but with a distinct maximum of rainfall at one period of the year.
   (iii) Monsoonal, with rain mainly in the hot season.
3. *Hot Desert.* (i) Continental, with little or no rain.
   (ii) Marine (west coast), with little or no rain, but much influenced by cold currents offshore. In part, areas with this type of climate lie outside the hot regions as defined by the mean annual isotherm of 70° F.

(b) Equatorial Climates
Main Controls

Regions with these climates are quite limited in extent, rarely stretching through more than ten degrees of latitude in all. Two characteristics of the climates are the constant high temperatures and the well-distributed rainfall, so that, in general, there is no season of drought. The control of the Doldrums belt with its constant temperature, low-pressure air, and regular convectional rainfall has long been regarded as of primary importance. However, air masses, whose sources are in the subtropical high-pressure cells, converge along the intertropical front, where air ascends in keeping with the earlier conception of convectional uplift in these areas. The humid warm air masses of oceanic origin are unstable, and productive of very heavy rainfall. The intertropical front oscillates north and south with the annual movement of the overhead sun, although it coincides fairly closely with the heat equator. In the northern summer it is well north of the geographical equator, so that there are marked transgressions by the south-east trade winds into the northern hemisphere, and both the Guinea coast of Africa and parts of the East Indies are influenced by air streams which have their origins in the southern hemisphere.

Temperature

Insolation is fairly uniform throughout the year, since noonday angles of the sun are never less than $66\frac{1}{2}°$ and, also, the length of the days is constant at the Equator. Mean monthly temperatures remain very steady in lowland areas at about 80° F, whilst in neighbouring uplands the values are about 55°-60° F (see Quito).[1] Mean annual ranges are remarkably small, rarely more than 5° F, and in oceanic positions they may be less than 1° F. Absolute maximum and minimum temperatures are of the order of 100° F and 60° F, respectively, in lowland regions. The keynote of the temperature is its monotony both as regards monthly and daily rhythms. Two equinoctial peaks of temperature may coincide with overhead sun (see Georgetown), but this feature is actually far from common.

Rainfall

Whilst the Doldrums belt is a zone of convergence, there is little contrast between the air masses, and thus frontal developments are unusual, apart from occasional squalls. The fairly constant insolation produces a regular convectional uplift of air, but rain does not necessarily fall every day and some months may have little rain. In general, the early morning is clear and sunny but clouds soon develop, with the mounting effect of convectional uplift of moist air. From noon onwards, rain falls in a series of violent downpours (accompanied by thunder and lightning) which are interspersed with sunshine. The period of maximum rainfall in the day is usually between noon and 4 p.m. but the showers may persist until midnight. Annual totals of rainfall are commonly between 65 and 80 inches, but local relief may produce greater totals, and peculiarities of régime are shown by many stations.

It would be expected that a maximum of rainfall should appear at each equinox or shortly afterwards, when convectional uplift should be greatest in view of the passage of the overhead sun. but there is usually a lag between zenithal sun and the highest temperatures. Such a double maximum is actually not very common, because sometimes one peak of rainfall is entirely suppressed (see Para) or is much smaller than the other.

With the movement of the overhead sun between the tropics there should be, theoretically, two periods in each year (about the solstitial dates, when the Doldrums rain-belt is shifted farthest north and south) when the rainfall should be less than at other times in equatorial regions. In fact, just north and south of the equatorial zone with well-distributed rainfall the regime shows two drier seasons (not rainless seasons) when the sun is overhead at either tropic (see Yaundé). Still farther polewards the drier seasons are more marked,

[1] Climatic graphs are on pp. 276–277.

but they are unequal in length, and still nearer to each tropic the interval between the two passages of overhead sun becomes shorter, and by about 10°-15° N the two rainy periods coalesce and there are, in essence, the two seasons in the year, one dry and the other rainy, of the tropical continental climates.

However, the Doldrums belt and the intertropical front are not placed symmetrically about the geographical equator at the equinoxes as would be expected. The heat equator is displaced northwards for most of the year, particularly in Africa, and to a less extent in South America. Thus the greatest heat, and therefore the most effective convectional rains, as well as the convergence of the two sets of trade winds are in the northern hemisphere rather than the southern. With this displacement the typical equatorial regime, with a double maximum of rainfall, is most likely to be found north of the Equator where it may be recognized as far north as 8° N.

Vegetation

The vegetation associated with the equatorial climates in lowland areas is best represented by the selvas or tropical rain forests of Amazonia, although these forests are best developed on well-drained uplands between the major streams (Fig. 17.2). This rain forest is dependent upon the maintenance of adequate and uniform precipitation and any significant departure from the normal régime, such as the appearance of a dry season, causes a deterioration of forest to grass woodland, which occurs locally within all the forest areas, but particularly in the Congo basin. The rain forest has trees rising to 150–200 feet, for the great heat and abundant rainfall promote vigorous growth. Trees grow straight and tall, competing for sunlight. Their crowns may form a canopy as low as 80 feet but usually it is well above 100 feet. There is usually a second storey of trees which rises to possibly 60 feet. These trees are not necessarily diminutive examples of the taller ones but different species (as well as tree ferns) which are adapted to existence between the canopy and the forest floor, on which fungi and small ferns may be found in the relative gloom (certain fungi do not need light for photosynthesis as is the case with other plants). This restriction of light means that plant growth on the forest floor is retarded and that undergrowth is sparse. On the edges of the rain forests, where light may penetrate more readily, undergrowth may become unbridled in its development—thus advances made by man into these forests have been repelled. The large trees are the hosts of parasitic plants and epiphytes (such as orchids) which lodge in the forks of branches, whilst vine-like lianas scale the giant trees and frequently link one tree to another in festoons (Fig. 17.3). Trees are found at all stages of growth. At any one time some are flowering, some are fruiting, whilst

E. Aubert de la Rüe, Pully-Lausanne

FIG. 17.2.—Tropical Rain Forest, Maroni Plateau, French Guiana

Dense rain forest, with trees rising to heights of 80-100 feet, surrounds the base of an inselberg (see pp. 121-2).

others may be casting their leaves. In general, the trees do not grow in pure stands, so that whilst valuable timbers are found in these forests, the practical difficulties of exploitation are great. Amongst the valuable trees are greenheart and mahogany, with rosewood and ebony of subsidiary importance.

Equatorial Regions

Congo and Amazon Basins

Both basins are in the zones of the trade winds of each hemisphere, but the Congo basin is shielded to a large extent by the East African plateau, so that its rainfall is, on the whole, less than that of Amazonia, which is wide open towards the east. Most of Amazonia receives 70 inches of rain in the year, but the central part has less rain than elsewhere. The greatest precipitation is in the west (see Iquitos), and this is often attributed to the effects of the relief of the nearby Andes mountains on the trade winds. Few stations show a double maximum of rainfall, and both Para and Manáos experience two seasons in the year, a very wet period before and after the vernal equinox (known as verão), and a period of low rainfall in the late months of the year (known as inverno). South of the Amazon there is a marked maximum of rainfall in the southern summer. Beyond the

273

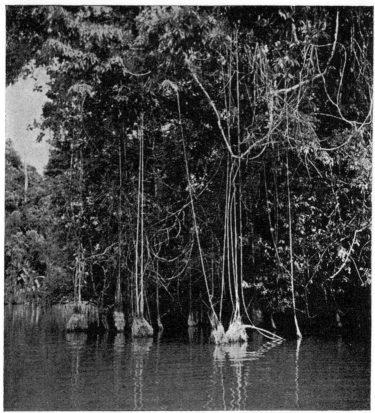

E. Aubert de la Rüe, Pully-Lausanne

Fig. 17.3.—Tropical Rain Forest along the R. Tampoc, French Guiana

The dense undergrowth, typical of the edges of these forests, is evident. Aerial roots of epiphytes hang down from the trees to obtain water—in appearance, these roots resemble lianas.

Andes on the Colombian coast north-east trade winds bring ample rainfall at all seasons, since the trend of the mountains gives access to these winds. Whilst many places in the Congo basin show a double maximum of rainfall, the annual totals are less than in South America, being of the order of 50–60 inches (see Yaundé). Whilst forest largely covers Amazonia, in parts of the Congo basin the rain forest is replaced by dry forest and grass woodlands where the annual rainfall is less and the rainfall in some months is slight. The Colombian west coast and the interior valleys have dense tropical rain forest.

The East Indies with Malaya and the Guinea coastlands of Africa are equatorial areas, but they have distinct monsoonal controls, and are therefore discussed on pp. 288 and 290 respectively.

274

(c) Tropical Climates

Main Controls

The areas which experience these climates lie immediately north and south of the equatorial areas, extending to the tropics in some instances (Fig. 17.4). Apart from the monsoonal climates, the facts of importance in the continental and marine types are as follows:

(a) The zones are under the continual influence of the trade winds.

(b) The regions are affected annually in the summer season on their equatorward margins by the Doldrums belt of convectional rains.

(c) Insolation is more effective than at the Equator at the time of overhead sun, since days are both longer and less cloudy.

The interaction of the first two controls distinguishes the marine type, which receives most rain from the trade winds at all seasons, from the continental type which receives most of its rain by the invasion of the Doldrums belt at one season of the year (Fig. 17.5). Both types are affected by convectional rainfall with the migration of the overhead sun and the related movement of the Doldrums belt into the hemisphere experiencing summer. The marine areas depend also upon the instability rainfall from warm oceanic air masses as they move onshore to the even warmer land. This rainfall may be regarded as of trade-wind origin.

Temperature

The temperature depends primarily upon the insolation, which shows seasonal variation owing to the difference between the highest and lowest noonday angles of the sun, which increases uniformly from the Equator (where the difference is $23\frac{1}{2}°$) to either tropic (where the difference is 47°). Nevertheless, the period when the sun is nearly overhead is not so cloudy as at the Equator, and at this time the length of the day is greater than at the Equator[1] so that the mean monthly temperatures in the hot season may be over 90° F. Cool-season temperatures rarely show monthly means of less than 70° F. It is more suitable to refer to hot and cool[2] seasons rather than to summer and winter in these latitudes. The mean annual range of temperature is thus greater than in equatorial regions, often as large as 15° F, but marine stations show much smaller ranges, as at Colon, 1·5° F, and this is largely true of places at higher levels, as at Caracas, with a range of 4° F. Marine stations are relatively cool, as a result of the fanning effect of the trade winds. Since cloudiness is often very slight, daily maxima of temperature may soar to 110° F, but these are balanced by low temperatures at night through intense radiation, and frost may occur in continental areas.

[1] At each tropic the maximum length of the day is $13\frac{1}{2}$ hours.

[2] The term 'cool', as applied to one season, is relative to the greater heat of the 'hot' season; it is always hot as judged by British standards.

FIG. 17.4.—Hot Regions—Equatorial and Tropical

277

Rainfall

The controls of the trade-wind influence and the Doldrums belt have been mentioned. Rainfall totals are dependent on:

(*a*) The latitude, since the encroaching rainfall of the Doldrums invasion, in the hot season, is restricted to low latitudes and decreases polewards, particularly, in the continental interiors. This is also true of the marine zones, as far as convectional rainfall is concerned, but the main source of rain in these areas tends to be of trade wind origin.

(*b*) Local relief, for islands like Madagascar and Cuba have heavy rainfall on one side and but scanty rain on the leeward or western side.

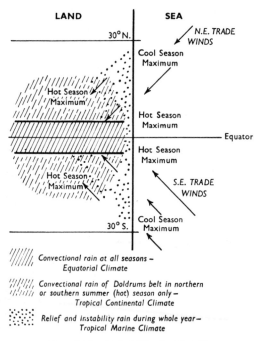

FIG. 17.5.—Rainfall in the Tropics

(*c*) Tropical storms, tornadoes on land, and hurricanes off the eastern coasts, may affect the rainfall totals in some areas.

There are, in the continental interiors, two seasons, one hot and rainy, the other cool and dry. The rainy season may last for seven or eight months in low latitudes and brings as much as 50 inches of rain (see Cuyaba), but this period shrinks to two months on the poleward margins, with as little as 10 inches. A double peak of temperature, apparently marking each passage of overhead sun, is shown in some graphs, but the incidence of rain in the hot season produces a marked cooling of the air and higher temperatures follow the rains (see Kayes). This effect may be observed at some equatorial stations.

In marine locations there are cool and hot seasons, both of which are rainy, but one is more rainy than the other, depending upon the relative effectiveness of the convectional and trade-wind influences. In general, marine stations show greater totals of rainfall than do corresponding places in the interiors (see Rio de Janeiro).

Vegetation

The continental interiors with their marked dry seasons are covered with tropical grasslands, although, as has been said elsewhere, 'grass woodlands' is often a more accurate description. Rain forest rarely ends abruptly, and there is a transition polewards through the grass woodlands to true savana (treeless plains). Schantz, the American geographer, has shown that, in the horseshoe-shaped zone enclosing the rain forests of equatorial Africa, the following types of vegetation may be recognized:

(a) High grass-low tree savana, which usually forms a fringe to the rain forests and is dotted with trees. The grass may rise as high as twelve feet in the wet season.

(b) Acacia-tall grass savana, having grass 3-5 feet in height and scattered clumps of trees.

(c) Dry forest, particularly in East Africa, which is park-like, with a grass floor, and has semi-deciduous or facultatively deciduous trees (Figs. 5.8 and 15.2).

In addition, there are areas of temperate rain forest on high ground and acacia-desert grass savana with sparse grassland and thorny trees (Fig. 15.1) on the poleward margins of the areas. Everywhere the trees are adapted to the dry season in having a water store, as in the case of the baobab, or by shedding their leaves (Fig. 17.12).

The grasses of savana areas grade from over 12 feet (Fig. 17.6) to under 2 feet with increasing latitude and decreasing rainfall. There is an immediate response to the onset of the rains, and the very rapid growth which ensues may, in the better-watered areas, result in the trees being submerged in a sea of grass. At full growth the grass is often yellow, and even red, but rarely is it green, except with the onset of the rainy season. In the drought season it withers and turns brown, to remain dormant until the next rainy season. Marine zones with their well-distributed and heavy rainfall have tropical rain forest, but on the leeward slopes of coastal mountains these are replaced by dry forest and grass woodland, and even semi-desert.

279

E. Aubert de la Rüe, Pully-Lausanne

FIG. 17.6.—Elephant Grass near Odienne, Ivory Coast, West Africa

This grass may reach 12 feet and obscure the lower parts of trees.

Tropical Regions

Africa

These regions of Africa have climates with varied régimes, but there are essentially three areas:

1. *Sudan.* In this region the climate is almost a perfect example of the tropical continental type, having a wet season when the Doldrums belt is displaced northwards from the Equator (see Kayes). The coastal margin in West Africa is of interest (see p. 290).

2. *East Africa.* Here the climate is essentially equatorial in régime. The graph for Nairobi shows two maxima of temperature and rainfall, but the elevation of the plateau reduces the total rainfall, so that grassland and dry forest are representative of the vegetation. The mean monthly temperatures are relatively low, but the mean annual range is small, as with equatorial climates. Local relief produces much variety over the plateau; the rift valleys show remarkable anomalies of rainfall, for in some places forests are found, whilst in others the rainfall is so low that solid salt is preserved in dried-out lakes. The water surface of Lake Victoria increases the humidity of the local southerly winds so that Entebbe, on the northern shore, has sixty inches of rain. which is well distributed throughout the year.

3. *South of the Congo Basin and of East Africa.* The east coast has tropical marine climate, with onshore south-east trade winds. However, much of the area is covered with tall grass savana and forests only extend along river courses. The interior receives but scanty rain from the trade wind source but it is invaded by the Doldrums belt of convectional rain in the hot season. Much of this region is covered with dry forest. The north–south extent of these southern savanas is greater than in the Sudan, where a sharp limit is imposed by the dry north-east trade winds over the Sahara.

South America

In the north is the area of the Guianas and the Orinoco basin with a fairly normal continental régime, except on the coast, which has rain forests. On the Brazilian Plateau and its adjacent east coast there is a fairly consistent distribution of the two types of climate, as in southern Africa. Interior stations show rather greater rainfall and longer wet seasons than are usual in Africa (see Cuyaba). In North-east Brazil there is an area of deficient rainfall that gives rise to thorn forest, with acacias, known as the caatinga. Various explanations have been given for this dry region, but none is entirely convincing. It would seem that the region is sheltered by high land to the east from rain-bearing trade winds. The south-east trade winds are dry winds on the north-east coast of Brazil and they rarely withdraw from this area in the period from February to May (see p. 219). Thus, the temperature inversion which is typical of the trade winds never weakens. This may be a possible explanation of the frequency of droughts in this region. Furthermore, the inter-tropical front rarely covers this part of Brazil to allow air masses to converge and give rain (see p. 270). Much of the Brazilian Plateau is covered with campos cerrados (with trees) and campos limpos (without trees). There are extensions of tropical rain forest along the upper courses of southern tributaries of the Amazon and, also, near the eastern edge of the plateau. It has been suggested that the term 'campos cerrados' be adopted widely for all tropical grass woodlands.

Tropical Highlands

Altitude has a marked effect on the tropical climates, as in the Andes and the East African region. In Latin America it is customary to refer to three vertical zones. Rain forests extending round the base of the tropical Andes in Peru, Colombia, and Ecuador, belong to the 'tierra caliente', which passes upwards above a level of about 3,000 feet into the 'tierra templada'. Here mean monthly temperatures are depressed to 65°–70° F. Ascending humid air gives mist and cloud, which support the tropical moss forest (sometimes known as cloud forest). This is a variety of rain forest in which mosses encumber the trees to an extraordinary degree so that their trunks and branches appear to be two or three times broader than they really are. Above about 6,000 feet the 'tierra templada' passes to the 'tierra fria', which rises to some 10,000 feet. Higher still are uplands that remain snow-covered for most of the year. The 'tierra fria' is obviously cooler than the lower zones, and has grasslands with some dry forest. The mean monthly temperatures are remarkably uniform, as is shown by the Quito graph. In Africa the mountains of Kenya and Kilimanjaro show a similar zoning, with grass and dry forest at the base, passing up to temperate forest and, at still higher levels, to temperate grass-land, which include alpine meadows.

(d) Monsoonal Tropical Climates
Main Controls

There are large areas of intertropical land and seas which are under the controls known as monsoonal. The main area is in India, South-east Asia including the East Indies, and North Australia, but there are smaller areas in Africa, Central America, and Mexico. The characteristics of a monsoonal climate may be summed up as follows:

(a) There are essentially two seasons which are characterized by opposite wind directions.

(b) At one season the winds are onshore and bring rain, whilst at the other season winds are offshore and dry or drier weather is experienced.

(c) The main criterion is this reversal of the seasonal wind directions, and in effect this means that the normal trade winds of these areas are absent during part of the year.

(d) The underlying cause of this reversal of the winds is the effect of continentality on temperatures and pressures in the interior of the land masses concerned.

In passing, it may be noted that the word 'monsoon' means season. Since there is a maximum of rainfall in the hot season, these climates resemble the tropical continental climate but they have special seasonal, or monsoonal, controls.

Monsoonal Regions
India

India is the classic area of monsoonal climate, and maps in Fig. 17.7 show the general seasonal conditions in the great theatre in the East, of which India is only a part. India is in some respects self-contained in that the plateau of the Deccan and the northern lowlands lie to the south of high mountains which form a climatic barrier. The seat of the controls is the plateau region of Inner Asia which, in winter, is covered by cold air, owing to the intense cooling, and this is reflected in the high pressure values. However, such cold air, as may descend from the plateaus, is warmed by adiabatic contraction so that January temperatures are of the order of 50° F in northern India whereas Ceylon has temperatures of 80° F at that time. As will be seen later

Fig. 17.7.—Pressure and Winds in Southern Asia and Australia

(p. 310), China receives surges of very cold air from the eastern side of this high pressure region of Inner Asia. Nevertheless, there are outblowing winds, in general, over India in this season. In summer, one of the most extensive hot zones of the world stretches from Africa over India and on to the inner plateaus of Tibet and Mongolia. This zone replaces the winter high pressure by markedly low-pressure air, which has its deepest centre in the Sind region of North-west India.

The Indian year may be divided climatically into three parts:

(*a*) A hot season (with inblowing winds from the sea that bring rain) which extends from June to mid-September in the north, and from June until mid-December in the south.

(*b*) A cool season, with outblowing winds, from the end of December until early March, which may be regarded as the normal winter.

(*c*) A hot season, which is dry, lasting from March until May.

The lengths of the three seasons given above may vary very considerably from year to year.

It is during the hot dry season that the overhead sun moves north from the Equator. At the beginning of this period the normal trade-wind circulation is present in each hemisphere, and the two sets of winds meet at the intertropical front, which is approximately equatorial in its position (Fig. 17.8). The culmination of this season brings a very different set of conditions (Fig. 17.9). The low pressure in northern India has reached a critical depth, and the Doldrums belt of low pressure near the Equator may be considered as having relatively high pressure. There is, in fact, a pressure gradient from the southern hemisphere, and the south-east trade winds transgress the Equator into the northern hemisphere.

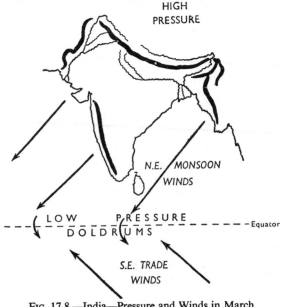

FIG. 17.8.—India—Pressure and Winds in March

The rainfall that follows is ushered in by the 'burst 'of the monsoon which is preceded by days and even weeks of very variable winds and intermittent storms of the hurricane type, known as cyclones in the Indian Ocean. The onset of the south-west winds of the wet or summer monsoon is usually accompanied by massive clouds, and the impact of warm tropical maritime air with hot land surface results in torrential instability rainfall, which is increased locally by high relief. On the flanks of the Western Ghats annual rainfall of over 200 inches is common, but a rapid decline to 20 inches can occur to the east of the crest of the Ghats. The extensive rain zone that lies over the eastern part of the Ganges plain and in Assam shows diminishing totals towards the Sind focus (Fig. 17.9). Probably the enclosing mountains help to produce the deflection of the winds from south-west to southeast in the north of India, but the indraught to the low pressure of the Sind is of paramount importance. The deficiency of rain in the Sind is surprising but, high above the area, hot dry winds from Baluchistan effectively restrict condensation in rising air and rain is unlikely. One feature of the rainy season in most parts of the country is the extremely high humidity which, accompanied by high temperatures, is both irksome and physiologically dangerous to Europeans, who resort to hill stations whenever possible.

The end of September marks the coolness that is consequent upon the return of the overhead sun to the southern hemisphere. The low pressure over India apparently retreats southwards with the establishment of high pressure in the interior of Asia. This change resembles the retreat of the convectional rains in the continental interiors of Africa, and it is therefore feasible to consider the low pressure that covers northern India in summer as the Doldrums belt which has been displaced northwards to an extraordinary degree. The ensuing season is cool and the outblowing air, from the north, tends to be very stable, so that most regions experience drought. Rain falls in eastern India, particularly on the south-east coast of the peninsula and in Ceylon, since north-east winds of the winter monsoon pass over a water surface in the Bay of Bengal (see Madras). North-west India also receives rain at this time from depressions that come from the west, probably from the Mediterranean Sea basin (see Lahore). After the winter solstice, with the northward march of the overhead sun, the cool season merges with the hot, dry season that leads to the following year's monsoonal 'burst'.

The vegetation of India is mainly tropical rain forest in the wettest parts and monsoon forest elsewhere apart from the drier northwest, where desert and desert grass savana prevail. Monsoon forest consists of semi-deciduous or facultatively deciduous trees, amongst which are sal and teak, both exhibiting xerophilous characteristics in the dry season. However, the Deccan has large areas of desert grass savana.

Fig. 17.9.—India—Pressure, Winds and Rainfall in the Wet Season

North Australia

This area is shown by Fig. 17.7 to be monsoonal, with the reversal of winds in relation to seasonal changes in the continental pressure. Unlike India, it has no 'burst' of rains heralding the wet season, when the north-east trade winds transgress the Equator and become north-west winds blowing into a focus of low pressure in North Australia.

Annual Rainfall

Over 60″

40-60″

30-40″

10-30″

⟵ January (Summer) winds

⟵--- July (Winter) winds

◯ January Isotherm (Actual) of 90°F. (Pilbarra Zone of Low Pressure)

W – Wyndham

FIG. 17.10.—North Australia—Winds and Annual Rainfall

The rains are heaviest on the coast and decrease inland as shown by Fig. 17.10—the winds rapidly lose their power of inducing rainfall as they approach the Pilbarra zone of low pressure. The dry season of winter has outblowing, south-east winds. On the Queensland coast, there is rainfall from onshore trade winds at all seasons, although there is a maximum of rain in the hot season. Coastal hurricanes and storms, known as willy-willies, bring additional rainfall to the north. These parts of Australia may be regarded as having a tropical continental climate, with a marine climate in the east. On the north coast a narrow forest belt passes inland to savana woodlands and savana with scrub as shown in Figs. 17.11 and 17.12. These eventually merge with the interior desert. In Queensland the east coast is forested, but local relief may produce a deterioration of rainfall, so that grass woodlands appear. The predominant forest trees are eucalypts. There is also a eucalypt scrub called mallee. Acacias are also common in the interior grasslands, and produce various types of scrub, the most widespread being called mulga. When certain species of acacia are

287

Fig. 17.11.—Savana Woodland in Northern Territory, Australia

South of Darwin, the savana is in the form of grass woodlands. The screw pine (Pandanus), in the foreground, is common in these regions and, particularly, in Malaya.

dominant the scrub is known as brigalow. This is common in interior Queensland and in areas lying inland, from the north coasts of Australia.

East Indies and Malaya

This equatorial area of islands and seas is almost continuously under monsoonal controls, and receives rain-bearing winds whichever way the air streams are moving between Asia and Australia (Fig. 17.7). The climate is probably most suitably described as monsoonal equatorial, because its régime shows a mixture of the two types, in that stations usually show a double rainfall and temperature maximum, but the rainfall maxima are primarily related to rain bearing

288

Black Sta

FIG. 17.12.—Baobab Tree, Kimberley District, Western Australia

Note the grass in the foreground and woodland in the rear.

winds rather than to increased convection with overhead sun. On the other hand the climate might be regarded as tropical marine, since the well-distributed rainfall depends on trade winds. The region receives an influx of warm, moist air at all times of the year, although when the winds are blowing from Australia the rain is rather less. Pressure gradients are rarely very steep so that there are steady airflows throughout the year, and these may produce marked contrasts in rainfall totals on windward and leeward sides of the islands, at any one period. Rainfall totals are rarely less than 80 inches per annum (see Singapore), and can be greater where high relief intervenes. In most areas, there are two rainy seasons which are separated by less rainy periods, marking the change-over of the pressure gradients between Australia and Asia. Temperatures are typical of equatorial areas (about 80° F for each month) so that the mean annual range is very small indeed (see Singapore). Much of the area has tropical rain forest but there are enclaves of various types of savana, both in lowlands and on highlands. The savana is probably the result of forest being cleared by man although deficiency of rainfall may explain some of these enclaves. Moss forest is also typical of many highland areas.

289

Other Areas

In Africa, there are two other regions with monsoonal climates. As Fig. 17.7 will show, Abyssinia is, in effect, a westerly extension of the Indian area. Summer monsoonal rainfall varies very much from year to year and this is reflected in the wealth or paucity of the floods of the Blue Nile. Air streams, associated with the southerly winds which affect Abyssinia, also give rain on the coasts of South-west Arabia which supports the coffee crops at Mocha.

The coastlands of the Gulf of Guinea may also be regarded as monsoonal. In general, the Doldrums belt and the inter-tropical front remain for most of the year along these coastlands. Dry north-east winds (harmattan) blow from the interior, and south-west winds, which are extensions of the south-east trade winds into the northern hemisphere, blow onshore and are responsible for the abundant rainfall. However, the north-east winds may bring a dry season to parts of the coast. At one point the configuration of the coast produces an upwelling of cold water (cf. Peruvian coast, p. 294) which reduces the rainfall on land, so that locally grass woodland replaces the rain forest. Some areas have a double maximum of rain (equatorial régime), whilst others have a marked wet season in the northern summer, when the inblowing south-west winds are most effective (see Cape Coast Castle). Mangrove swamps fringe this coast, and these may be regarded as extensions of the land forests on to the sea.

Finally, a brief mention of Central America and the Caribbean area may be made. Whilst north-east trade winds prevail throughout the year, there is in the hot season an indraught of rain-bearing winds to the islands and the mainland because of low pressure. The warm waters here induce this low pressure and in summer winds may blow from the south-west on the west coast of Central America. In all seasons, local aspect plays an important part in determining the rainfall and vegetation. Windward coasts tend to be clothed with tropical rain forest, and at high levels there are cloud forests.

(e) Hot Deserts

The normal positions of the hot deserts are on the poleward margins of the tropical grasslands, within the trade-wind belt and athwart one of the tropics. They usually extend to western shores, but rarely to the eastern shores of land areas. The aridity of the deserts depends mainly on the trade winds, which are dry, having blown far inland from the oceans to the east. Furthermore, these areas usually have the high pressure of the subtropical cells which are associated with low rainfall. Even on their western margins the proximity of the ocean is of no avail in relieving desert conditions, since any inblowing winds can give very little rainfall because of the high temperatures on the land combined with the effect of cold currents offshore (see p. 294).

Temperature

The maxima of temperature in the hot deserts are certainly as high as anywhere in the world. A minimum of cloud cover gives unrestricted insolation and heating of the land is increased by the almost complete absence of water surfaces and of vegetation. In the hot season daily maxima of 130° F (55° C) are common, but the great loss of heat at night, owing to the very great radiation with cloudless skies, may produce freezing temperatures. Diurnal ranges may be as great as 60° F or 70° F—at Insalah, a range of 100° F (between 26° and 126° F) has been recorded in twenty four hours. The mean annual range of temperature is usually less than 30° F, with the mean monthly temperatures varying from about 80° F to 50° F, although higher maxima are common in the interiors (as at Insalah, whose hot-month temperature is 100° F). Compared with the monotony of the temperature in equatorial climates, it will be appreciated that the deserts enjoy relatively invigorating climates.

Humidity

The aridity which is characteristic of deserts may be defined in terms of the relative humidity of the air. Values of 50 per cent and below are quite common and, in some extreme instances, 10 per cent or less has been recorded. It may be of interest to note that measurements of the absolute humidity may show that there is, in some areas, a fairly large water-vapour content in the desert air, but with the prevailing high temperatures of the daytime, much water would have to enter the air as vapour before it could become saturated. In view of the general absence of water surfaces from which evaporation may proceed, it is virtually impossible for high values of relative humidity to be recorded in the daytime except on western coasts. Dew, and even hoar frost, may occur at night.

Rainfall

It is not so much the low annual rainfall as its incidence which determines a desert. For instance, desert may prevail where about fifteen inches of rain falls in the year if this precipitation is restricted to a few torrential downpours. On the other hand, it is possible for crops to flourish in areas with less than 10 inches of annual rainfall provided that sufficient falls in the vegetative season of the plant concerned. In general, it may be assumed that desert climates are experienced where the mean annual rainfall is less than 10 inches.[1]

[1] Köppen in his early classification of climates distinguished deserts and their neighbouring steppes by annual rainfall of less than 10 inches and 10–20 inches, respectively (where the mean annual temperature was 65° F or over). In the case of high latitude deserts and steppes, the distinction was made with 5 inches and 5–10 inches of annual rainfall, respectively.

Within the interiors of the hot deserts there is so great an uncertainty of rainfall that it is generally true to say that rain is negligible: in several years only one storm of rain may occur. Torrential showers are not unusual in some areas, but their duration is limited and their effects are short-lived. However, in some deserts it is possible to distinguish definite seasons of rainfall.

The vegetation of desert regions is discussed on p. 249. There is rarely, if ever, a clearly marked boundary to a desert. In most cases a transition through semi-desert, with scanty seasonal rainfall, may be traced from north and south. On the equatorward side this transition zone has hot-season rainfall (related to the savana areas), whilst on the poleward margins the rain has a winter incidence (related to Mediterranean areas). In passing, it may be noted that there are very few areas of waterless desert, as will be seen by a reference to Fig. 17.13, which shows the world distribution of hot deserts.

Hot Desert Regions

Continental Areas

In Africa there is a great difference between the east–west breadth of the deserts of the north and south. In the south the south-east trade winds blow from sea to land, whereas in the north the prevailing north-east trade winds arrive as dry winds, having blown from Arabia, with little or no chance of gaining water vapour as they cross the Red Sea. In addition, subsiding air over the desert restricts convectional uplift. The south of Africa has a relatively well watered east coast, so that, in conjunction with the narrowness of the continent in these latitudes, the area of desert is restricted. In the north, aridity prevails over a zone which is 3,500 miles wide, and, indeed, the Sahara must be regarded as part of a greater desert zone which continues eastwards into Arabia and Iran. In Australia the controls which produce the hot desert are similar to those in southern Africa, but the greater east-west extent on the continent gives a correspondingly wider area. North-west monsoonal winds blow in the hot season from the seas to the north of Australia, but they have only marginal influence as regards rainfall, although they are attracted inland by the seasonal low pressure. Here conditions recall those of the Sind region in India (p. 285), where in the hot season little or no rain falls. In North America the hot desert is very limited on the narrow Mexican plateau.

Marine Areas

In Peru and northern Chile the hot deserts are entirely marginal, and a study of local controls will be fairly typical of those prevailing in similar areas on the west of the other hot deserts. In Fig. 17.14 the

°C
°F

100 ── 40 °C
      ── 35
90 ── ── 30
80 ── ── 25
70 ── ── 20
       ── 15
60 ── ── 10
50 ── ── 5
40 ── 32°F 30 ── 0°C
       20 ── ─5
30 ── ── ─10
       10 ── ─15
0 ── 0 ── ─18
            ─20
─10 ── ── ─25
─20 ── ── ─30
            ─35
─30 ── ── ─40
─40 ──

Tropic of Cancer

Equator

Tropic of Capricorn

Waterless Desert (mainly sand and bare rock)

Semi-desert

Acacia Semi-desert, steppe in some regions

70° F. Mean annual sea level isotherm

In   Insalah
C   Carnarvon
Iq   Iquique

Carnarvon (15)

Iquique (30)
Insalah (920)

Rain-nil at both

FIG. 17.13.—Hot Regions—Hot Deserts

293

essential controls are shown. The trade winds are offshore, and are related to the high-pressure cell in the south Pacific Ocean. These winds are partly responsible for the current of cold water which flows northwards along the coast, producing an upwelling of deep ocean water which is much cooler than the surface water (p. 350).The desert areas of western South America show continentality in the development of low pressure in the hot season, which causes a movement of air towards the shore from the ocean. The moist oceanic air is chilled in passing over the water of the cold current, and condensation occurs in the form of mist, which extends on to the coastal lands, where it is dispersed by the warmth of the land, so that not far inland the typical desert climate is preserved. The mist (known locally in Peru as the garua) often produces a gloom, accompanied by the dripping of moisture from trees which can grow with some success.

FIG. 17.14.—Controls on West Coasts of Hot Deserts

The moist cool air reduces the hot-month temperatures, and the mean annual range of temperature is smaller by some 10° F than that experienced in interior desert areas (see Iquique). Locally, hot dry air may flow from the interior, and give much higher temperatures at the coast. However, in general, the mean monthly temperatures range between 55° F and 70° F and show the usual equability of marine zones. Rainfall is very scanty, and generally coincides with onshore winds in the hot season.

The Peruvian-Atacama Desert is a marine hot desert, and is very narrow from east to west, since the high wall of the Andes mountains almost completely isolates the area from continental and eastern influences. The cold current helps to maintain the aridity, and this is the hot desert with the greatest north-south extent in the world. It stretches from just south of the Equator to lat. 30° S. The importance of the cold current is shown in the northern part of Peru, where copious rainfall may interrupt the desert régime approximately every seven years (sometimes it is after a fourteen-year interval), when a warm current of water[1] sweeps southwards from the northern hemisphere. This counteracts the influence of the cold water, and moist, onshore winds produce very heavy rainfall on the land. Trujillo received 15·4 inches, in March 1925, whereas its total rainfall, for the previous seven years, was only 1·4 inches.

Aridity is also controlled by cold currents which flow offshore from the coastal deserts of South-west Africa and Lower California. However, in Western Australia, and along the western fringe of the Sahara, the aridity is much less marked. This is partly explained by the fact that the cold currents offshore are less effective along these coasts and also, the relief is low, so that there is no marked descent of winds from high land to give warm, dry air, as is true of most other coastal deserts.

There are two cases of east coastlands, in the tropics, with a desert climate—Somaliland and Arabia. These areas lie just within the western limits of the theatre of monsoonal controls, as shown in Fig. 17.7. Winds tend to blow either offshore, or parallel to the shores, but slight rain falls at favourable situations, such as near Mocha (p. 290).

(f) Soils of Regions with Hot Climates

Apart from the hot deserts, the most widespread zonal soils in these regions are those in which laterization has been dominant as a soil-forming process. As indicated on p. 258, one of the main characteristics of tropical soils is the red colouration, at most levels. However, amongst these red soils there is a variety which depends on the effectiveness of the leaching which is by no means uniform throughout the year, even in areas with an equatorial climate. Dry seasons are by no means uncommon, within the humid tropics.

Amongst the most common pedalfers are the markedly red lateritic soils which are associated with the tropical rain forests—they are typically dark red to yellowish brown in colour and are best developed on well-drained surfaces. These soils are permeable and friable but they dry out rapidly at the surface, after rainy periods—on the other hand, they do not erode very readily. Their humus content is low, despite an apparently inexhaustible supply of vegetable material—this is rapidly converted to soluble colloids which are washed down through the soils. With the clearance of the forest, these soils appear to have a high fertility but this declines rapidly and can only be maintained by increasing amounts of fertiliser, as time passes. Some tree crops are well suited to these soils, such as rubber, coffee and bananas, but the readiness with which the surface dries out makes them less suitable for sugar and maize.

[1] This current arrives off Peru about Christmastide, and is known as El Niño (the boy child).

Some of these tropical red soils may have a surface layer, as shown in the profile (Fig. 17.15), where leaching of the silica and other soluble materials has left a hardpan of red iron oxides, sometimes accompanied by whitish aluminium oxide. The red material is laterite, and the white is bauxite. A reference to the footnote on p. 258 will show that it is necessary to distinguish between the relatively fertile

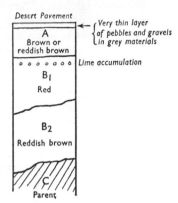

FIG. 17.15.—Profile of Tropical Red Soil (Lateritic)

FIG. 17.16.—Profile of Desert Soil (Arizona)

lateritic soils, as discussed in the previous paragraph, and these much less valuable soils, with a well-defined laterite horizon at the surface (such have been described by some as ground water laterites).[1]

Closely related to the savanas are tropical red soils in which laterization has not advanced to the full extent—in these soils the clays near the surface are very water retentive. However, they shrink and crack on drying out, making them liable to erosion as well as difficult to cultivate. Nevertheless, they are more fertile than the red lateritic soils and, given careful cultivation, they prove to be some of the most valuable soils in the tropics.

In addition to these soils are yellow tropical soils where abundant rainfall, as on trade wind coasts, or impeded drainage, has resulted in hydration of the red iron oxides to yellow-brown (limonite). These soils are otherwise very similar to the red lateritic soils. Both red and yellow podzolic soils are found in upland areas, in the tropics, and, polewards, towards cooler regions—they are transitional between the lateritic soils and the true podzols of the cool temperate regions.

[1] As has been said above, laterization removes practically all but iron and aluminium oxides, so that the upper horizons are left with a deficiency of silica. Most tropical soils have a $\frac{SiO_2}{Al_2O_3}$ ratio of more than 2, near the surface, but, in some cases, this ratio is less than 1·33, when the clay so formed is truly laterite or sometimes bauxite, the latter being almost pure alumina.

Other soils in these regions are the black tropical soils, which are probably intrazonal rather than zonal. They develop on a parent rock which is rich in lime and their dark colour is possibly produced by particular colloids. Since these colloids do not flocculate readily, the soils have a fine-grained surface horizon which is sticky when wet, but shrinks and cracks on drying out. Thus the soils are easily

E. Aubert de la Rüe, Pully-Lausanne

FIG. 17.17.—Transition of Steppe to Desert in Issa, Eastern Ethiopia

This photograph demonstrates the steppe-desert transition and is typical of most arid regions, in both tropical and temperate latitudes.

eroded. The Deccan of India has this type of soil in the cotton-growing region. It is developed on a basaltic lava which contains a fairly high proportion of calcium compounds. A similar area of such soils is found in the central parts of the Transvaal. Areas of black soil occur elsewhere in the savanas, and some have been regarded as chernozems (p. 335), but they resemble the latter only in colour. However, reddish-brown pedocals, also found in savana areas, seem to be the tropical equivalents of the chernozems. These soils have a deep layer of lime accumulation and the reddish hue is probably dependent on the high rates of evaporation, oxidation and decay which are typical of the tropics. Intrazonal soils include the grey-black clays of forest swamps, which are organic peat and muck soils (p. 336). They depend, respectively, on the acidity or alkalinity of the local ground water.

Near the margins of the tropical deserts red and grey zonal soils occur. Owing to the bare rock surfaces and sand dunes, large areas of the deserts are unlikely to possess true soils but the desert margins

297

have some rain, and leaching leads to the development of a soil profile, as shown in Fig. 17.16. The soils have little organic material, so that light colours are common at the surface, but digging reveals red and brown horizons below. Drought produces an upward movement of various salts and there is usually a zone of lime accumulation at, or just below, the surface. In the hotter margins of these deserts such pedocals tend to be more markedly red whilst the cooler margins are more likely to have grey desert soils (serozems). The latter are very common in the marginal areas of temperate deserts (p. 314). With irrigation and the addition of large quantities of organic fertilizer, to encourage the retention of water and plant foods near the surface, excellent crops have been raised on these soils. In the interior basins of both tropical and temperate deserts, saline soils (pp. 259 and 261) are the only ones which are likely to be developed.

CHAPTER 18

Warm Temperate Climates

Introduction to Temperate Climates

Polewards from the regions with hot climates lie areas with temperate climates. Whereas hot climates are differentiated primarily by rainfall and its seasonal distribution, the temperate climates are subdivided primarily by temperature distinctions, so that there are warm, cool, and cold types.

Warm temperate areas are essentially subtropical, in that they lie just outside the tropics and have very hot summers, although their mean annual temperatures are less than 70° F. Winters are never cold enough to arrest all plant growth, as never does the mean temperature of the coldest month fall below 43° F.

Cool temperate climates have at least one month (on the equatorward margins) and often five months (on the poleward margins) with mean temperatures below 43° F. Thus, a rest is imposed on the growth of plants. Cold temperate climates have longer cold seasons, with at least six months with mean temperatures below 43° F.

The cool and cold temperate areas lie wholly within the westerly wind belt with its associated depressions, whereas warm temperate zones are alternately under trade-wind and westerly wind influences during the year, since they lie close to a significant meteorological boundary, namely, the Horse Latitudes.

The warm and cool temperate climates are each capable of a subdivision into west marginal, interior, and east marginal types. Both the margins have rainy seasons during the year, but the interiors are fairly dry, and include cool or temperate deserts. This is particularly true of the northern continents, where the continentality of the interior produces this triple division. Cold temperate regions are not so clearly divided, as desert does not appear in the interior areas. In Asia the eastern margins of all the temperate areas have monsoonal controls, which also, to some degree, affect the east marginal areas in the warm temperate latitudes of North America.

Distribution of Warm Temperate Climates

Lying mainly between 30° and 40° N and S, these regions are under the influence of the trade winds and westerly winds, with depressions, in alternate seasons of the year. Fig. 18.1 shows the essential contrast between the west and east margins. The former have offshore winds in summer and onshore winds in winter, the rainy season. The latter have onshore winds in summer and outblowing winds in winter, but both seasons are rainy, as will be seen later, although summer is

(a) Average Position of Winds

(b) Winds in Summer

(c) Winds in Winter

S.W. Winds   Rain — decreasing inland

N.E. Trade Winds

N.B. Similar diagram applicable to Southern hemisphere

Fig. 18.1.—Winds and Rainfall in Warm Temperate Areas
(Northern Hemisphere)

the more rainy. West and east marginal areas are found paired with one another in all continents (see Fig. 18.2). In South Africa the two marginal areas are practically contiguous, but elsewhere there is a gap of varying width between the margins which is occupied by fairly arid regions.

West Marginal Areas

The warm temperate west marginal climates are commonly known as 'Mediterranean'. Outside the Mediterranean Sea basin, which has a very great east-west extent, the west marginal zones are very restricted, being merely coastal strips and, therefore, truly marginal. They have a breadth of about 100–200 miles, whereas the Mediterranean Sea is about 2,000 miles long.

Temperature

Mean temperatures of the coldest months are usually between 43° F, and 50° F, but in the hot months they rise to 70° F and even 80° F, so that the mean annual range is commonly about 25° F or 30° F. On the coasts the range may shrink to 10° F, partly because of the proximity of the ocean, but often because of the effect of cold currents (as off the Peruvian coast, see p. 294), and the arrival of the highest mean monthly temperature may be delayed by two months. Inland from coastal stations the mean annual range of temperature is much greater. In California it is 11° F at San Francisco and 27° F at Sacramento, eighty miles inland, whereas in the 2,000 miles from Gibraltar to Smyrna the range increases from 20° F to 34° F. Diurnal ranges are large, with daily maxima of over 100° F, particularly on the desert margins.

Rainfall

The rainfall is determined largely by the equatorward movement of the westerly wind belt in winter and is mainly brought by depressions, although in most areas mountains produce local relief rainfall and snow may lie on the mountains. Although most places show a peak of rainfall in the winter season, some places have an autumnal maximum of rain (see Gibraltar). In summer, the absence of onshore westerly winds produces a season of drought, broken by rare rainstorms. Annual totals of rain are of the order of 15–35 inches, with as many as 50 inches on coastal mountains but, in general, smaller totals are found both inland and towards the hot desert margins.

Vegetation

There is no winter pause in plant growth, since the mean monthly temperatures remain above 43° F. A rhythm is perceptible, however, in view of the summer drought, which, owing to the great evaporation, is rarely relieved by effective rains so that a pause in plant growth in summer is almost inevitable. In other words, the vegetation is xerophilous and most plants are adapted by nature to resist the drought as described on pp. 238 and 242.

There are woodlands of evergreen oak, and chestnuts but, probably, the most widespread vegetation is degenerate woodland. In the

301

Fig. 18.2.—Warm Temperate Regions

Climatic graph for Buenos Aires is given in fig. 17.1.

303

latter low bushes, such as myrtles and laurels form thickets which, in parts, are almost impenetrable. In the several 'Mediterranean' regions, such plant associations are so common that local names have been given to them, such as maquis (France), macchia (Corsica), mallee (Australia) and chaparral (California) (Fig. 18.3). As many of the Mediterranean areas are mountainous, there are frequently coniferous forests at high levels—these include the Aleppo pine and various cedars, in the Mediterranean Sea basin.

E. Aubert de la Rüe, Pully-Lausanne

FIG. 18.3.—Maquis near Azegour, Morocco

Here is degenerate woodland, mainly of evergreen oaks and cedars, on the slopes of the High Atlas.

In areas with scanty rainfall, and on pervious limestone in better watered regions, the characteristic vegetation is very sparse and is known as garigue in the Mediterranean Sea basin. Garigue consists of small, brightly coloured, sweet-smelling shrubs and plants, such as thyme, lavender, rosemary, rockrose and broom, with bare rock and soil lying between the separate plants. Grass is usually very restricted, because its short roots are unable to draw upon deep moisture supplies in the warm dry season. It is possible that some grassy areas have been destroyed by over-grazing, in the past—today, the goat is about the only animal that can graze sufficiently on the thickets.

Mediterranean Regions

Mediterranean Sea Basin

This great embayment is quite exceptional amongst 'Mediterranean' regions with its east-west structural trends which guide depressions passing in winter between the high-pressure areas of the Azores and the European continent. Annual rainfall is greater on west-facing coasts than on the eastern sides of the peninsulas of the European shore, but decreases on the whole gradually from about 35 inches at Gibraltar to slightly less than 25 inches on the coast of Israel, over 2,000 miles farther east. Cold winds, such as the bora and the mistral (p. 220), blow in the rear of depressions, and warm winds drawn from the Sahara, such as the sirocco (Algeria) and the khamsin (Egypt), arrive on the European coasts both humid and warm.

In summer the basin is covered by an extension from the west of the Azores high-pressure zone, which effectively shuts out depressions, although convectional rain-storms may occur. Etesian winds, from the north, blow in the eastern part of the basin on to the Libyan coast, giving fog. The peninsula of Iberia, and high parts of southern Italy and the Balkan region, exhibit continental features which make their climate more like that of Central Europe. The steppe-like grasslands of the Meseta, and elsewhere, reflect this continentality whilst, in the Plain of Lombardy, it is the summer rainfall which distinguishes it from the 'Mediterranean' area of Italy.

California and Chile

These two areas of the New World are alike in having north-south trend lines, with an interior central valley backed by high mountains and separated from the sea by coastal ranges, occasionally broken by gaps, such as the Golden Gate in California. Cold currents offshore give cool air, which is drawn in summer through the coastal gaps into the valley that is a local centre of great heat and low pressure. Fog keeps the coasts cool in summer, and until the indraught of cool air ceases in late summer, the highest mean monthly temperatures of 60° F and 67° F are not recorded at San Francisco and Valparaiso, respectively. Winter rain, which is somewhat variable in amount, is brought by depressions, which often pass across the coast on the poleward side of these areas. Warm tropical air, drawn north by depressions, gives the wind, known as the Santa Ana in Southern California, with air which becomes warm and very dry, as it descends from the mountains into the valleys. In spring, this wind may have a very adverse effect on the fruit crops. Aspect and altitude have a bearing on the rainfall totals, for the valley floors are less well supplied with rain than the seaward-facing slopes of the ranges, although the maximum precipitation is below the crest of the interior mountains. Redwood and yellow pine forests flourish in the northern coast ranges and on parts of the Sierra Nevada but, in California, the typical vegetation is degenerate woodland, or chaparral (Fig. 15.8). On the Andean slopes, in Central Chile, are forests of Araucaria pine.

Cape Region and Swanland (with the Adelaide District)

Both these areas lie on the southern margin of a continent and are backed by plateaus. Throughout the winter the proximity of the sea to the west and the south prevents very low temperatures. Perth, in Western Australia, is practically frost-free, and its lowest mean monthly temperature is 55° F. The Berg wind, which is föhn-like, descends from the plateau in the Cape region in winter, giving day temperatures as high as 100° F, but there is no counterpart of this wind in Swanland. Depressions crossing the seas to the south bring very reliable winter rainfall, as well as some in summer, but this declines inland. Eastwards from Swanland the northward curve of the Great Australian Bight causes rain-bearing winds to miss the land. Farther east the coast trends southward, and in the Adelaide district and parts of Victoria the rainfall increases: there is no summer drought here (see Adelaide), but there is clearly a winter maximum of rain. In summer temperatures are moderated (slightly) by the proximity of the ocean and also by a northward-moving cold current, off the Cape region, in particular. The areas have a succession of vegetation, related to the decrease of rainfall inland. With forty inches of rain, on the south-west coast of Australia, there are eucalypt forests, of jarrah and karri (Fig. 18.4), which pass inland to mallee. In a few places, above 2,000 feet, in South Africa remnants of coniferous forest remain, with trees akin to the cypress. Otherwise, this region has scrub forest.

East Marginal Areas

The eastern areas in warm temperate latitudes have rain at all seasons, although summer is very often the wetter half of the year with onshore trade winds. However, both temperate and tropical cyclones affect the areas. In winter temperate depressions, with their contrasted winds, may produce rapid changes in the weather which are characterized by sudden falls of temperature through 30° F to 40° F in a few hours.

Temperature

Despite the possibility of very cool weather, the mean annual range of temperature is generally small. The oceanic influence on the southern hemisphere regions may be contrasted with the continental-

Australian Official Photograph

FIG. 18.4.—Karri Forest, Western Australia

The botanical name of karri is *Eucalyptus diversicolor*.

ity that affects the northern areas. In the south, mean monthly temperatures range from 50° F to about 70° F (occasionally rising to 75° F), whereas in the north a mean annual range of 30° F or more is common with a hot-month temperature of over 80° F (see New Orleans). In summer the high humidity of the onshore winds gives wet-bulb temperatures of over 70° F, and thus the activities of white people are restricted in these areas.

Rainfall

In summer generous and heavy instability rainfall is produced by moist, warm, oceanic air moving on to the heated land surfaces. Locally this rainfall is augmented by relief, and also by typhoons and hurricanes. Winter rainfall is often brought by depressions. Almost everywhere near the coasts the annual rainfall exceeds forty inches, and often fifty inches, although the totals decrease inland. Summer is not everywhere the wettest season, and, in any case, evaporation tends to reduce the effectiveness of the summer rain.

Vegetation

The mild, and even warm, winters permit the perennial growth of plants, and since there is no marked dry season in the year, forests are common, especially near the sea margins. Trees are similar to those of the west margins, with conifers (cypress), laurels, and evergreen oaks, but in addition there are the magnolia, the mulberry, the maple, the walnut, and the hickory, which form broad-leaved evergreen forests. Lianas and bamboos occur in some areas, and recall the tropical rain forests (Fig. 17.3). Deficiency of rainfall in the interiors results in the formation of scrub, and eventually this passes to grass-and and steppes.

Southern Regions

It is convenient to discuss the east margins in the southern hemisphere separately from the northern areas. This is because of the marked continentality which gives monsoonal characteristics to the latter areas, particularly in China. Furthermore, tropical cyclones are common in the northern regions, whereas they are more or less absent in the southern hemisphere.

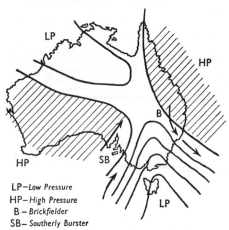

LP—Low Pressure
HP—High Pressure
B — Brickfielder
SB— Southerly Burster

FIG. 18.5.—Pressure Distributions in Australia with a Trough of Low Pressure giving Southerly Burster

New South Wales and Victoria

Much of the winter and autumnal rainfall (see Melbourne) is produced by depressions which pass eastwards through Bass Strait, although they may penetrate northwards. Troughs of low pressure, particularly in summer, separating migrant anticyclones, give brick-fielders and southerly bursters. The former are hot winds blowing from the continent and are accompanied by much dust, whilst the latter are quite cool and violent blasts from the south, usually marked by a dark roll cloud associated with a cold front (Fig. 18.5). The burster often brings, with its coolness, relief from the suffocating heat of the brickfielder. Annual rainfall decreases from twenty-five to forty inches and more on the coast, where forest occurs to under twenty inches inland, where grassland and scrub flourish on the highlands and the interior plains.

Black Star

FIG. 18.6.—Veld Plateau in Orange Free State

The vegetation is warm temperate grassland. Note also the plateau surface, which is broken by mesa-like hills, and the strato-cumulus clouds.

South-east Africa with Natal

Eastwards along the coast from Cape Town towards Port Elizabeth, there is an almost perfect transition from the west to the east marginal warm temperate climate. Knysna is often regarded as marking the boundary, with more rain in winter to the west and with a summer maximum of rainfall to the east. Durban, with the moderating effect of the sea, has very warm winters and a mean annual temperature of 70° F, which places it on the edge of the tropical marine zone of South-east Africa. Its mean annual range of temperature is 13° F, between 64° F and 77° F. No cold winds of polar origin are experienced, although a föhn wind may elevate the diurnal temperatures in winter. Decreasing rainfall towards the interior results in a change from forest to steppe, with grassland on the Veld (Fig. 18.6) and dry forests of wattles (acacias) in some areas.

South America—Central Argentine and Uruguay, with Southern Brazil

Migrant depressions in winter passing eastwards bring the zonda, a warm, humid wind from the north and the cold pampero from the south (a squally wind but not so vigorous as the southerly burster of Australia), as well as south-east winds off the sea to the east. In summer low pressure develops over the interior and splits the sub-tropical high-pressure belt into two oceanic cells to the east and west of the continent. Onshore winds from the north-east, east, and south-east blow inland from the Atlantic Ocean and account for the summer rains. The annual rainfall totals decrease steadily inland, an effect of the subdued relief of the region, but only in Southern Brazil is there forest, elsewhere are grasslands. However, Schmieder has advanced the theory that an earlier forest cover on the Pampas has been destroyed by burning and clearance. Local scrub or 'monte' supports this view, and wind-breaks on estancias prove that trees can flourish in the area. The climatic graph for Buenos Aires is given in Fig. 17.1.

Northern Regions

The 43° F mean January isotherm is taken as the poleward limit of the warm temperate climates, and this lies close to the River Yangtse Kiang, so that North China, despite its warm summers, has quite cold winters (see p. 324). The same isotherm marks, by chance, the northern edge of the North American cotton belt. Both South and Central China, as well as the Gulf-Atlantic States, are monsoonal, although winter depressions tend to mask the seasonal reversal of the wind directions, particularly in North America. Tropical cyclones are common in the coastlands of these northern areas.

South and Central China

In winter, the normal north-east trade winds are reinforced by northerly outblowing winds from the high-pressure zone of inner Asia, from whose southern margin almost inexplicable depressions emerge into China, and bring rainfall to the Yangtse Kiang valley. Behind these disturbances polar air may surge southwards and give freezing temperatures in Canton. Nevertheless, Szechwan (see Chung-king), in the track of these depressions, has extraordinarily mild winters, with January mean temperatures about 11° F higher than has Shanghai. In summer, as temperatures mount, there is a period somewhat like the hot, dry season in India, but rain is not entirely absent, and there is no 'burst' of rain when the south-east winds set in from the sea towards the continental low pressure. Much of this summer rainfall is apparently brought by local depressions. Mean monthly temperatures may surpass 80° F for several months, and with the great humidity the climate is almost equatorial.

Typhoons in late summer and autumn affect ports between Hong Kong and Foochow, the latter showing a distinct peak of rainfall in August (see graph). With their recurvature around the western margins of the North Pacific high-pressure cell, Shanghai enjoys a relative freedom from these storms.

Fifty inches of rain, and even more at coastal stations, are usually well distributed throughout the year. On the south coast rain forest occurs but is replaced northwards and inland by broad-leaved evergreen forest, except where clearance has been made, as is very true of China.

Gulf-Atlantic States of the United States of America

Here monsoonal controls are weaker than in China. Depressions from the Pacific Ocean follow tracks as shown in Fig. 19.4, and bring winter rainfall, with the tropical air drawn off the Gulf of Mexico. Behind these depressions the cold northers, in Texas and farther east, may lower temperatures by 50° F in a few hours. In summer the indraught of warm humid air from the south gives high temperatures and great humidity over a large part of the Mississippi lowlands; 80° F, with 80 per cent relative humidity, is frequently recorded as far north as St. Louis. Summer is the season of abundant rainfall and most stations show a maximum then, despite the considerable precipitation in winter from depressions. On the coasts hurricanes may give heavy autumnal rainfall, but these storms are less numerous than the typhoons in China. (In the Far East, typhoons are about three to four times more common than hurricanes, in the American area). Although much land is under cultivation, there are still tracts of virgin forest, including mixed oak-pine forest, but the sandy coastal plains are of interest in having coniferous forests. In fact, this is the most extensive area in the world where conifers flourish with abundant and well distributed rainfall, as well as with high temperatures (Fig. 18.7). Trees include the southern long-leaf pine, loblolly pine and pitch pine. In Florida are the Everglades, with swamps and almost impenetrable woodland, as well as mangroves near the sea.

Temperate Deserts

In Eurasia there is a wide intermediate zone between the east and west margins in warm temperate latitudes which is occupied by desert that may be regarded as a northerly extension of the hot deserts. A similar but much more restricted area is found in North America. The more northerly position, the elevation, and the rather

Fairchild Aerial Surveys, Inc.

Fig. 18.7.—Coniferous Forest in Florida, United States of America

The lakes are in hollows which have been formed by solution of the low-lying limestone surface. Chemical solution of limestone is discussed on p. 125.

special physical nature of these regions make them different from the tropical deserts.

They are cooler than the hot deserts, having in Asia January mean temperatures that often fall below 32° F, partly because of the elevation above sea-level, but also because of the effects of continentality (see p. 163).[1] However, the summers are hot, and the lack of cloud gives daily maxima of temperature equal to those of the tropical deserts, that is, frequently greater than 100° F. Much of these areas consists of upland basins shut in by high mountains which isolate them from rain and snow in winter. In any case as these are centres of very high-pressure air in winter the chance of precipitation is slight. The dryness of the regions in winter is reflected in the rapid rise of temperatures in spring; little insolation is required for the snow melt prior to the heating of the ground surface.

Rainfall is slight but mainly of summer incidence because of the

[1] This marked continentality is shown by the remarkable southward bend of the 32° F mean January isotherm as seen on world maps.

312

continental régime (see p. 234). The climatic graph for Kashgar is typical. Some winter rainfall is received in the Eurasian zone from occasional depressions which have come from the Mediterranean Sea basin, although such rainfall is mainly in the western parts.

Literary Services Mondiale Ltd.

FIG. 18.8.—Steppe in Mongolia

The vegetation consists of very sparse grass in an intermontane plateau region of Central Asia.

The vegetation is very commonly steppe (Fig. 18.8), or sage brush (in North America). On the ranges surrounding the intermontane basins precipitation may be relatively great, so that grasslands and even woodlands are found. Polewards, in North America, and farther into the interior of Central Asia, these deserts persist, although in some parts mountain climates with their special features are found (see pp. 323 and 325).

Soils of Warm Temperate Regions

The warm temperate regions are transitional in regard to their soils, lying, as they do, between areas with the laterized soils of the tropics and the podzolized soils of the cool temperate and cold regions. The threefold division of the warm temperate regions, into relatively well-watered east and west margins and the semi-arid zones of the interiors, is reflected very closely by the soils, in that

313

pedalfers are more or less typical of the marginal areas, whilst pedocals are predominant in the interiors. There are, however, no very clear cut types of zonal soil, rather are there variants of the better-defined soils to the north and south.

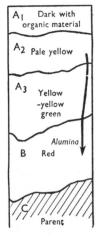

FIG. 18.9.—Profile of Warm Temperate (Subtropical) Red and Yellow Soil (South-east U.S.A.)

The east margins, with their well distributed rainfall, have zonal soils which resemble the tropical red and yellow soils but laterization has been replaced by podzolization, largely because of the lower temperatures which prevail. The soils have fairly shallow profiles and the B horizon is darker than the A horizon—this is indicative of a degree of podzolization. Markedly yellow soils, where hydration of the iron oxides has occurred, are common, in the well watered south-eastern parts of the United States of America (Fig. 18.9), Similar red and yellow soils are found in parts of the Mediterranean Sea basin, and in south-west Australia. In general, the fertility of these soils is not high. In the rainy western fringes of the Mediterranean area of Europe, grey-brown podzolic soils are found— these are described on p. 334.

In the marginal areas are intrazonal soils known as rendzinas, which have been discussed on p. 263. These soils have a parent rock of limestone which, in the Mediterranean Sea basin, weathers to a reddish soil (terra rossa), largely the residues left on the surface as the limestone dissolved. Similar soils, on a soft limestone parent, are found in Alabama and these support cotton crops on their dark, lime-rich clays.

Whilst there are serozems on the desert margins of the interior parts of the warm temperate regions, similar to those described on p. 298, towards the poleward margins there are two other pedocals, known as brown steppe and chestnut soils, respectively. As these are more widely distributed in cool temperate regions, they are discussed on p. 335. These brown soils are of marginal importance to agriculture. Towards the tropics they show a marked tendency to become more red. These reddish-brown pedocals (some of which are known as reddish prairie soils and others as reddish chestnut soils) are truly transitional, and link up with the reddish-brown pedocals of the savanas, referred to on p. 297. They are found in most continents, between approximately 10° and 35° of latitude, north and south.

314

CHAPTER 19

Cool Temperate Climates

Distribution and Major Controls

The cool temperate regions lie on the poleward side of latitude 40° in each hemisphere. The major areas are in North America and Eurasia, where there is a marked contrast between the interiors and the margins (Fig. 19.1). In the southern world the areas are small and do not permit of the threefold division mentioned on p. 299.

The west margins are in the direct path of the westerly winds which blow at all seasons, but depressions are so common that the climate may be regarded as a sequence of weather which shows some sort of seasonal rhythm. The east margins are much influenced by the seasonal pressure distributions of the interiors, but again in the east depressions play their rôle, whilst in eastern Asia there are monsoonal controls of some importance.

Temperature

As well as having one to five months with mean temperatures below 43° F, there are wider ranges of temperature to distinguish these areas from warm temperate regions. In fact, the very wide ranges experienced in the interiors make the term 'temperate' quite inappropriate. Nevertheless, the western margins have very equable climates, since there is a fairly regular importation of warm air of tropical origin, particularly in the winter. The oceans adjacent to these western margins in the north have large positive anomalies of temperature in January. In effect this means that the eastern parts of the North Pacific and Atlantic Oceans are at least 20° F warmer in January than would be expected for such a high latitude. The course of the January reduced mean isotherm of 32° F demonstrates this quite well, as it runs from the Pacific shores of Canada south through some twelve degrees of latitude to St. Louis. A similar course may be noted from Norway to the Black Sea, thus enclosing an extensive zone of the Atlantic margins. including the British Isles, known as the gulf of winter warmth.

Increasing continentality towards the interior of each northern land mass is shown by the mean annual ranges of temperature at successive stations lying from west to east in approximately the same latitude.

	January Mean Temperature (° F)	July Mean Temperature (° F)	Mean Annual Range (° F)
Eurasia			
Valentia, 52° N	44	59	15
Berlin, 53° N	30	66	36
Warsaw, 52° N	26	66	40
Kiev, 50° N	21	67	46
Vladivostok, 43° N	7	69 (Aug.)	62
North America			
Portland (Oregon), 46° N	39	67	28
Denver, 40° N	30	72	42
Chicago, 42° N	26	74	48
Boston, 42° N	27	72	45

Hot-month temperatures are obviously higher in interior areas than on the margins, and extreme mean annual ranges of temperature as large as 80° F may be recorded in the interiors. East coasts are markedly colder in winter than at corresponding latitudes on western shores. Cold currents offshore are partly responsible for this, but cold air moving from the continental interiors helps to produce this contrast.

In the southern hemisphere large ocean surfaces separating the quite narrow land areas help to reduce the effects of continentality to a minimum. Mean annual ranges of temperature are never large, 20° F being rarely exceeded.

With the quite regular passage of depressions, rapid changes of temperature related to alternating warm and cold fronts are common in practically all areas and at all seasons. Such thermal fluctuations are of some importance since muggy, warm air tends to produce a decline in most human activities, whilst the cold, bracing air in the rear of a depression encourages physical activity.

Rainfall

The most effective source of rainfall within these regions is unquestionably the westerly wind circulation, although it must always be remembered that these winds are more often than not related to depressions. In general, the west margins are the wettest areas, particularly on coasts backed by high mountains (see Vancouver and Valdivia), but on the leeward slopes of these mountains there is much less rain (see Punta Arenas and Denver). The interiors have much less rain, but in the two northern continents there is an increase of rain as the east margins are approached.

316

Frontal, relief, and convectional rainfalls prevail in the various areas and at different seasons, so that distinct régimes may be recognized:

1. Both west and east margins have well-distributed rainfall which is mainly frontal and relief in origin (see Brest and Halifax).

2. The continental interiors have convectional rains, often from thunderstorms in summer, coinciding with the greatest heat (see Odessa). In spring depressions may bring additional rainfall to the western parts of the interiors (see Denver).

3. Eastern Asia has a marked summer maximum of monsoonal rainfall which is both frontal and relief (see Peking).

Transitions between the well-distributed rainfall of the western areas and the summer rains of the continental interiors are commonly found. For instance, Paris receives more rain in summer than at other seasons, and yet in the whole year there is less rain here than at Brest in the west of France. In all cool temperate areas snowfalls are usual in winter, but rarely does snow lie for long in the western margins except on very high ground.

Vegetation

In many of these areas the natural vegetation has disappeared since land has been cleared for farming. In the western margins with mild winters there is only a short period when temperatures are low enough to stop plant growth, whereas in the interiors growth is arrested for several months.

Whilst it would be expected that the west margins with their abundant rainfall should support forest, the salt spray blown by the prevailing winds clogs the leaf pores, so that trees are restricted in coastal areas. It is the transitional areas of mid-England, eastern France, and much of Germany, which carry, under natural conditions, broad-leaved deciduous forests of ash, oak, and beech in particular, as well as birch (Fig. 15.3). In the western margins of the Americas there are coniferous forests, and in southern Chile there are Antarctic beech trees. It is only at high levels or on poor soils that conifers are found extensively in cool temperate areas of Europe. In the Scilly Isles and the south-west coastlands of Ireland, subtropical evergreens of 'Mediterranean' type flourish out of doors, but, from the course of the 43° F mean isotherm for the coldest month, these remote western areas have, strictly speaking, a warm temperate climate.

The continental interiors, with light spring and summer rains, carry steppe and prairie grasslands and along the banks of rivers are mixed coniferous and deciduous woodlands. The grasses are relatively tough and dry in comparison with the meadow grasses of the western margins. The eastern margins of the northern continents, with well distributed rainfall, have also mixed forests. In these cool temperate regions the forests, nearly everywhere, provide good

317

West Margins

Forests—Coniferous in N. America, mixed in most other areas
(unless cleared for cultivation)

Continental Interiors

Grasslands

Intermontane Steppes and Deserts
(including Patagonia)

East Margins

Mixed Forests

Other Forested areas

– – – – 70° F. mean annual sea level isotherm
enclosing hot regions

· · · · · · Isopleth of 43° F. for lowest monthly
mean temperature

– · – · – Isopleth of six months below 43° F.
mean temperature

FIG. 19.1.—Cool Temperate Regions

lumber, particularly in the mixed forests, where the choice of timber is good. In high demand are pine, spruce, hemlock, Douglas fir, elm, oak and beech.

Northern Regions

Since there are significant differences between the regions of the two northern continents it is best to consider each as a whole. Nevertheless, the major controls of their cool temperate climates may be discussed together.

Fig. 19.2.—Seasonal Controls of Pressure in Cool Temperate Areas (Northern Hemisphere)

(a) *Winter*. As shown schematically in Fig. 19.2 there are three main pressure distributions, high pressure centred over each of the continents, high pressure in the subtropical parts of the northern oceans, and low pressure which is centred over Iceland and the Aleutian Islands respectively. The long arrows show the southwesterly winds, but these are essentially parts of the anticlockwise circulations of depressions as shown by the short, curved arrows.

The courses taken by depressions are mainly north-east towards Scandinavia in Europe, although a few pass southwards through the Mediterranean Sea basin (Fig. 19.3). These courses are largely determined by the buffer of high pressure over the continent. In North America the guidance and the obstruction of the western mountains cause a southerly circuit along the shores of the Gulf of Mexico to be the most favoured route, although some depressions pass directly across the continent in this season. All depressions in North America tend to issue from the Laurentian lowlands or New England into the Atlantic area (Fig. 19.4).

FIG. 19.3.—Tracks of Depressions in Europe

(b) *Summer*. As shown by Fig. 19.2 the oceanic low-pressure area of winter has been relatively reduced by the development of major low pressure zones over the land masses to east and west, whilst the sub-tropical oceanic high pressure belt has moved north and extended eastwards towards the continent. Depressions are now much more prone to take courses which lead them into the heart of each continent, although in Europe there is still a strong tendency for tracks to the north-east to be followed.

It is possible to discriminate between the tracks followed in the four seasons of the year. Thus in spring and to a less extent in autumn the Mediterranean corridor is frequented. However, it is undeniable that many depressions follow northern routes throughout the year in both continents.

321

Eurasia

(a) Western Europe and the British Isles

Despite the vagaries of weather associated with depressions, there are fairly common patterns characterizing the various seasons. In winter the western margins often enjoy mild and humid weather when the continental high pressure is restricted to eastern Europe where intensely cold weather is experienced. Practically the whole of the sea-

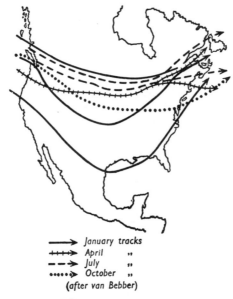

⟶ January tracks
+++⟶ April ,,
− − ⟶ July ,,
•••••⟶ October ,,
(after van Bebber)

FIG. 19.4.—Tracks of Depressions in North America

board of Western Europe, including Scandinavia, receives frontal rainfall from depressions and is under the influence of the gulf of winter warmth. Norway may have milder weather than places on the northern shores of the Mediterranean Sea. Occasionally in winter the continental high pressure extends considerably and covers the western margins. Such an extension may be very persistent, and with east winds and clear skies, and therefore unimpeded nocturnal radiation, severe frosts are common. An extension of the Azores high pressure towards Europe often brings fog and anticyclonic gloom as warm humid air is chilled by contact with the relatively cold land surfaces of the coastal regions. Radiation is reflected back from low stratus clouds, and frost is unusual. If the continental high pressure extends towards Britain then it may be quite cold, particularly in the south and east of England. Snowfall in Western Europe is often produced when a wedge of cold air protrudes westwards and forces tropical air upwards, thus giving abundant frontal precipitation which falls as snow.

In spring, Western Europe is frequently the site of a large col through which depressions move rapidly from Britain towards the Mediterranean Sea basin when squally weather, at a succession of fronts, and typical spring showers are common. Many depressions pass south of Britain in this season, causing easterly winds to prevail over our islands. These winds are reinforced by continental high pressure and the weather is cold and dry.

In summer, with the northward spread of the Azores high pressure area and the development of low pressure in Europe, slow-moving anticyclones pass inland accompanied by intervening depressions. Sometimes the latter may be predominant, and the British summer is very wet. Rainfall is mainly convectional and often associated with troughs of low pressure and thunderstorms. A persistent anticyclone may give a heat wave lasting for several weeks in England, but usually the settled weather of an anticyclone lasts for perhaps nine or ten days, when it is replaced by cyclonic weather. At this time of the year Eastern England has more rain than at any other season, thus showing the continental feature of a summer maximum of convectional rainfall.

Autumn is somewhat like summer, with anticyclonic weather which may last until late October. Night radiation is considerable, so that ground frost and mists or fogs are not uncommon. Depressions give the western coastlands much frontal rainfall, which may be heavy, since warm, humid air is moving on to a land surface which is cooling steadily (see Brest).

(b) Interior Zone—Eastern Europe and Inner Asia

As a whole in Europe the rainfall decreases towards the east, although an extensive region, reaching at least 1,000 miles from the Atlantic seaboard, has over twenty inches of rain in the year. Eastwards the significant change is from rain at all seasons to a markedly summer maximum of rain, but parts of the Russian steppes receive spring rain from depressions. Sheltered basins, such as the Alföld of Hungary, are drier than would be expected for so westerly a position, and carry areas of steppe and semi-desert. On the other hand, inland seas increase the humidity of local winds, so that there may be quite large totals of rain, as at the southern shore of the Caspian Sea, where deciduous forest flourish. Still farther east, increasing continentality, combined with the physical nature of the intermontane basins, produces steppe and desert in inner Asia (Fig. 18.8). The word 'steppe' is of Russian origin and refers to 'waste land'. The observations already made on temperate deserts (p. 311) are relevant.

(c) Eastern Margins—North China and Japan

In this monsoon region intensely cold air from inner Asia covers North China, and also affects Japan, in winter. Peking has mean temperatures below 32° F for three months, and much of northern Japan is similarly very cold (there is also a cold current of water moving towards Japan from the north). Depressions, moving out of China, draw air from the seas, which gives light snow in North China. Many of these depressions follow the two streams of the Kuro Siwo as it branches and passes along both sides of the islands of Japan. With outblowing winds from China, which have to cross the Sea of Japan and gain water vapour, and with these depressions, heavy winter precipitation of both rain and snow is experienced on the northern and western shores of the Japanese islands, whereas their south and east coasts are drier (compare Niigata and Miyako) and also, with lower humidity, more tolerable.

In summer onshore winds give a maximum of rainfall in North China and Japan, although in the latter area the north and west coasts are less rainy than those on the south and east. Additional rain may come in spring from depressions and in autumn from the northern fringes of typhoons whose active centres are well to the south. Mean temperatures in the hot months approach 80° F in North China, but the oceanic influence in Japan prevents temperatures rising much above 75° F, and the hottest month may be delayed until August. Within so limited an extent of latitude (about fifteen degrees) Japan shows a remarkable range of vegetation passing from coniferous forest in the north, through deciduous forest to the southern areas, where subtropical plants such as bamboos and camphor trees flourish.

North America

The west marginal zone of this continent is very limited in comparison with that of Europe, and the intermontane basins and plateaus of the western cordillera carry steppe and desert to within 200 miles of the west coast. The eastern part of the continent has, however, a very extensive region, which receives adequate rainfall as far west as about 100° W, some 1,000 miles from the east coast.

(a) West Margins—Pacific Province

In winter the controls are as shown in Fig. 19.2 but the air accompanying the North Pacific Drift is not so warm nor as humid as that in the North Atlantic Ocean, so that January mean temperatures are some 5° F lower than in corresponding latitudes on the European seaboard. The high mountains, near the western coasts, limit the area enjoying relatively high winter temperatures—but, whilst temperatures fall rapidly on the mountain slopes, the latter induce very heavy coastal rainfall, despite the lower humidity of the oceanic air referred to above. Some of the rainfall is frontal in origin, associated with incoming depressions from the Pacific Ocean and most winter months are very wet (see Vancouver). Annual rainfall totals of over 100 inches are not uncommon on the Canadian coast.

In summer, the northward shift of the high pressure cell and the decline of the low pressure in the North Pacific Ocean cause prevailing north-west winds. Depressions are less common and the air is moving on to relatively warm land, so that there is but moderate rainfall. In Oregon, the rainfall is even less as the 'Mediterranean' region of California is approached.

This coastal province probably has the most luxuriant coniferous forest in the world and includes Douglas firs (Fig. 15.4).

(b) Interior Areas—Basin and Ranges Province and the High Plains

This region shows some of the characteristics of inner Eurasia. The continental nature of the climate is shown by the large mean annual ranges of temperature, usually well over 40° F, with January means below 32° F and July means of the order of 70° F (see Denver). Depressions bring rain in spring and summer and also in winter, but the annual total is only about 15 inches (in some parts less than 10 inches are received) which is in contrast to the western coastlands. Immediately east of the Rocky Mountains there is little winter precipitation, and the continentality is shown by the well-defined summer maximum of convectional rainfall. In summer, tornadoes, which are the most intense form of temperate air swirl, may occur. These are produced by intense convection, frequently developing on the fringe of a thunderstorm. It is probable that they are also influenced by the downdraughts of the thunder cloud (p. 230). As in the Russian steppes, spring rain from depressions is not uncommon in the area of the High Plains.

The Basins and Ranges area carries sage brush (a species of Artemisia) and desert but the high ranges have appreciable rainfall on their western slopes and may be covered with thin coniferous forest. The High Plains to the east have steppe and prairie grasslands but there are some very arid areas, with bare rock and sandhills, known as the 'bad lands'. Steppe grassland is seen in Fig. 15.5.

(c) Eastern Areas (mainly east of 100° W)

This area lies north of the Cotton Belt, extending to the St Lawrence lowlands and the Ontario Peninsula. Its great width gives it both marine and continental characteristics. In winter, depressions are limited, since high pressure air restricts the majority of them to the southern circuit (Fig. 19.4). However, those which pass through this region draw polar maritime air off the Atlantic Ocean and this may cause heavy falls of snow. Behind these depressions may come sudden cold waves, when polar continental air sweeps south. In summer, continental heat produces convectional rainfall everywhere, and this is supplemented by frontal rain which, in the western parts of this area, is brought by tropical air drawn, by low pressure, from the Gulf of Mexico. Farther east, such rain is of Atlantic origin. Chicago exemplifies the continental west of this great area, with a large mean annual range of temperature (48° F) and a summer maximum of rainfall (33 inches per annum), whilst Halifax is typical of the marine east, having a range of 42° F and well distributed precipitation (57 inches per annum).

In winter, temperatures are not excessively low, since the water bodies of the Great Lakes (which are never completely frozen over), like the oceans, have a moderating influence. In the winter months the isotherms show a northward bend over the Great Lakes region—thus, Toronto is not so cold as Montreal, at this time of the year.

Hot waves develop in summer, when tropical air in the warm sectors of almost stationary depressions raises temperatures to over 100° F on several consecutive days (night temperatures rarely fall below 75° F). Relief only comes with the shift of the depression and the onset of winds which bring cooler air from the north.

The natural vegetation of this eastern region consists mainly of mixed deciduous and coniferous forest, but today there are few extensive forested areas apart from the uncultivated uplands, such as are found in the Appalachian Mountains. The forests pass westwards into tall prairie grasslands.

Southern Regions

The areas of Southern Chile (with Patagonia), Tasmania, and New Zealand have several features in common. There are no distinct eastern margins, nor do interior areas occur. All of these areas are close to extensive oceanic surfaces, so that the mean annual ranges of temperatures are usually less than 20° F and only the southernmost parts of South America and New Zealand are high enough in latitude to have mean winter temperatures below 40° F. All lie in the Roaring Forties, where a more or less continuous series of depressions gives constant westerly winds which, on meeting the elevated terrain that lies on all the western shores of these areas (apart from North Island, New Zealand), give excessively heavy annual rainfall; many coastal stations have over 100 inches (see Valdivia). Eastwards in the lee of the mountains the rainfall decreases, so that parts of Patagonia have less than ten inches and in both Tasmania and New Zealand there are areas with less than twenty inches of rain in the year.

South America

Southern Chile and Patagonia are extraordinarily contrasted, with dense forests of conifers and Antarctic beech trees as well as much swamp in the former, whilst in the latter there is steppe and even desert. However, in Patagonia the rainfall, though slight, is well distributed throughout the year, and in some valleys, fed by Andean streams, woodlands appear, whilst an acacia scrub, called espinal, is found in the Rio Negro district.

New Zealand

These islands enjoy the oceanic moderation of the summer heat, and some places have hot-month temperatures which are considerably lower than places in corresponding northern latitudes. Most of New Zealand appears on the map in Fig. 19.1 as a warm temperate region. However, whilst the south is strictly cool temperate, in many ways the whole region is of this type. Whilst westerly winds prevail over most of the country, the northern areas of North Island receive trade winds with rain from the south-east in summer. Rainfall is well distributed during the year, since there is a constant succession of depressions (see Dunedin), and yet there is a very high incidence of sunshine in these islands. In South Island the mean annual isohyets trend parallel to one another and to the longer axis of the island, and there is a fairly uniform decrease of rainfall from west to east. North Island does not exhibit this pattern of rainfall distribution, as its relief is more complex. New Zealand has temperate rain forests, with Antarctic beeches and other trees, such as the kauri pine in the north, whilst grass with woodland flourishes in the drier parts of the country.

The soils of the cool temperate regions are discussed with those of cold temperate areas (p. 333–336).

CHAPTER 20

Cold Climates – Soils of Cool Temperate and Cold Regions

Types and Distribution of Cold Climates

Polewards from cool temperate regions there may be distinguished three types of climate, two of which experience mean temperatures that permit only a very short growing season for plants. The three type of climate are:

   (i) *Cold Temperate Climate*. With at least six months having mean monthly temperatures below 43° F.

  (ii) *Tundra Climate*. With a warm-month temperature of not more than 50° F.

 (iii) *Polar Climate*. With perpetual frost and with no significant plant and animal life.

(*a*) Cold Temperate Climates

These climates are found exclusively in the northern hemisphere (Fig. 20.1). Lying mainly in the westerly wind belt, the regions have climates which are much like those of cool temperate areas. West margins are very restricted in both the northern continents, since western coasts are backed by mountains. Very wide interior zones have the usual characteristics of continentality. Eastern margins are less clearly differentiated but in Siberia there is a monsoonal control.

Temperature

In the narrow west margins mean annual ranges are small, usually between 20° F and 30° F. In winter, the gulf of winter warmth is an important factor and keeps most of the Norwegian coast free from ice and this is true of its North American counterpart. The course of the reduced mean January 32° F isotherm lies slightly inland, along the west coast of each continent. Highlands prevent the warming influence of the ocean penetrating far, and the heads of the larger fjords of these coasts are often icebound, having January mean temperatures some 10° F lower than at their sea ends. In the summer, the tempering effect of the ocean prevents the west coasts from having very high temperatures (Bergen—hot month temperature of

FIG. 20.1.—Cold Regions

58° F); in addition there are frequent fogs which also have a cooling effect.

Interiors have exceptionally large mean annual ranges of temperature. It has been noted that the cold pole of the northern world is not polar in its location, since it lies within north-eastern Siberia. Almost everywhere in winter, mean monthly temperatures descend to, at least, 0° F and, in parts of Siberia, to −58° F, as at Verkhoyansk. Cold air from the interior spreads to the eastern margins, which are only slightly less cold. However, cold sea currents and ice, offshore, give these east margins exceedingly severe winters. This is particularly true of the coasts of the Sea of Okhotsk.

In summer, these interior regions have mean temperatures in the hot month which nearly always exceed 65° F and may reach above 70° F. Spring and autumn are virtually non-existent. Within the Arctic Circle long hours of insolation in summer offset the disadvantages of the low elevation of the sun's rays, and insolation can be very effective on south-facing slopes, particularly if they are steep, in view of the low angle of the sun's rays.

Rainfall

In west margins, there is considerable frontal rainfall which is increased by the high relief. Much snow falls in winter, even at sea level, and this must be regarded as the wettest season, although summer is by no means dry. Annual totals of rainfall decrease northwards along the coasts, where the cold air has a low capacity for water vapour. In northern Norway, the annual rainfall is about half that at Bergen, which has eighty-four inches fall per annum.

The interiors have much less rainfall than the coasts and there is a very sudden eastward decline across the western mountains (compare Bergen with Stockholm). These areas enjoy a very large freedom from rain or snow-bearing winds in winter on account of the high-pressure control, although occasionally depressions do penetrate the areas. Nevertheless, although winter is not without its precipitation, it is in summer that the interiors receive the largest proportion of their annual rainfall, which is rarely more than twenty inches, and of this total some ten or fifteen inches are of summer incidence.

Vegetation

Both west coasts and interiors of these regions support coniferous forests, which, in fact, replace polewards the cool temperate deciduous forests. Some deciduous trees persist but, like the coniferous trees. other than spruce, these are relatively underdeveloped (Fig. 20.2) and none can compare in size with either the deciduous trees, or the Douglas fir, of the cool temperate forests. The value of the short warm season is enhanced by the long hours of sunshine in the far north and, whilst the rainfall is not great, it is adequate, since evaporation is low. Conifers are predominant since there is a lack of competition with deciduous trees but, on exposed coasts, strong winds and salt spray inhibit tree growth.

The coniferous forest is known as taiga and forms a more or less continuous belt across both Canada and Eurasia—the forests extend some 10° of latitude further north on the west sides of these belts

Paul Popper Ltd.

FIG. 20.2.—Coniferous Forest, near Maals River, Northern Norway
In the foreground are some deciduous trees. In the uplands may be seen corries.

as compared with the east. Where fires may have destroyed the coniferous forests, deciduous trees have succeeded in establishing themselves. Such is known as white taiga in Russia and consists of aspens, birchs and willows (the coniferous forest is often called black taiga). In addition, bogs, with mosses and marsh grasslands, may also interrupt the forests.

Regional Types

North America

(*a*) *West Coast—Alaska and British Columbia.* The maritime conditions which have been described above are true of this region. Mountains rising to well over 15,000 feet give excessively high annual totals of rain and snow, over 100 inches at some stations, although, in general, there is a decrease from British Columbia in a northward direction.

(b) *Intermontane Zone of the Cordilleran Region.* Behind the forested coastal mountains the Alaskan interior has less than twenty inches of rain per annum. Much of the area is very high and winters are very cold. The predominant vegetation is tundra.

(c) *Canada, east of the Cordilleran Region.* Most of this area may be regarded climatically as a continental region, but the winter high pressure is less rigid in its control than is the case in Eurasia. Depressions bring not infrequent blizzards with their intensely cold, humid air of polar origin, which makes the winter chill very irksome. Immediately east of the Rocky Mountains rapid increases of temperature are experienced at the time when the chinook wind blows (see p. 220). Although this wind is not regular in its occurrence, it has a frequency which appears to affect the mean winter temperatures of West Albertan towns that, despite their being more northerly and at a greater elevation, are actually rather warmer than Winnipeg (see Winnipeg graph with Calgary temperature curve).

Towards the east of Canada, frequent depressions issuing by the Laurentian region into the North Atlantic Ocean have, it is thought, a moderating effect on the winter chill, and also the water masses of the Great Lakes, as referred to on p. 326, play their part in reducing the severity of the season. Both Labrador and Newfoundland are affected by the cold Labrador current which in summer keeps the mean temperatures below 60° F. Fog is also common on these coasts, particularly in winter.

Immediately east of the Rocky Mountains, the rainfall is, in general, less than twenty inches for the year. The western part of this zone has a typical continental summer maximum of rain that passes eastwards into a region of well-distributed precipitation with somewhat greater annual totals nearer the Laurentian lowlands and in Newfoundland. An annual total of 20·2 inches at Winnipeg increases to 54·6 inches at St. John's, in Newfoundland.

Eurasia

(a) *North-west Europe.* The contrast between Norway and Sweden with Finland may be regarded as an epitome of the contrast between martime and continental regions in high latitudes. Whereas the Norwegian coast is almost completely ice-free, the Gulf of Bothnia is frozen over for some six months of the winter and spring. Although continentality is shown by the summer maximum of convectional rainfall in Sweden, the summer temperatures are lower than those experienced in Siberia (see Stockholm and Yakutsk—on the other hand, the latter is much colder in winter).

The rainfall on the Norwegian coast is generally lighter than in western Canada and Alaska, since the mountains are not more than 6,000 feet in height. In winter, Norway may suffer from very cold easterly winds derived from the continental high pressure, although mild air of Atlantic origin is more common. These cold winds create advection fogs as they pass out over the relatively warm water. Depressions, with west winds of gale force, affect the Norwegian coast on an average once every week in winter and give a winter maximum of rainfall and snow.

(*b*) *Interior Eurasia.* Here continentality of climate is most pronounced (see Yakutsk), but despite the intense winter cold the air is dry, and only rarely do depressions bring humid polar air with the wind known as the buran. The summer rainfall is sufficient, with temperatures of over 60° F, to support coniferous forest.

(*c*) *Eastern Siberia.* The whole Siberian coast as far south as Vladivostok is frozen in winter since it is under continental influences, and in northern sections temperatures fall almost to the level of those at Verkhoyansk. In summer, inblowing monsoonal winds directed to the continental low pressure give coastal rainfall, sometimes in excess of twenty inches, which declines inland towards the eastern edges of the interior plateaus. These winds blow from cool seas and prevent summer temperatures even in the south from rising above 70° F. As in the interior zones, so here winter passes directly to summer and vice versa, so that there is neither spring nor autumn.

(*b*) Soils of Cool and Cold Temperate Regions

The soils of these adjacent regions are best discussed together as many of the major soils are common to both. The podzol is the zonal soil which is particularly associated with the northern coniferous forests but in fact, it is much more widespread. The dominant rôle in the formation of this soil is played by the process of podzolization A typical profile is shown in Figs. 20.3 and 16.2*a*. The needle leaves and twigs which form the litter in the coniferous forests are poor in regard to basic compounds, so that the surface humus layer is fairly raw and acid; furthermore, bacterial action is restricted by low temperatures in these regions. The A horizon shows the effect of strong leaching in that light colours (often nearly white or ashgrey) are characteristic. Eluviation of brown iron oxides and organic material is responsible for this bleaching whilst illuviation of these materials into the B horizon gives a markedly dark (red or yellowishbrown) colour. The acid nature of the A horizon is also accompanied by poor structure of the soil, whereas the much less acid B horizon is reasonably well flocculated. With a deficiency of plant nutrients and the loose texture near the surface, these soils are not suited to agriculture, unless improved by fertilizers when, with the short cool summers, they can be used to grow rapidly maturing crops, such as roots, potatoes and buckwheat.

Fairly closely related to the podzols are the grey-brown podzolic soils which develop, generally, in the rather warmer marginal areas, particularly, of the west. Again, the dominant process is, of course, podzolization but this has not progressed so far as in the true podzols. There is no ash-grey layer in the A horizon but the effect of leaching is seen there in the grey-brown colour, resulting from the removal of brown iron oxides and organic material, whilst the B horizon is typically yellow-brown and of good structure. These zonal soils are quite valuable in comparison with the podzols. There are two special varieties of grey-brown podzolic soils; the grey forest soils which are found in areas where trees have encroached on grasslands, as in parts of the Canadian prairies and the Russian steppes, and the brown forest soils which are more or less intrazonal in character. The latter soils have abundant calcium compounds which may be derived from a limestone parent (they are found on the calcareous

Fig. 20.3.—Profile of Podzol

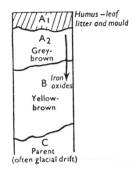

Fig. 20.4.—Profile of a Grey-brown Podzolic Soil

scarplands of England and France). On the other hand, the leaves of deciduous trees, which absorb calcareous material from soil solutions, on decaying, provide this basic content. These forest soils have a very much darker B horizon than is typical of the grey-brown podzolic soils. Most northern areas that were covered with ground moraine, during the Ice Age, have developed these various podzolized soils. A profile of a grey-brown podzolic soil is seen in Fig. 20.4.

In addition to the podzols, the interior regions have two important zonal soils, namely, the prairie soils and the chernozems. Both have a very dark (almost black) surface horizon but the prairie soils are pedalfers and, whilst they are not markedly podzolized, have a reddish-brown B horizon which is non-lime accumulating. On the other hand, masses of calcium compounds are found in the yellow-brown B horizon of the chernozems which are pedocals. The distinction between the two soils is sometimes very difficult to make, since their surface appearances are so similar, but prairie soils tend to occur in more humid areas than do chernozems, which are the 'black earths' of the Russian steppe grasslands. The profile of a prairie soil is given in Fig. 20.5. The high humus content of the A

FIG. 20.5.—Profile of a
Prairie Soil

FIG. 20.6.—Profile of a
Chernozem

horizon is related to the grass cover but slight eluviation has resulted in an enrichment of the B horizon, with some iron oxides and organic material. The chernozem profile (Figs. 20.6 and 16.2b) shows a dark upper horizon (also related to a grass cover) which may extend down as much as five feet. Very little eluviation occurs in the A horizon and calcium compounds therein produce very stable clay colloids so that a good, granular structure is developed. Calcification leads to increased lime accumulation at lower levels in the soil profile, so that pH values show increases from 6·8, at the surface, to about 7·5 in the brown B horizon. Both these zonal soils are of high agricultural value, and the temperate wheat and maize belts are closely related to them. They have such high fertility that some have produced crops for several decades without the use of fertilizers.

FIG. 20.7.—Profile of a Brown
Steppe (Chestnut) Soil

In the more arid interiors, brown steppe and chestnut soils are developed. These pedocals have brown rather than black humus layers and a zone of lime accumulation which lies quite high (Fig. 20.7). Their A horizons are slightly alkaline and have a platy structure. Parts of the intermontane plateaus of the northern continents have these soils. Crop production is not impossible, with dry farming methods, on the chestnut soils but usually they are left undisturbed for grazing (Fig. 15.5). These brown soils are transitional between the chernozems and the grey desert marginal soils which are found in the very dry and remote, interior parts of these regions.

Soils on loess are similar to steppe soils, although loessic soils must be regarded as almost intrazonal in character. Loess is formed as a rock by æolian deposition (see p. 122), but the finely comminuted rock material, the raw mineral content of soil, is readily changed into a loessic soil by the humus derived from the grass cover, and in most cases the soil is very fertile indeed. Both chernozems and prairie soils may have a loess parent.

Intrazonal soils in these temperate areas include rendzinas on chalk and limestone, and, with impeded drainage, there are also peat soils. Peat, like loess, is a rock, but it contains the raw organic material of a soil which is readily converted into a true soil. Fen peat soils form in marshes whose water contains dissolved alkaline minerals. Without such alkaline waters the peat soil is acid, although this type of peat soil may be formed when vegetable matter decays in very wet ground, where the exclusion of oxygen results in the production of much acid humus. These peat soils are sometimes referred to as bog soils and are, in fact, reasonably common in the river plains of most regions.

Tundra soils are discussed in detail on p. 338.

(c) Tundra and Polar Climates

Both the other types of cold climate may be classed as polar in the sense that they are largely under the control of the polar caps of high pressure. The distinction between tundra climate with its short growing season and the polar climate with no period of the year which is free from frost reflects the relative importance of the former. At best the tundra climate is one that must repel man, so that the geographical importance of these regions is slight.

The Arctic region consists of a central ocean basin that is almost completely landlocked, whereas the Antarctic area is a land mass centred on the South Pole and reaches at several places just north of the Antarctic Circle. Surrounding this continent of Antarctica is a complete ring of ocean, so that tundra is almost exclusively located in the northern hemisphere.

The regions are not known well and there exist few long-period records of meteorological observations.[1] The dominant feature on the ground is the outblowing katabatic winds from the polar caps of high pressure, and these are easterly. There is clear evidence that this

[1] The International Geophysical Year (1957–58) has improved our knowledge of Antarctica.

easterly circulation is replaced at no great height above ground-level by a westerly one. This westerly drift is shown by clouds and by smoke from Mt. Erebus, the volcano near the South Pole. The high pressure cap in each hemisphere covers an area which coincides fairly closely with the extent of the pack ice. Around these caps of high pressure move families of depressions in an easterly direction—they are particularly common in the Southern Ocean and many penetrate Antarctica to give snow. Even in winter, low pressure, around the margins of Antarctica, apparently gives access to depressions—in August 1958 about twenty of these penetrated inland at various points. Such influxes of maritime air ameliorated the severity of the cold. At some stations the temperature rose to −60° F.

Temperature

In these very high latitudes the insolation over the year is quite abnormal, since there are very long periods when the sun's rays are cut off completely, which are balanced by periods when insolation is not interrupted for more than a few nocturnal hours in every twenty-four. Both at the Arctic and Antarctic Circles there is one complete day with sun and another without sun in each year. With increasing latitude, within these circles, the number of complete days in the year with and without sun increases to a maximum at each pole, which has a six-month day and a six-month night in each year. Since temperature may be regarded as the result of a balance between heat received by insolation and heat lost by radiation, the significant dates in the year are not the solstices but the equinoxes, because it is after the equinoxes that the long night, or day, commences near the poles. It is usual to expect the lowest mean temperatures after the winter solstice of the hemisphere concerned,[1] but such temperatures may be delayed in these regions until the following equinox (see Spitzbergen). Highest temperatures are similarly postponed in the summer months.

A more important result is that, despite the long hours of insolation in the so-called summer, the angle of the noonday sun at any period is so low that the heat received is very slight. Furthermore, much of this heat is used in melting the ice rather than in heating the ground and the air lying above. The tundra zones are only slightly more fortunate than other polar areas for, although maximum temperatures may on occasions soar to 60° F and 70° F, the majority of places have rarely more than three months with mean temperatures above 32° F. As would be expected, situations near the sea are the most favoured. Mean annual ranges of temperature in both

[1] At Vostok (12,000 feet high on the Antarctic plateau), during the period 1958–60 the lowest recorded temperatures in each year occurred one or two days after the sun reappeared on August 22nd or 23rd. The lowest record of all was obtained on August 24th, 1960, with a temperature of −88·3° C (−127° F).

tundra and polar climates are large, but the amplitude never reaches that of stations in eastern Siberia. The Arctic basin is ice-covered but the water below has a temperature of about 29° F, and this prevents the minima at the surface from being very low. It is of interest that, near the South Pole, the temperature remains almost constant during the long winter period.

Precipitation

Under the prevailing high pressure of the polar caps the chance of precipitation is very limited and, although snow falls, the air is so dry that usually there is very little. At the same time there is probably even less chance of a great loss of moisture, because the melting of snow and ice is slight. Apart from coastal and marginal areas, where depressions and blizzards may bring heavier falls of snow, rarely do annual totals exceed the equivalent of 10 inches of rain. This general statement applies to Antarctica, as well as to the northern tundra regions.

Vegetation and Soils

The tundra regions have, with the annual release from frost, a chance of supporting plant life, but the plants are adapted to the very limited period of growth and the exceptional soils. The life-cycle of some plants must be accomplished in a period of less than two months. Growth is, undoubtedly, encouraged by the long hours of sunshine, but so handicapped are the plants that the normal process of seeding is largely abandoned and in its place there is vegetative reproduction, by budding or from root shoots.

FIG. 20.8.—Profile of a Tundra Soil

After the mean temperatures have risen above 32° F the soil is unfortunately of little worth, since it is clogged with water, and has a glei horizon (see p. 262). The soil is ice-cold and, as at no great depth it is permanently frozen, its drainage is largely impeded. Tundra soil is essentially anaerobic, and in it organic processes are inhibited. Little humus is formed; it remains raw and is therefore very acid and has a low content of nitrogenous compounds (Fig. 20.8). Plants are

E. Aubert de la Rüe, Pully-Lausanne

FIG. 20.9.—Tundra in Summer, Ungava Peninsula, Canada

Much of the ground, frozen at a depth of not more than 2 feet, is covered with marsh and small pools. The slopes in the background carry stunted trees.

compelled to behave in such a manner that they resemble some desert plants in that the frozen subsoil compels the root systems of the plants to spread extenively in the upper layers of the soil. Dwarf plants, including small trees of willow, alder, and birch, may succeed on better-drained slopes, but they have no great vertical development for quite slight winds will produce too rapid a transpiration for their well-being. On slopes which are sunny and well drained, plants such as Iceland poppies, the saxifrages, and other familiar members of our British rock gardens may flourish. Lichens are quite common, being well suited to the tundra in that they have little competition to face from other plants. They are double plants, being both algae and fungi (the fungi are probably parasitic on the algae). One of the largest lichens (Cladonia) is, incorrectly, called reindeer moss. Lichens, mosses and coarse grasses provide the food for the animals of the regions (Fig. 20.9). In Antarctica, there are some plants including algae, lichens and liverworts, in a few favourable coastal situations, but animal life is almost non-existent, apart from some insects and microscopic animals (seals and penguins are, of course, not land animals). Paradoxically, the waters around Antarctica have been shown to be extraordinarily rich in marine life, both animal and vegetable.

P.G.C.—12

Part IV   Oceanography

CHAPTER 21

Oceanography

Physical Features of the Ocean Basins

The oceans, with their marginal seas, occupy about 70 per cent of the global surface. Our study of the oceans must be limited in comparison with that of the land surfaces and the atmosphere. Our chief aim will be to examine fairly closely such aspects of the oceans as have a bearing on meteorology and climatology. Nevertheless, the oceans possess fairly well known features of relief.

Most oceans occupy basins which may be divided into several zones (see Fig. 21.1). Nearest the continental margins is the contin-

Fig. 21.1.—The Floor of the Ocean

Note.—In general, slopes are quite gentle (not to scale)

ental shelf which is of varying width: 0 to 940 miles with an average of about 50 miles. The depth of its outer margin also varies, from 65 to 1,800 feet with an average of about 420 feet. Beyond the shelf the ocean floor plunges steeply by the continental slope to the ocean plain; the steepness of this slope, of the order of 1:40, is only relative to the gentle gradient of the shelf which is of the order of 1:1,000. The ocean plains, as deep as 12,000 feet or more, are interrupted by significant features such as mid-ocean ridges, deep trenches, and sea mounts and guyots.

The continental shelves appear to be the outer edges of the continents and carry a surface layer of deposits largely derived from the neighbouring lands. It is possible to regard some continental shelves as zones which are determined by some form of outer barrier against which terrestrial deposits have accumulated. Such barriers may be faulted blocks of continental origin whilst others, as in the Gulf of Mexico, in particular, have been developed by rising salt uplifting the ocean bed in the form of a salt dome (see p. 17). A third form of barrier is that of a reef which may have been built by living coral organisms (see p. 154). Nevertheless, many of the continental shelves do not seem to be related to such dams or barriers. Clearly, in the shallow inshore parts of the shelves wave action can modify the shelf surfaces. However, recently—during the Pleistocene Ice Age—the ocean surface was much lower than it is today (see p. 154) and shelves in high latitudes have, in fact, been eroded by ice, as revealed by surveys off the coast of Maine.

The shelves may possess submarine canyons. These are steep-sided channels with cross-sections that suggest they have been eroded by running water. In fact, some show a correspondence, in depth and cross-section, to the Grand Canyon (see Fig. 7.10). They are found both on the shelf and the continental slope. Some are in direct line with existing valleys whose rivers may have eroded the adjacent shelf when it was exposed in Pleistocene times. Other submarine canyons are totally unrelated to existing rivers but many may be said to notch the continental slope. Such canyons are believed to be the product of turbidity currents. These are massive flows of sea water, heavily charged with fine unconsolidated sediments, which move with speeds as great as 50–60 m.p.h. Such a current was initiated by an earthquake on the continental shelf to the south of Newfoundland in 1929. The turbid water, on a front some 100 miles wide, extended southwards for well over 500 miles and severed several telegraph cables which lay in its path. Such currents, moving at the speeds mentioned, would erode on a much greater scale than do fast-flowing rivers on the land and, therefore, they could cut these deep canyons. It is believed that the turbidity current, referred to above, swept off the Grand Banks and deposited an apron of sediments some three feet deep over a large area of the ocean plain.

At one time, extensive ocean plains were regarded as typical of the ocean basins beyond the continental slopes. However, in recent years, it has become apparent that such plains are interrupted by mid-ocean ridges. The Mid-Atlantic Ridge has long been recognized but, in fact, the system of such ridges is virtually world-wide (see Fig. 21.2). These ridges have dimensions which make them comparable with continental mountain ranges. With widths of the order of 500 miles or more they rise from the adjacent ocean plains to heights of 5,000 feet or more. Perhaps the most remarkable feature of these ridges is the dual crest line, separated by a median rift valley whose floor may be as much as a mile below the level of the crests (see Fig. 21.1). Cross-sections of these rifts show a close resemblance, including their overall dimensions, to the rift valleys in east Africa. The ocean ridges are dislocated by extensive transform faults, resulting from horizontal movements, which have caused adjacent sections

Fig. 21.2.—Mid-Ocean Ridges and other features of the Ocean Basins

of the ridges to be offset from one another in regard to the median line. Thus, the smooth curves shown in Fig. 21.2 should be regarded as a series of relatively short sections, offset from their neighbours—in some cases dextrally and in others sinistrally—by as much as 300 to 600 miles. Such faults have produced underwater scarps that rise as much as a mile from the sea floor.

It is further believed that, in two instances, at least, these ridges may link up with continents—as in California, with a relationship to the San Andreas fault system, and in the Red Sea and east Africa. The Mid-Atlantic Ridge appears above sea level in Iceland.

Associated with these ridges are volcanoes and earthquakes. It is generally accepted that from the median rifts, basaltic lavas are extruded and on the flanks of the ridges rise volcanic peaks. Some of these volcanoes may be supplied with lava from the transform faults. A map of the world showing the epicentres of earthquakes in the ocean basins reflects remarkably the distribution of the ridges.

In addition to these major features, the oceans possess very deep trenches. These are narrow, longitudinal belts which may descend to depths of 30,000 or even 35,000 feet. Some of the outstanding deeps are indicated in Fig. 21.2. Whilst relatively limited in their distribution many deeps are closely related to island arcs (see pp. 37 and 52-5), as in the Asiatic and Caribbean zones, or to the trend of the Alpine fold mountains, as off Central and South America. However, in western parts of the Pacific Ocean, the Mariana and Kermadec-Tonga trenches lie well out in the ocean basin.

Finally, isolated peaks, known as sea mounts and guyots, which rise to heights of the order of 10,000 feet above the ocean plain, must be discussed. The sea mounts have the shape of volcanic cones and, indeed, some give rise to present-day submarine eruptions. On the other hand, guyots seem to be sea mounts whose upper parts have been reduced by sea erosion so that, in essence, they are truncated extinct volcanic cones. To account for this truncation by wave action the gradual sinking of a volcanic island (or the gradual rising of the sea surrounding such an island) must be invoked. It is possible that some of the atolls of the Pacific Ocean are based on guyots (see p. 154). Guyots and sea mounts have been recorded from several parts of the Pacific Ocean, as shown in Fig. 21.2, but it seems likely that many may lie in groups on either side of most of the mid-ocean ridges.

Ocean Deposits

The floors of the oceans are covered with layers of sediments which belong to two classes. On the shelves and to a lesser extent on the continental slopes there are mainly terrigenous deposits (derived from the land), whilst in the deeper areas there are very fine deposits known as oozes, which are composed of the finely divided remnants of shells and skeletons of various sea organisms, together with fine volcanic dust and other material. The organic deposits are derived from various groups of sea creatures and marine plants, some being calcareous, whilst others are siliceous. Sea organisms may be divided into two groups according to their habitats. There are, for instance, the corals, mussels, and sea-weeds which are benthic, that is, they live usually rooted, on the sea floor, and since they are limited to depths of not much more than 100 fathoms, they inhabit the waters of the continental shelves and add their quota to the terrigenous deposits. The other group of sea organisms are planktonic, in that they live in the surface waters of the seas and float about quite freely. This group includes pteropods and foraminifera, which have calcareous shells and structures, and radiolaria whose skeletal material is siliceous. In addition, there are diatoms or microscopic sea plants which have siliceous material in them. The diatoms are a source of food for most of the planktonic creatures. Since diatoms require light and this does not penetrate farther than about 650 feet in sea water, most planktonic life is restricted to depths of about 100 fathoms. Although most of these organisms are very minute, their numbers are countless, and they represent in all a much greater bulk than do the fishes and whales.

The terrigenous deposits have been briefly discussed in Chapter 1, where it was shown that rivers carry out to sea particles of sand and clay together with carbonates in solution. The carbonates may be taken out of the sea water by various organisms in order to produce their shells, and on the other hand the carbonate may be deposited directly from sea water through temperature variations. Terrigenous deposits of sand and clay are laid on the continental shelves at varying distances from the land according to the size of their particles, together with carbonate deposits derived from sea water in one way or another. There are also various coloured muds which are very finely divided clays. Their colour depends on chemical changes which produce different compounds of iron. Blue mud obtains its colour from ferrous sulphide, red mud from iron oxide, green mud from glauconite, a silicate of iron and potassium resulting from organic decay.

Large areas of the ocean floor beyond the continental shelves are covered with various oozes, and some muds and clays which consist largely of the minute remnants of the calcareous and siliceous organisms. Most oozes are greyish-white in colour. After death the shells of the organisms sink slowly downwards, and at the same time a considerable amount of solution of these shells occurs in sea water; they are small to begin with, rarely larger than a pin's head, but they become even thinner and smaller with solution. Calcareous remains are unusual below 3,500 fathoms, since their solution is more rapid than is the case with the siliceous material which may not be completely dissolved until depths of 5,000 fathoms are reached. Whilst the depth of the ocean floor determines to some extent the type of deposit that will accumulate in a given area, there is a further control, namely, that of temperature in the surface waters. For instance, diatoms, whilst occurring in all surface waters, are most common in the colder seas, and the most extensive deposits of diatomaceous ooze are on the floors of the Southern Ocean on the equatorward side of the terrigenous deposits which are derived from Antarctica. On the other hand, radiolaria flourish in warm tropical seas, and their siliceous oozes are found in the deeper parts of the Indian and the Pacific Oceans.

Below 5,000 fathoms most material of organic origin is absent and the commonest deposit is red clay, which is composed of fine volcanic ash, wind-borne dust from the land surfaces, minute remnants of the bones and teeth of large sea creatures such as whales and sharks, and even some terrigenous deposits that have been released in the open oceans by the melting of icebergs. This clay accumulates extremely slowly, and long-period decomposition produces much iron oxide which is responsible for its predominant red colour. It must not be thought that red clay is restricted to the great depths of the oceans, as it is a constituent of most oozes. Radiolarian ooze is, in fact, red clay with a high proportion of radiolarian remains, and the same is true of calcareous and other deposits.

Of the many organisms which produce calcareous oozes, two are outstanding, namely, the pteropods (which are molluscs) and Globigerina, the commonest of the foraminifera. The oozes of the former are restricted to fairly shallow depths, usually no more than 1,000 fathoms, and to tropical and subtropical seas where they are associated with the ridges and plateaus rising from the ocean plains. This pteropod ooze has a very limited distribution, mainly in quite small areas on the central ridge of the Atlantic Ocean, but other areas are found in the Mediterranean Sea and in parts of the Pacific Ocean off Australia. The Globigerina ooze has, on the other hand, a very wide distribution, particularly in the Atlantic and Indian Oceans, and to a less extent in the Pacific Ocean. Whilst foraminifera are capable of standing quite wide ranges of temperature in the surface waters of the ocean, they are usually found between 60° N and 60° S latitude, although in the North Atlantic Ocean, relatively warm surface water enables these deposits to form in latitudes as high as 70° N. This ooze is limited in depth by the complete solution of the calcium carbonate of the shells at about 2,500–3,000 fathoms, and towards these levels red clay becomes an increasingly important constituent and finally replaces the calcareous ooze in deeper waters. There are also certain zones of the oceans, around coral islands, where a distinct coral mud is deposited.

Temperature of Ocean Water

The temperature of the surface of the sea varies in much the same way as that of the land surfaces, since insolation is responsible for the varying quantities of heat which are received at different latitudes and in different seasons. However, there are significant differences between water and land surfaces which have been reviewed on pp. 162-3, and as water is a liquid, there is a distribution of the heat by mixing which is, of course, impossible with land areas. Surface temperatures of the oceans show a fairly considerable range during the year at most latitudes and in some zones, admittedly limited, this range may be as great as that which is experienced in certain continental interiors. Although ranges of 50° F are on record, it is usual for the range to be of not more than 20° F. The surface temperatures vary with latitude, and mean annual temperatures of 80° F, and even higher, are common in tropical seas, but there is a general decrease towards the poles where there are mean temperatures of slightly less than 32° F. Owing to sea water being saline, it may not freeze until temperatures of 29° F or 28° F, are reached, the depression of the freezing temperature depending very much on the concentration of dissolved salts. There is not a constant decrease of surface temperature with increasing latitude, since drifting warm water from the tropical seas may move into high latitudes and give a local increase of temperature, as in the North Atlantic Ocean, where there is, as has been described on p. 168, a positive anomaly of temperature in winter. On the other hand, upwellings of deep, cold water may reduce locally the surface temperature of tropical and subtropical sea water.

The distribution of surface temperatures in the oceans during the year may be summarized as follows:

1. In tropical waters extreme temperatures may be as high as 90° F, or as low as 70° F, but the mean annual range is usually about 10° F.

2. In polar waters the lowest surface temperatures are experienced, approaching 32° F (and may be lower, as explained above), and rarely does the temperature rise above 50° F. The mean annual range of surface temperature is usually of the same order as that for tropical waters, about 10° F.

3. The temperate seas which may be regarded as intermediate to the above zones have somewhat wider ranges of temperature. Adjacent to certain continental areas, as off eastern Canada and in a comparable area, the Sea of Japan, the mean annual range may be as large as 50° F. In general, however, it is between 20° F and 40° F.

There is a fairly close connection between the temperature conditions of the surface waters and the sea organisms present. Thus, the high mean temperatures and the small ranges of the tropical waters encourage corals and many calcareous organisms, whereas in the cooler waters of higher latitudes the secretion of lime is much reduced and siliceous material is more commonly used for the structures of marine creatures. On the other hand, planktonic organisms are most abundant in temperate waters in fairly high latitudes, and this is reflected in the great fisheries of the subarctic seas.

Salinity of Ocean Water

The salinity of the oceans is produced by a large number of dissolved chemical compounds. The salt of the sea is the residue of solid material, left after the evaporation of sea water, that can be weighed and is expressed as a fraction of the whole weight of water, before evaporation. Salinity is therefore defined as the weight in grammes of solid material left after the evaporation of 1,000 grammes of sea water. If the weight of solid material is 35 grammes (and it is usually very near this figure) the salinity would be shown as 35‰.[1] In the marginal seas of the oceans the salinity has a wide range of values. In the Baltic Sea fresh water entering from the surrounding lands reduces the salinity to 7‰, and it may fall in this sea as low as 2‰, but great evaporation combined with a very dry climate in the Red Sea region gives the water of that marginal sea a high salinity value of 41–42‰.[2]

Although a great number of salts can be identified in sea water, something like 80 per cent of the salt is sodium chloride, whilst magnesium chloride, magnesium sulphate, and calcium sulphate together account for much of the remaining 20 per cent. In addition, very small quantities of many other salts account for less than 1 per cent of the total dissolved salts. Irrespective of the salinity value, whether high or low, the proportions of the different salts remain practically constant. This is explained by the thorough mixing which occurs throughout the waters of the several oceans. Estimates of salinity are therefore considered quite reliable when the content by weight of any one element in a sample of sea water is determined. The element used for this purpose usually is chlorine.

The origin of the various salts is somewhat problematical. Much of the salt content is derived from river water, but there is by no means an obvious relationship between the salts in river water and those in sea water. River water has a considerable content of dissolved carbonates, but these are relatively uncommon in sea water, having been abstracted for the formation of the shells of various marine organisms. On the other hand, chlorides, which have a low proportion in river water, become quite common in sea water largely

---

[1] It is usual to express salinity in this way rather than as a percentage.
[2] Salinity of the Dead Sea may be as great as 250‰.

because of the removal of carbonates in the sea, which thus increases the relative proportion of chlorides.

The salinity of open ocean waters varies within certain limits, although the value is rarely much above or below 35‰. A dilution of the salt water may be caused by the influx of water from large rivers, by heavy rainfall, and in polar seas by the melt of ice, whilst a concentration of the salts is produced by great evaporation, with great heat and strong winds. Dilution may be brought about by the transport of less saline waters into very saline waters and concentration by the reverse movement.

Lines of equal salinity or isohalines may be drawn on maps from salinity observations in the same way as isotherms may be traced. An investigation of such maps shows that in rainy tropical and equatorial zones the surface salinity values are low (below 35‰), whilst immediately north and south of these zones in the areas affected by the trade winds which cause much evaporation, the salinity rises to 36‰ and over. In temperate latitudes with fairly heavy rainfall at sea, the salinity is reduced and decreases still more in a poleward direction, so that in Arctic and Antarctic waters the value may be as low as 33·5‰ and in some areas a value of 31‰ has been recorded.

In addition, sea water dissolves gases from the atmosphere, and apart from nitrogen and oxygen there is a remarkably high content of carbon dioxide. Bacterial action is also important in sea water, and there is the fixation of nitrogen to form nitrogenous and ammonium compounds. It is possible to regard these various dissolved substances as playing a similar rôle in relation to the life within the ocean waters as do the mineral and organic particles which affect the growth of plants in the soil of the land.

Surface Circulations of the Oceans

The circulation of the waters in the oceans can be regarded in two ways. There is a series of horizontal movements of water across the surface of the oceans, but owing to the depth of the oceans there are also both vertical and horizontal movements within the body of ocean water. The complete circulation is extraordinarily complex, and can be discussed but briefly in this book. Movements of water at any level in the ocean body and in any direction depend upon the difference in the density of the water. The density depends upon the temperature and the salinity of the water, but movements at the surface also depend upon the major wind flows which are controlled by atmospheric pressure distributions. These surface movements are in the form of currents and drifts. The former may be readily observed, as they have speeds of 1–5 knots, and are of importance to navigation; the latter are slow, almost imperceptible, movements of large masses of water with a large surface area.

The Atlantic, Indian, and Pacific Oceans are sufficiently extensive from north to south to have surface circulations which may be shown by a generalized diagram for one ocean (Fig. 21.3). The most significant features of this diagram are the two anticyclonic gyrals of currents that are clearly related to the subtropical oceanic cells of high pressure in each hemisphere. These two circulations approach one another in equatorial latitudes, so that westward-flowing currents are found immediately north and south of an eastward-flowing counter current. The two westward currents are thought to produce a piling

Fig. 21.3.—Generalized Surface Circulation in an Ocean

up of water on the western sides of the oceans, and some of this returns to make good the loss of surface water from the eastern side. In fact, near the Equator, there is a surface gradient in the ocean giving a gentle fall eastwards. It is reasonable to assume that the North and South Equatorial Currents are induced by the surface drag of the trade winds of each hemisphere. On the western sides of the oceans these currents are deflected by the continental margins and turn poleward, moving into higher latitudes, and eventually coming under the influence of the westerly winds, they become eastward-moving currents. In part, at least, these eastward currents are deflected towards the Equator on the eastern sides of the oceans. There is a shift of the latitudinal position of the currents in the equatorial zones, with the migration of the overhead sun during the year. This is most noticeable in the Atlantic Ocean. Fig. 21.3 shows also that in high latitudes there are currents which move in an equatorward direction and are of polar origin. The diagram also indicates what are known as cold and warm currents. The former are currents which bring surface water that is relatively cold into areas of the ocean which are relatively warm, whereas the latter are opposite in character. Whilst warm water from an area of cool sea surface will warm up as it moves towards areas of warm surface water, it will tend to have a temperature which is lower than that of the water it enters and than that of the overlying air, so that it will have a cooling effect. The reverse is true of warm currents as they move water into cooler areas. A cold current may be caused by another factor, namely, the upwelling of deep water which is common on the eastern sides of the oceans in tropical and subtropical latitudes. Here the westward-moving trade winds, in removing surface water from the eastern sides of the ocean, induce deep water to rise and take the place of this displaced surface water. Although each of the three major oceans has a basic pattern of currents which is very like that shown in Fig. 21.3, there are certain distinctions characterizing each one. Whilst the southern parts of these oceans show a close similarity to one another, it is the parts lying north of the Equator that show the greatest diversity. The Indian Ocean is also somewhat exceptional, in that is northern limits are in low latitudes, whereas both the Pacific and Atlantic Oceans extend to very high northern latitudes. Figs. 21.4 and 21.5 show the essential points of resemblance and contrast between the circulations of these three oceans.

The two Equatorial Currents, with their Counter-Equatorial Current, are different in the Atlantic and Pacific Oceans (Fig. 21.4). In the former, water from both Equatorial Currents enters a westward-flowing current which passes mainly through the Caribbean Sea. Cape San Roque in South America seems to act as a deflecting point, so that whilst most of the South Equatorial Current turns southwards as the warm Brazilian Current, some of its water flows north-westwards. Almost the exact opposite occurs in the western Pacific Ocean, where near the Philippine Islands the North Equatorial Current is partially deflected southwards, and enters the Counter-Equatorial Current of that ocean. The current of the Atlantic Ocean which leaves the Caribbean Sea through Florida Strait becomes the warm Gulf Stream that can be traced as the West Wind Drift (that is, it loses the character of a well-defined current and broadens), and farther east it is known by yet another name, the North Atlantic Drift, which flows

FIG. 21.4.—Surface Circulations in the Atlantic and Pacific Oceans.

Note.—Part of the North Equatorial Current in the Atlantic Ocean enters the Gulf of Mexico.

Cold Currents
Warm Currents

GS—Gulf Stream
KC—Kamchatka Current
KS—Kuro Siwo
LC—Labrador Current
PC—Peru Current

CC—California Current
CaC—Canaries Current
EC—Falkland Current

AC—Alaska Current
BeC—Benguela Current
BrC—Brazil Current

NEC—North Equatorial Current
CEC—Counter Equatorial Current
SEC—South Equatorial Current
WWD—West Wind Drift
NAD—North Atlantic Drift

351

to the very northern limits of the ocean and enters the Norwegian Sea. It is true that quite large offshoots of the West Wind Drift occur; one swings southwards around the Sargasso Sea, and farther east part of this drift, usually known as the Canaries Current, turns south to join the North Equatorial stream. The counterpart of this quite exceptional current and drift in the North Pacific Ocean is much less extensive. The major part of the North Equatorial Current in the Pacific Ocean turns north near the Philippine Islands and proceeds as the Kuro-Siwo, a warm current, past the main islands of Japan (with two branches) and then eastwards as a drift, although it is highly doubtful if this reaches the coasts of North America. Like the West Wind Drift of the North Atlantic Ocean it sets southwards in a series of offshoots, the most easterly of which is in the neighbourhood of the Hawaiian Islands. Farther east there is a comparable current to the southerly drift on the east side of the northern Atlantic Ocean, which is known as the California Current, but this arises from an entirely separate gyral in the North Pacific Ocean to the south and east of the Aleutian Islands. Here water comes south and swings east, and then bifurcates into the northward-flowing Alaska Current which is thus relatively warm, and the southward-flowing California Current which is relatively cool. In the northern regions of both these oceans there are cold southward-flowing currents off Labrador and Greenland in the one ocean and off Kamchatka in the other.

South of the Equator both oceans merge with the Southern Ocean, and the anticyclonic gyral in each gives rise to a very regular pattern of currents. It will be observed that the southern margin of each gyral merges with the circumpolar West Wind Drift of water, and in part the waters of the southward-flowing and warm Brazil Current and of the similar current off Australia enter this circulation. The configuration of the coasts of Southern Chile and South-west Africa create a deflection of some of the West Wind Drift that moves north as a cold current along each of these coasts. Both the Benguela and Peru Currents are markedly cold, but a complete account of them has yet to be given. For instance, the Peru Current, which has been very well studied, is not cold just because it flows from south to north, but owes its low surface temperature to upwelling of cold water. It is not by any means uniform in its chilling effect, and recent investigations suggest very strongly that there are local minor swirls within the current at various places off the coasts of both Chile and Peru which cause warm water to prevail instead of cool or cold water. In all probability, these are produced by influxes of relatively warm water from the ocean surface, lying to the west of the main currents. Nevertheless, upwelling of cold water from the depths is regarded as the most important feature near the coast, although farther west there is what is known as the Peru Ocean Current which consists largely of water of Antarctic origin moving northwards. It has been suggested that the Falkland Current is caused, in part, by the offshore effect of the westerly winds which induce cold water to flow northwards off Patagonia.

In the Indian Ocean the circulation north of the Equator is quite exceptional, since in this region the ocean surface is under the controls of the monsoonal circulation of the atmosphere. This means that whilst in the winter half of the year the wind direction is practically identical with the normal trade wind flow from the east, this direction is completely reversed in the summer half of the year. Consequently no North Equatorial Current flows in summer; in its place, and also apparently in the place of the counter-current, is an eastward-flowing current which may be referred to as the Monsoon Current (Fig. 21.5).

AgC	Agulhas Current	
CEC	Counter Equatorial Current	
MC	Mozambique Current	
NEC	North Equatorial Current	
SEC	South Equatorial Current	
WAC	West Australia Current	
WWD	West Wind	

All Year Currents
Northern Winter Currents
Northern Summer Currents (Monsoon Current of North Indian Ocean)
Warm Current
Cold Current

FIG. 21.5.—Surface Circulation in the Indian Ocean

In winter there is a westward-flowing current north of the Equator with a counter current between it and the South Equatorial Current of the Indian Ocean. In its southern part the Indian Ocean has a circulation which is comparable with that of the corresponding areas of the Pacific and Atlantic Oceans, with one slight difference, namely, that the warm western current off Mozambique sends some water around the southern margins of Africa into the Atlantic Ocean. This flow is opposed to that of the main West Wind Drift and results in a series of local swirls or eddies. The cold current off

Western Australia is much less marked in its coolness than are the corresponding Peru and Benguela Currents.

Circulation within the Water of the Oceans

It has been shown that currents and drifts of surface water in the oceans can be linked closely with the frictional drag of winds across the surface, but it has been mentioned that these movements of water depend upon differences of density which can produce gradients in the surface waters, much as differences of atmospheric pressure will create pressure gradients and winds. The density of the surface water of an ocean can be both increased and decreased locally. Increase occurs when the surface waters are cooled, when there is great evaporation which increases the salinity, and where there is freezing of saline water. In the latter case the ice which forms does not contain all the soluble salts, and this means that the surrounding water which remains unfrozen has a greater concentration of salt and therefore a greater density. Decrease of density occurs when great heating causes the expansion of the surface water, also when great rainfall, or an influx of much fresh water from rivers or the melting of ice dilutes the water. When there is an increase in the density of sea water, as happens when saline tropical water moves into higher latitudes and cools, the water usually sinks to the level of the ocean which has the same density and there spreads out as a distinct layer. To compensate for this sinking of some surface water there must be a return of water to the surface. This may be in the vicinity of the sinking water, but it may occur in parts of the ocean very remote from where the water sinks.

In tropical latitudes the effect of great heating is to maintain a fairly low density in the surface waters, and even where high salinity values prevail there is little chance of the water sinking very deep. It is in high latitudes that water on chilling can become sufficiently dense to sink to the deeper parts of the ocean, and form what is known as bottom water and deep water. Particular areas, where this deep sinking occurs, are in parts of the North Atlantic Ocean and off Antarctica. In the former ocean, saline tropical water moving north with the Gulf Stream and its continuation, the North Atlantic Drift, becomes so very chilled in the seas between Greenland and Iceland that it sinks to very great depths. Off Antarctica the water not only becomes very dense through chilling, but its salinity is increased through the formation of much ice in this region. Much of this water finds its way down to the lowest levels of the South Atlantic Ocean (Fig. 21.6), and creeps at a very slow pace (it has been estimated that some of this water moves only about five to eight miles in a year) northwards, to the mid-latitudes of the North Atlantic Ocean. The temperature of this water is very slightly higher than the freezing temperature of sea water, that is, about 28° F. The densest water in the oceans is thought to lie on the floor of the Arctic Ocean, but it cannot move out of this basin, since it is hemmed in by the surrounding shelves of the shallow seas. There is little chance of water sinking to displace this bottom water in the Arctic Basin, since the surface waters are light, having a very low salinity because of the great discharge of fresh water into it, particularly from the great rivers of Siberia. Since there is no confinement of the waters in the Southern Ocean it is here that most of the deepest bottom water of the Atlantic Ocean originates.

The fairly dense waters, caused by chilling, which sink in the North Atlantic Ocean, do not reach the greatest depths, but form what is known as the North Atlantic deep water, which moves southwards, creeping over the northward-moving bottom water from the Antarctic zone. This North Atlantic deep water permeates the whole of the southern part of the ocean, and finally rises over the denser Antarctic bottom water which is descending from the surface in high southerly latitudes (Fig. 21.6). This Atlantic deep water is accompanied

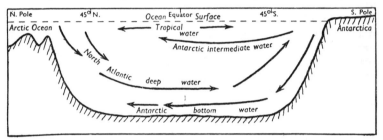

Fig. 21.6.—Generalized Circulation within the Atlantic Ocean

by dense saline water which flows out of the Mediterranean Sea basin as a deep current below an eastward-flowing surface current passing through the Straits of Gibraltar from the Atlantic Ocean. The circulation of the water at the Straits of Gibraltar is of interest, and is shown by Fig. 21.7. It will be seen that there is a shallow sea over the sill at the Straits of Gibraltar which separates the Atlantic Ocean from the Mediterranean Sea. There is a strong surface current of shallow depth, bringing fairly warm saline water from the west. This current may be accounted for by the gradient which is produced through the lowering of the surface level of the inner parts of the Mediterranean Sea by great evaporation. This evaporation is accompanied by an increase in salinity, and some water sinks as a dense layer to the floor of the Mediterranean Sea. There is set up a difference of density which produces a return flow of saline deep water into the Atlantic Ocean over the sill at the Straits of Gibraltar and this sinks and joins the Atlantic deep water. It is usual for an inward-moving surface current to be above an outward-moving deep current

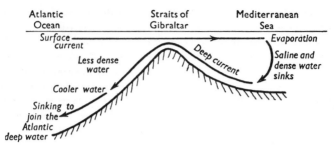

FIG. 21.7.—Movements of Waters at the Straits of Gibraltar

at an opening from an ocean into a more saline marginal sea. The reverse is true of a marginal sea, which has relatively fresh water in comparison with the outer ocean water. Thus, there is a westward surface current over a deep current moving eastwards in the Skaggerak and Kattegat between the North Sea and the Baltic Sea. Two comparable currents flow between the Mediterranean Sea and the fresher Black Sea.

Hence, there is a stratification of the ocean waters, and the section of Fig. 21.6 shows several types of water from various sources at different levels. It is certainly quite common for warm but highly saline water to lie below relatively cold water that is only slightly saline. This is exemplified by what is known as Antarctic intermediate water which, although quite cold, is diluted to such an extent that it is not so very dense. It flows northwards in the South Atlantic Ocean above somewhat warmer southward-flowing North Atlantic deep water and below surface tropical waters. There has come into being a conception of 'water masses' in the oceans which are analogous to air masses in the atmosphere, and, with movement, a 'water mass' may be brought to a position where it mixes with water of a different mass, so that it is transformed as regards its temperature and salinity.

The vertical circulation, which seems typical of the Atlantic Ocean as shown by Fig. 21.6, is not found in the Pacific or Indian Oceans. The bottom and deep waters of the South Atlantic Ocean apparently spread eastwards and enter the Indian Ocean. Farther east still this water serves the Pacific Ocean. In both of these oceans a return of these deep waters seems to take place with a reversal of the northward flow in the northern parts of the oceans. Just as in the Atlantic Ocean, there is some supply of water to the deep waters of the Indian Ocean from the Red Sea. This supply is somewhat analogous to that which moves from the Mediterranean Sea into the Atlantic Ocean. It is almost certain that much, if not all, the deep water in the Pacific Ocean is of Atlantic origin.

As has been suggested, there must be a compensating elevation of water in certain areas of the oceans to make good the loss to the surface of water which sinks. It has been shown that deep water rises over the denser Antarctic bottom water, as the latter sinks in the South Atlantic region, but there are, of course, several zones of up-welling such as those off the western coasts of Peru and South-west Africa. Quite obviously the whole circulation is extraordinarily complex, but there is little doubt that the surface circulations are merely one aspect of the complete picture which, as yet, is far from being fully understood.

Effect of Oceanic Circulations on Climate and Weather

Throughout the studies of climatology, in particular of those regions in middle and high latitudes, the contrast between continental and marine areas is frequently presented. Although the land masses undoubtedly play their part in producing this contrast, there is an oceanic influence as well. As Fig. 21.3 shows, there are westward-moving sea currents near the Equator which bring water to the eastern shores of the land masses, and from here surface water, that is obviously quite warm, moves into high latitudes to become eastward in flow. Within the tropics the contrasts in temperature between maritime areas off the west and east margins of the continents are never very great. However, the coastal fringes on the west of hot deserts are somewhat cooler than most other coastlands in the tropics, as a result of the up-welling of cold water (see p. 294).

In temperate and high latitudes of the north, the eastward flow of winds and water is of significance. Thus, west coastlands in high latitudes tend to be markedly warmer than east coastlands in winter. West coasts are favoured then by warm water of tropical origin. Air, passing from this warm surface over adjacent coastlands, often keeps mean temperatures remarkably high for the latitude. In contrast, east coastlands tend to be cold, for their latitude, in winter because of outflowing cold air of continental origin. Nevertheless, isotherms show poleward bends over the oceans which are quite ample near west coasts but somewhat less so near east coasts. It would seem that the oceanic water offshore from east coasts has some tempering effect on the winter cold of the coastlands, despite the additional chilling by cold currents and ice along these shores. A comparison of two places on opposite sides of an ocean in approximately the same high latitude shows that there is usually a greater annual range of temperature near east coastlands than is true of west coasts.

On the other hand, west coasts in warm temperate latitudes may show the effect of cold water offshore by the equatorward loops in the isotherms, as, for instance, along the coasts of Northern Chile and South-west Africa. However, isotherms bend polewards on eastern shores in these latitudes because of warm currents offshore.

A brief reference must be made to one other effect of the oceans. It can be shown that in oceanic areas such as those affected by the Gulf Stream and its related drifts, or by the Kuro Siwo and its extensions, there are large areas of water surface that are relatively quite warm, and from such surfaces there is much evaporation into the cooler overlying air. Furthermore, it may be shown that there is a great transfer of energy from the ocean water to the atmosphere above as a result of this evaporation. It so happens that this access of energy to the atmosphere occurs in the neighbourhood of the average position of the polar front in both the North Atlantic and North Pacific Oceans. Thus there appears to be a close relationship between these currents and drifts and frontal developments, so that it is suggested that the ocean water here is the source of the energy of depressions. Recent studies suggest that the Southern Ocean receives much heat from the adjoining oceans by southward-flowing warm water. This water warms the cold Antarctic air masses which, in turn, have a significant influence on the atmospheric circulation in the southern hemisphere.

Tides

The tides in the oceans are a study in themselves, and it is intended to give here a very brief résumé of the processes which are involved.

(a) *Effect of the Attraction of the Moon and the Sun.* A tide is the periodic elevation and depression of the ocean surface which occurs locally very nearly every $12\frac{1}{2}$ hours. There would be a pair of high tides and a pair of low tides at any one time if the earth had a uniform cover of water. Fig. 21.8 shows this, and it will be observed that the two high tides (H_1 and H_2) are antipodal in position, so are the two low tides (L_1 and L_2). The explanation of this phenomenon, reduced to the simplest terms, may be followed by reference to Fig. 21.8. The attraction of the earth and the water of its oceans towards the moon is dependent upon the distances between the moon and H_2, the moon and the centre of the earth, and the moon and H_1. The water at H_2 is attracted more than the earth, and the latter is attracted more than the water at H_1. The fluid nature of water permits a distortion of its surface, and so produces the high tides and the low tides. It may be mentioned that the pull of the sun is also of some importance in raising tides in much the same way as that of the moon; the high tides caused by the sun are less elevated and the low tides are less depressed than those caused by the moon.

As the earth rotates on its axis, the high and low tides progress in longitude. Assuming that there is a high tide at a given line of longitude, then a half-rotation of the earth will not bring this line into a

FIG. 21.8.—Tides produced by the Moon

position to receive its next high tide (caused by the moon) since the moon has moved in its orbit around the earth during this interval, and this delays the theoretical onset of the following high tide by about 26 minutes.

During a lunar month the moon moves completely round the earth, and during that period the sun and the moon are continually affecting the earth as regards its tides. The sun may be regarded as fixed in position, and thus on two occasions in each month the moon and sun collaborate to give very high and very low tides (spring tides) and on two other occasions their influences are in oppositon, and they produce less high tides and less low tides than usual (neap tides) as shown by Fig. 21.9.

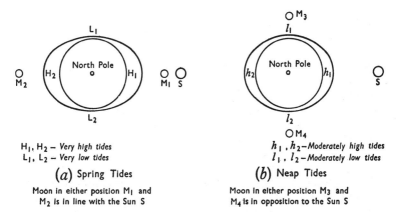

FIG. 21.9.—Spring and Neap Tides

(b) *Progression of Tide Waves.* The theory of a progressive wave of high water moving across the surface of the Southern Ocean (as the earth rotates from west to east this wave would move westwards) and sending branch waves northwards through the other oceans is now considered erroneous.

Today tide waves are explained by considering large sections of each ocean as very large tanks of water, rectangular in shape. The water in such a tank may be made to rock, so that its surface oscillates in a manner which is dependent upon the depth of water and the length of the tank. The tide-producing forces described above set up the oscillations in the form of stationary waves which move across the ocean surface in a succession of high and low tides. Each section of an ocean surface which can be recognized as oscillating in a particular way is determined very largely by the depth of water in that zone. In marginal seas, and in parts of the open ocean, the dimensions often prevent direct waves of this type from being set up, but tides are induced in such areas from neighbouring sea surfaces which are oscillating under the tide-producing forces.

Fig. 21.10.—Co-tidal Lines in the North Sea
Figures show hours of high tide.

As a result of the effects of the rotation of the earth, the tide waves must be regarded as pulses of high and low water which are gyrating around fairly well-defined points in the seas. For instance, in the North Sea there are three such points, and the radiating lines in Fig. 21.10 show by the sequential numbers the progress of high water around the coasts.

(c) *Effects of Tides on Shore Regions.* In the open ocean the difference between high and low tide is usually very small, of the order of two or three feet. In many cases the tide experienced on the shores of continental regions is caused by a progressive wave which has been induced by the pulsations of a stationary wave in the nearby seas.

This progressive wave, on entering the shallow water over the continental shelf, tends to increase in height, and give tidal ranges of several feet in some cases, as much as forty feet.

In bays and estuaries the effects are quite varied. On entering an estuary the tide is rising against the gradient of the river-bed and the flow of the river. The rising tide may, in narrowing estuaries, produce a wall of water three or four feet in height, as in the case of the Severn bore with spring tides. With the fall of the tide in an estuary there is the additional force of the river flow which has been temporarily dammed, and this is helpful in creating effective scour. In bays, such as the Bay of Fundy, in eastern Canada, the water apparently oscillates as an independent unit, with a stationary wave. The exceptionally high tides of this bay are caused by its decreasing width which produces a tidal range of fifty feet at its head, on some occasions.

The double tides at Southampton have been explained in various ways. The most acceptable explanation of this phenomenon turns on the variations in the channel in which the tide flows, as well as on friction, between the water and the bottom of the channel. Incidentally, near Portland, on the Dorset coast, there is a double low tide. Another feature of interest is typical of some ports on the shores of the Gulf of Mexico and in North Australia which have only one high and one low tide in a day.

Finally, a brief reference may be made to storm surges. These are not caused by the tides, but their effects appear to be the result of exceptionally high tides. Storm surges, such as produced the disastrous floods in early February, 1953 on the shores of Eastern England and Holland, are determined by very low air pressure, which results in a local elevation of the sea surface. Such, in combination with a period of high tide, can produce serious incursions of the sea on low-lying shorelands. On the occasion referred to, high water rose six to ten feet above the predicted height. Furthermore, the surge was accompanied by very powerful storm waves.

Index

(References in heavy type indicate illustrated items.)

362